COMING
OF
AGE

HAMLYN

COMING OF AGE

A positive guide to growing older

Consultant Editor:

DAVID HOBMAN, CBE

Former Director of Age Concern England

HAMLYN

ACKNOWLEDGEMENTS

The publishers would like to acknowledge their special thanks to Frances Hughes for her invaluable contributions to the text on the legal aspects of housing, money, marriage breakdown, ill health, bereavement, wills and probate.

The publishers would also like to thank John Murray (Publishers) Ltd. and Central Independent Television plc for permission to use the Face Exercises from Healthy Living Over 55, (1984) by Laura Mitchell.

Thanks are also due to Caroline Butterfield at SAGA Photographic Services; Liz Dendy at the Sports Council; Jan Green; Olive Newsome; Jean Royes of the Margaret Morris Movement; Rosalind Milne; Frederick Sitter; William Perry.
Special thanks to Pat Ingrams of Getting On (Central Independent Television plc) for her help and advice.

Project Editor: NICKY ADAMSON
Art Editor: PEDRO PRÁ-LOPEZ
Editor: DIANA CRAIG
Designers: WILLIAM MASON, ANDREW BAIN
Illustrators: PAUL COOPER, ELAINE ANDERSON
Photographer: PETER CHADWICK (exercise sequences)
Picture Research: RACHEL DUFFIELD, CHRISTINA WEIR
Production: AUDREY JOHNSTON, ALYSSUM ROSS

The publishers would like to thank the following organizations and individuals for their kind permission to reproduce the photographs in this book:

Age Concern 17, 20, 26, 87t; A&M Hearing Ltd. 106; Anchor Housing Trust 68; The Bolingbroke Hospital 76; Central Independent Television 18; Choice Magazine 7; Mary Evans Picture Library 10, 11, 12; John Glover 57; Sally and Richard Greenhill 83, 90, 98, 101t, 167, 170, 175; Help the Aged 94; Jacqui Hurst 86; S & O Matthews Half title, 101b; Eric Midwinter 8, 9; National Federation of Women's Institutes 15; The National Gallery, London 103; Octopus Group Picture Library/Chris Crofton 128, 129, 130, 132, 134; Saga Holidays plc 80, 89, 92, 93, 96, 97; Science Photo Library 120; Sports Council 112; Sports Council/Ian Weightman 111; Tony Stone Worldwide 104; Judy Todd 63, 70; John Walmsley 109, 119, 169; WRVS/Wiltshire Times and News 87b; Zefa Frontispiece, 79.

This edition published in 1989 by
the Hamlyn Publishing Group Limited
a division of the Octopus Publishing Group,
Michelin House, 81 Fulham Road, London SW3 6RB

ISBN 0 600 56541 6 (p/b)

ISBN 0 600 56534 3 (h/b)

Produced by Mandarin Offset
Printed and bound in Hong Kong

CONTENTS

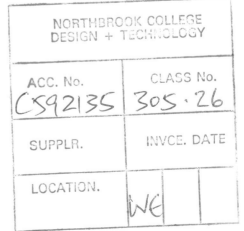

INTRODUCTION

Most of us can now expect to live a good deal longer than the generations who came before us. If we are fortunate, we can look forward to remaining active into extreme old age. We can also begin to enjoy new experiences which may have escaped us before, when we had other preoccupations to absorb our time and energy. Love, liveliness, and laughter are by no means the prerogative of the young.

The great majority of us are better educated and more travelled than previous generations. As a result, we are more sophisticated and have come to expect higher standards than older people tolerated in the past. We are not prepared to be written off or segregated simply because of our age. We want to remain involved in the decisions which affect our lives, for as long as possible, or to transfer these personal responsibilities to people we choose for ourselves and on whom we can rely.

With the rapid growth in occupational pensions, many of us will have reasonably decent incomes in retirement. More than half of us own our own homes. With cheaper travel, our horizons grow daily wider.

THINKING AHEAD

To some extent, our destiny lies in our own hands. But, of course, there are still factors over which we may have little or no control, such as illness, reduced circumstance, or isolation. Adversity, in any of its guises, can strike any one of us, even though we may think we anticipated all possible eventualities.

However, with better knowledge and a little help, even the bleakest prospects can be transformed. If only we know where to turn for advice with, at least, an idea about the questions we ought to be asking, we are on the beginning of the road to recovery.

This is why we have produced *Coming of Age* and invited experts in their own fields to share their knowledge and experience with us in producing this practical guide to making the most of later life.

Of course, many readers will already know about some of the information we have included; but we live in a complex and fast-changing age in which there can be few, if any,

of us who really know all there is to know about money management, housing adaptations, or leisure opportunities. And even if we are aware of ways in which to keep ourselves fit and well, reminders about a sensible diet, taking the right kind of exercise, or generally treating our bodies with respect, may still be useful.

For many older people life has been overwhelmingly involved in work and family rearing, so that little time or thought has been given to considering the future and exploring the wonderful new possibilities opening up, whether it is in pursuit of new knowledge through active involvement in a hobby, or in doing something useful for other people through service in the community. For those with an inadequate income, limited paid employment may also be important. All these ideas are explored in the chapters which follow.

We have written this book with older people in mind, although thinking about retirement long before it happens is no bad thing either. It is a practical no-nonsense guide, whether you have an older relative or friend, are on the threshold of retirement, are a working housewife who never retires (but who may have a rather bored partner around the house all day for the first time), or are well into your later years. It must be remembered that retirement is, itself, a new phenomenon for the majority of people. It may well last longer than childhood, adolescence or a working career; so it is well worthwhile taking it seriously, so that this last stage of life is a bonus to be enjoyed rather than a burden to be endured.

CARING FOR OTHERS

Although this book is about finding fulfilment in the later years, some readers will find themselves in the unexpected position of caring for an older person in what can become a full-time occupation. It may be a husband, wife, brother, sister, parent, or even an old friend and companion. It is also not unknown for a mother in her nineties to find herself caring for a frail seventy-year-old son.

The need to assume the carer's role may well come suddenly with little, or no, warning and certainly no preparation or training. People seem to cope wonderfully well in these circumstances, often discovering a hidden strength; but here again, there is plenty of room for practical advice, as well as psychological help in supporting those for whom we feel a sense of responsibility.

This is why we include sections on caring, and on some of the early indications of illness or distress, which it is sensible to acknowledge and understand, rather than ignore. Many disabilities associated with old age can be stemmed, if not actually cured, when they are dealt with in their early stages.

LIVING WITH AGEING

Ageing is not a disease. It is a perfectly natural process in which we are all busily engaged from the moment we reach adulthood. Many of its so-called problems are a reflection of the way in which we view the ageing process in other people. Sometimes our vision is distorted because of a mistaken attempt to deny its reality within ourselves.

It is natural enough for older people to look back on those parts of our lives which are over, both the good times and the bad. They help to make us what we are. But living is about the present, and the future. This means keeping as many options open for as long as possible, so that personal choice rather than force of circumstance determines what we do and where and when we do it.

For example, for some people life in a residential home, free of personal responsibilities, may be much more satisfying than trying to struggle on alone in a house which is too big, surrounded by indifferent neighbours. The important thing is to make sure the older person directly concerned is making an informed choice. This means knowing what the alternatives are and not simply acquiescing with what is suggested by other people. It is also about having our opinions heard with respect.

But all life has its ending, and although the later years can be about gains, there are also losses to be borne, and eventually the closing of our own chapter. For many older people religion, or sometimes a renewed contact with a minister, is a source of comfort, providing an explanation of our place in the scheme of things. For others, there are only rational explanations; but in either case, being ready to face death in both practical and emotional terms may ease the passage, and help those who are left behind. Quite unnecessary fears can often be allayed by gentle conversations with family, friends, or counsellors. There are also important financial and legal matters to deal with which are discussed where appropriate in this book.

THE FLAME OF ENJOYMENT

There is nothing morbid about making sensible provisions for our departure. But in the meantime, life is for living, and it is this sense of keeping the flame of enjoyment burning which runs through the pages of this book. All the ideas we discuss, the suggestions we make, the sources of information we point to, are designed to meet that simple objective.

It must never be forgotten we are unique personalities in old age, just as we always have been. Our capacities and our interests are different, as are our hopes and fears, strengths and prejudices. We are not a homogeneous group, but a collection of individuals. The needs and aspirations of the young sixty-year-old are as different from those of the old ninety-year-old, as they are between the infant, the adolescent and the adult. This is too easily forgotten but not, we hope, in *Coming of Age*.

DAVID HOBMAN

LIFE-STYLES

The fly-leaf of A Pilgrim's Progress, *used as a family register of births and deaths.*

A bulky, battered copy of *A Pilgrim's Progress*, printed in the mid-nineteenth century, is a treasured possession of mine. John Bunyan's inspirational allegory was used by some families like a family Bible, in that the register of births and deaths of the household are recorded on the fly-leaf.

My great-grandfather, Joseph Clare, was born in 1838, and his wife, Margaret Lingley in 1845. He was a chief ostler on the Bridgewater Canal, eventually at Deansgate, Manchester. He was of the artisan class, with a little house, one or two guineas a week, and

coals. Given the vote by Disraeli's shrewd 1867 Reform Act, he became a member of the Primrose League, a Tory voter and low churchman until his death in 1898. He was 59, and he was still tending the chain-horses.

Joseph and Margaret Clare had fourteen children, lovingly inscribed in *A Pilgrim's Progress*. The first, Levi, was born in 1864, when Margaret was still 18. The last, Doris, was born in 1889, when she was 44. Her child-bearing years thus spread over 26 years. She died in 1897, aged 52, when Doris, the youngest survivor, was still only eight. Indeed, my grandmother, Ada, born in 1876, from whom I inherited *A Pilgrim's Progress*, spent her own formative years looking after Doris. Of course, not all fourteen children survived. Six died in infancy, one or two of them within the first four months of life. When Queen Victoria opened the Manchester Canal in 1894, Joseph and Margaret had but a couple of beribboned children clustered around them in the canal company's rather paternalist 'family pen'.

So much for life-style a hundred years ago. The Clares were not untypical of a huge swathe of working class and lower middle class families that constituted the majority of the Victorian population. Quite simply, they did not contemplate old age, nor did they actively prepare for it. But they were not feckless. In part, it was because money was scarce, but, in the main, it was because the ordinary man or woman didn't expect to live long. There

No. 51

Book 45. Page 42.

1862. Marriage solemnized at the Parish Church, in the Parish of Warrington, in the County of Lancaster.

No.	When Married.	Name and Surname.	Age.	Condition.	Rank or Profession.	Residence at the time of Marriage.	Father's Name and Surname.	Rank or Profession of Father.
84	Dec 29th 1862.	Joseph Clare	23	Bachelor	Labourer	Rixton	Joseph Clare	Deceased
		Margaret Lingley	17	spinster	—	Rixton	Thomas Lingley	Deceased

Married in the Parish Church, according to the Rites and Ceremonies of the Established Church by _____ after Banns by me, W. Hamilton.

This Marriage was solemnized between us
Joseph Clare
Margaret Lingley X

in the Presence of us.
William Berry
Ann Hughes

I Hereby Certify that the above is a true Copy or Extract from the Register of Marriages of the Parish Church of Warrington, made this 11th day of January 1898.

non. A Markham
Asst: Curate.

By the Act of 6 & 7 Will. IV. c. 86, s. 35, it is enacted, "That every Rector, Vicar, or Curate, and every Registrar, Registering Officer, and Secretary, who shall have the keeping for the time being of any Register Book of Births, Marriages, shall at all reasonable Times allow Searches to be made of any Register Book in his keeping, and shall give a Copy certified under his Hand of any Entry or Entries in the same, on Payment of the Fee hereinafter mentioned; for every Search extending over a Period not more than One Year the sum of One Shilling, and Sixpence additional for every additional Year, and the sum of Two Shillings and Sixpence for every single Certificate."

Keeping track of family histories is rewarding as well as illuminating. Left: The marriage certificate of Joseph Clare and Margaret Linley, the author's grandparents, which was solemnized on 29th December 1862. This marriage was blessed with fourteen children, of whom six died in infancy.

Left: *Joseph and Margaret Clare's daughter Ada, born 1876, with her husband Harry and son Harold Midwinter, the author's father, in 1910. Right: A little over twenty years later, Ada with her grandchildren Bryan, and Eric (the author) as babe in arms.*

was a built-in lack of anticipation about old age. In turn, this had two strands. On the one hand, there was the distinct possibility of dying relatively early. After all, only 6 per cent of the Victorian population was over 60, so the odds seemed stacked against you. On the other hand, there was the knowledge that the two principal planks of life-style – work and family-rearing – were lengthy commitments, and, in the case of Joseph and Margaret Clare and thousands of their fellow-men and women, unending.

Therein lies the key to the switch in life-styles then and now, a change at once devastating and triumphant. Of course it is affected by longer average life-spans, but it has more to do with changing status and social condition.

A NORMAL LIFE-SPAN

One hears it said that people are living longer, but that is a little misleading. It suggests some new biological or medical plateau has been reached, or that we have taken a spectacular evolutionary leap. There may be a bit of longevity creeping into the equation, but a chief factor is survival.

Margaret Clare was unlucky. A woman towards the end of the last century might have expected another thirteen or so years of life if she reached the age of 60. If a woman reaches 60 today that actuarial expectation has only risen by two years to a little over 15. The real difference between then and now is that far more people are surviving to enjoy this more 'natural' lifespan. There are 10 million over 60 now,

In an age that tends to romanticize 'Victorian values', it is worth noting that they themselves felt obliged to do the same, since work and family-rearing were literally a lifetime's commitment, without any prospect of retirement from either.

compared with two million a hundred years ago. And there are now 180,000 people over 90 in the United Kingdom alone. A hundred years ago it was just a handful.

Nevertheless, don't be misled into the popular belief that the greater proportion of older people in our society is mainly due to more living longer. It is true that the *proportion* of older people in Britain has trebled this century, from 6–7 per cent to 20 per cent, a fifth of the population. This amazing leap has been sudden and it is unprecedented.

But the basic and underlying reason why the proportion of older people is so large *is because the proportion of younger people is so low*. In the hundred years under review the number of people 16 years and under has dropped steeply from close on 40 per cent to about 22–23 per cent. In Victorian society, half of its members were under 20.

An interactive mesh of features was at work. Mortality fell, especially in the earlier age groups. Death no longer strikes as randomly. Death is no longer a part of our daily consideration. Death, on the whole, is something which happens to older people. Translated into figures, each year there is only one death of an under-five per thousand of the population, compared with 25 deaths of over-60s.

Advances in public health and preventive medicine for children meant far more babies survived infancy. Birth control, at first in desultory fashion, began to have a role, and, gradually, people had the confidence to believe that you didn't need to have so many pregnancies to ensure that at least two or three children survived.

Now this change in the proportions of young and old in the population is extremely important for older people thinking about their place in the community. Old age is like the common cold: there's a lot of it about. The norm in the past has been of a few, relatively isolated and lonely ancient figures in any community. Not so these days. If you are older, you are in the ascendant, quantitively speaking. It is the younger people who are less in numbers; it is the school-rolls that are falling and the youth clubs that are closing.

Let this seminal fact boost your confidence. Let this background knowledge inform your willingness and urge to develop a new life-style, for there are, literally, thousands of people like you just waiting to be befriended, just waiting for you to seek them out and enjoy common interests.

Of course, there is a disadvantage. For those fascinated by cross-generational link-ups, there may be fewer opportunities. Grandchildren are not in the profusion they were. Nonetheless, the first step is belief in the new

reality. The shape of the population has changed – but so few people realize this and react accordingly. Yes, you are, in your thousands, in the same boat. Metaphorically speaking, it is up to you to decide whether it's a luxury liner or a drifting raft.

PARENTHOOD AND WORK

So what is the authentic nature of the older life-style today? Joseph Clare's collapse and demise while still at work and his wife's decease while still with young children would not now be a typical case. Most women now will have had far fewer babies, perhaps planning them in and around career prospects, in a short span of maybe four or five years, rather different to Margaret Clare's spread of pregnancies over 26 years. This means that, for a majority if by no means all, the mainstream obligations of parenthood have been discharged by the early fifties. Youngsters have grown up, gone to college, started work, left

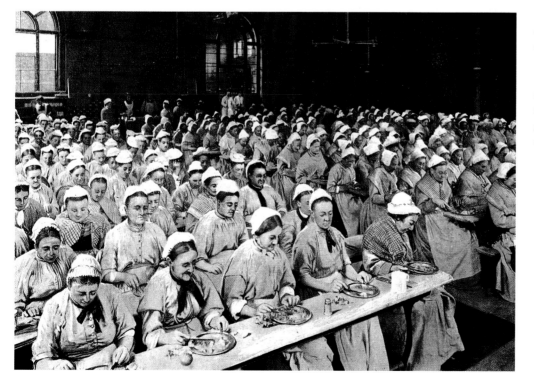

Women's dinnertime at a London workhouse in 1895. For women and men of working age, the workhouse was seen as a sign of failure, but it was often the only solution for the minority of the poor who managed to survive into old age.

In the 19th century, domestic gadgets only rose to the level of this simple wooden laundry twist (1873). Nowadays, washing machines, vacuum cleaners and all the other electrical appliances in the home have provided leisure time which was unthinkable in Victorian days.

tacked her brood's sundry garments with the same scrub-brush she utilized every Friday night to scour their wearers, boiling all the water for either function on an open fire. Via the washtub, mangle and dolly-blue, we arrive at the electrical washing machine of modern times, and that applies to many household chores.

All this means that, taken in the round, men and women are progressively released from the dictates of both vocational demands and family ties. And this is what, irrespective of birthdays, crucially defines older age. Put simply, it starts much earlier, as well as going on later.

THE CHALLENGE OF OLDER AGE

This is why, to escape the oppression of birthdays that set retirement at 60 or 65 or whenever, we use increasingly the nomenclature of 'ages' rather than age. Thus the First Age is that of childhood and education; the Second Age is that of waged work and family responsibility; the Third Age is the independent and active phase of retirement beyond that; and the Fourth Age is the dependent and frail endpiece of life.

You will see immediately that this is a more helpful and relevant measure. There are plenty in their seventies or eighties who are not 'old' in the outmoded sense of being ill; there are many of these who, because they are still employed or earning money, are still in the Second Age. Equally, there are, by definition, umpteen thousands embarked on their Third Age by the time they are 50 or 55. By this measure, you are not 'older' because of your birthday, and you are not 'older' because of some arbitrary assessment of your failing health. In terms of life-style you are 'older' when you change status.

Let us hazard a guess at the numbers involved. It cannot be too precise because, obviously, statistics are collected

home. That is not to say they do not sustain their nuisance value and anxiety quotient: but *raising* the family is complete.

Similarly, in the work-place. Slowly, from the mid-nineteenth century, the concept of retirement was introduced. Its dateline has gradually fallen so that, today, retirement or late redundancy in one's 50s is not uncommon.

This really is significant. Although the state retirement age for men remains at 65, the number of economically active males aged 60 to 65 has dropped from over eight out of ten to under five out of ten in the last dozen years. Incidentally, those same labour-saving devices that have fundamentally reduced the work-load have also radically affected domesticity. Think of the history of laundry. Margaret Clare at-by age, and not by status. However, we know there are nearly ten million state and private pensioners, and we know how many men and women over 50 are out of work or retired. We have some estimate, too, of those who have never had a permanent career, but who have perhaps stayed at home to care first for children and then for an elder relative. At the end of the day, it is still imprecise, but an educated guess might put the Third and Fourth Age population at between thirteen and fourteen million. That is not far short of a *third* of the adult population.

This must immediately be underlined by an allied fact. Because on this scenario older age begins earlier and ends later, it is self-evident that this arc in the life-cycle is enormous. These vast regiments of Third and Fourth Agers are enlisted in their new colours for long terms of service – 25, 30, even 40 years. Given late starts to the working life – going to college or, more bitterly, youth unemployment – it means that the phase of retirement for some people is as long as their period of work.

Retirement is no longer the bit at the end, the old pit pony put out to graze at pasture for a few months after countless years down the shaft. We are talking about a *third* of people's lives in many cases.

Retirement cannot therefore simply be seen any more as a 'writing off' of life. A third of the population could be spending a third of their lives in so-called retirement. That is the extent of the revolution. So many older people feel that being old or retired is out of the ordinary, but the reverse is true. 'Thank God I'm normal', sang Archie Rice, the seedy comedian in John Osborne's *The Entertainer*. In a rather different context, it is a tune which might be chorused by the teeming millions of people enjoying long years of – in the definition utilized here – being old.

There is no point, however, in dispensing advice in blinkers. It is important for you to *know* what's happening around you in society, and thereby to make more informed decisions about your own life-style. Just as it is difficult to persuade the public, including its older members, that older people are in abundance, it is difficult somehow to cajole them into the belief that older age – as defined here – goes on, and on, and on. Before now, the 'old' part of life has, rightly, been regarded as the short, brutish bit, swiftly dispensed with. Older people can no longer fall back on the excuse that 'I'm not long for this world': in the main, they are, and it's high time they realized it and started making something of it.

Long Third; Short Fourth

Third Age, Fourth Age: let us mark out the ground plainly and starkly. The object of one's life-style should be to lengthen the Third – active – Age and postpone and curtail the Fourth – passive – age. The ideal would be a Third Age of forty years, and a Fourth Age of forty seconds. When it comes to illness, the last should be first and the last should be short, like Bing Crosby, who popped his clogs – or rather his golf shoes – as he walked off the eighteenth green after a pleasant and rewarding round. As Bill Shankly, the old Liverpool football manager, used to say: 'I want to die healthy.'

THE ACTIVE RETIREMENT

How is this new normalcy played out? What are – what, more importantly, should be – the types of life led by older people? Well, a number of issues arise directly out of the sheer quantities of people and time under review.

Because retirement is still perceived as the postscript to the long letter of life, rather than a glaringly fluent last paragraph before you sign off with a flourish, a good deal of advice is of static variety. The messages, overt and hidden, counsel you to sort out your finances, sort out your house, sort out your hobby, sort out your health, and then, by inference, stay sorted out. In this scenario, by accident and by design, retirement is seen as a rut. Find yours, make it as comfortable as possible, but stay in it. Be it ever so palatial, it's still a rut.

But think over the thirty years or so of your Second Age, your little epoch of work and family-raising. It might be worth jotting down on the back of an envelope the changes that occurred in your personal world, changes either sought by yourself or dictated by other circumstance. You found a job; you became engaged; you broke it off; you had a promotion; you became engaged; you were offered another job; you were married; you found a house; you fought a war; you obtained a job; you had a child or two; you passed some professional examinations; you moved areas and found a better job and a different house; you were divorced; you moved house again; you became married again; you had a second family; you lost your job; you moved house another time; you found work. . . .

Of course, not all of these experiences happened to everyone, but enough of them probably happened to most people to underpin the point. Life was dynamic, not static. It was a whirligig of altering patterns over time.

Keeping out of the rut
Should you abandon that life-style, to the degree that it was so vibrant and busy, for the advertised groove of retirement? Of course, you might, and for good personal reasons, but please don't select the rut without weighty thought. Consider the possibility that you might, especially in the earlier decades of post-work, move around a bit, sniffing the air

and indulging in different rather than the same exercises. It might be a matter of moving house a couple of times, if that takes your fancy. It might be a matter of learning Serbo-Croat for four years, before devoting the next three to mastering the ukelele. In other words, put yourself about.

One whispers this softly but it might be worth taking a risk. Because the ageing process is thus and thus and our culture teaches us to worry about older people, we do tend to molly-coddle ourselves rather. So consider the balance of *social*, as opposed to *medical* risk. The 70-year-old lady, with most of her chief responsibilities over and done with, is, by that yardstick, the one who should be parachuting, and maybe not the young man with, as Tommy Handley used to remark, three widows, sixteen orphans and a football team to support.

Age need not wither . . .
All this illustrates a number of features that we associate with being old, but which you must constantly remind yourself are seldom, automatically and directly, the consequence of older age. Many older people are impoverished; many older people are unwell or disabled in some way; many older people feel insecure and anxious about safety, especially on the streets. Yet none of these factors are or need be linked irrevocably with age. Put simply, many older people, equally, are well-to-do, hale and confident. That is not to say the difficulties of poverty, ill-health and anxiety should not be treated, and treated forcefully. What it does mean is that they should be attacked head on. An old person is not poor because he or she is old, but because we have a pitiful and outmoded system of income maintenance. An old person is not necessarily ill because he or she is old, but because he or she, simply, is ill. Old

people are not vulnerable because they are ancient: they are vulnerable because they are vulnerable.

Listing them will not cure the ills of mankind, but it is right that older people, attempting to live positive lives, should accept nothing as the *inevitable* post-requisite of older age. Question everything on purely individual grounds, especially if it emanates from an official source.

'Cultural malnutrition'

The consequence of this cultural pressure to conform to a stereotype of old age is terrifying. Its most worrying aspect is that a large majority of older people naturally and inevitably believe implicitly in that value-system. Older people tend to play out the role for which they have been cast. They retire, literally. They withdraw. They yield place. They cede ground. They steal away into their shell.

Yes, yes, yes: one hears the irascible reader shouting back: 'What about Fred Snooks who ran the marathon at 83 or Bertha Bloggs who goes ballooning at 84?' But they are the exceptions. They would not hit the headlines if they were not the exceptions. What is exceptional about the silent majority is precisely that; their silence.

The involvement of older people in constructive activities of all kinds is, frankly, so negligible as to be frightening. Whether it is formal educational or recreational pursuits, do-it-yourself, going to the cinema or going for a walk in the park, it is very, very low, compared with the mass of the population. Lack of money, poor services and declining health explain some of this, but the major reason must be the older person's self-perception: 'You don't do as much when you're older.'

Here, then, is a gigantic paradox. Our civilization has created the jubilant triumph of untold leisure for millions of older people, when they can realize all manner of ambitions and wishes. And, in the main, they do substantially less than when they were up to the ears in dashing to work and getting the youngsters to school. The 'I don't know how I had the time to go to work' group is, in practice, a tiny elite.

Consider what this means in terms of social amiability, physical suppleness and mental vigour. Consider what has been called 'the cultural malnutrition' of so existing. The effects on health and well-being could be damaging. It is certain that the effects on man or woman in the round, as a whole person, are devastating and, what is more, cruelly wasteful of human resources.

Intellectual exercise
Older people are assailed with advice about keeping their arms and legs in trim or making sure their heart and lungs are in good nick, but who counsels them on keep fit for the head? P.E. for the pate; needle for the noddle; mind fields; head mastery; call it what you will, it is important. Older people who are not habitual readers, say, or regularly engaged in a pastime which makes vigorous mental demands, would be well-advised to adopt a daily intellectual exercise, the mind's equivalent of jogging.

Two-thirds of older people state that watching TV and listening to the radio is their chief leisure activity, by far the largest of all such activities. Of things people do *more* often rather than less in retirement, television is again easily top of the list with 55 per cent of people saying they watch more. High figures – 26 or 28 hours a week – are recorded for older viewers. And there is no harm in this. Television can be a stimulating and colourful medium, full of delights and surprises.

This is not about to degenerate into one of those sobersided homilies about the awfulness of the telly. It is more a plea not to be a passive watcher. React and participate. If a novel is serialized, read it at the same time, and watch with three or four others, in order to have a more interesting discussion. If a documentary on science or current affairs strikes you tellingly, follow it up with some specialist reading. Become a TV critic. Choose a programme a day, and write an article praising it or faulting it. Send bouquets and brickbats to the producers and performers. All in all, be an active viewer.

That is about the size of it. It is about being active, rather than passive, in whatever style or habit of life is chosen. In French medieval history there was a royal family called the 'do-nothings'. They came to a sticky end.

The other side of the coin
You may consider yourself one of the unlucky older people, and there are very

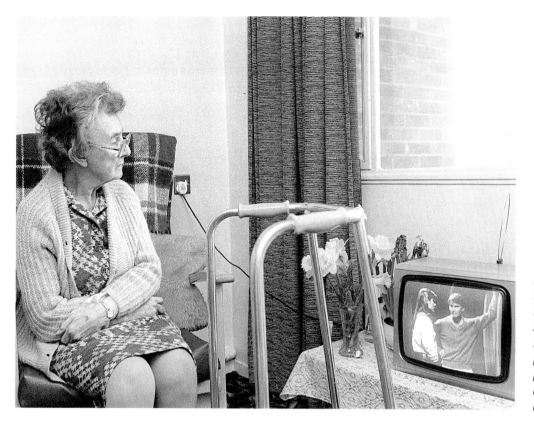

Restricted mobility means that television may become an important source of mental stimulation. Viewing can be made active rather than passive by writing to programme makers with constructive comments and criticisms.

many, who *are* poor, lonely or in frail health. These jollying paragraphs about doing this, that and the other must seem a little irksome. It is a question of adapting the letter of the general advice to your particular situation, for the tenor of the suggestions is unarguable. It must sound a little harsh, but, whatever the disadvantages suffered, the tired, worn cliché must be dragged out and utilized again. Here it comes. If you don't help yourself, no one else can help you. There. It could have been worse. It could have been God helps those who help themselves.

For what must be urged is that there is nothing more debilitating in older age than inactivity, social, physical and mental. People use the harrowing phrase 'giving up the ghost'. It is a very poignant and telling aphorism, and it is certain that if one has disadvantages, one must seek as active an adjustment to one's lot as possible. What is sure is that, without some self-motivation, things may only deteriorate.

Your response may be simple. It may be just a decision to do the crossword every day, without fail; or to get to the shops every other day, without fail; or to visit your friend every week, without fail. Indeed, routine is a significant aspect of the positive life-style: it is the simple skeleton that helps you to organize and lift yourself.

Once more, one must compare with the Second Age: the commitment of work and family imposed its structure, sometimes pleasing, sometimes drab, but, nonetheless, a structure. Now it is up to you. The major change to the Third and Fourth Age is that you are rather more on your own. Less design is imposed on your life, and you have to construct the base and the relationships through your own endeavours.

Right: *Gillian Reynolds. She is one of the few female TV presenters testing attitudes by refusing to fit the mould of being glamorous or thirty-ish, or both.*

ANTI-AGEISM

The maintenance of this kind of independent and dignified self-autonomy depends, like liberty, on eternal vigilance. It is amazing how many people and agencies are keen, perhaps unwittingly, to construct dependence for older people, and, paradoxically, good intentions are partly to blame. It might be close family, anxious to help, or officials, eager to assist, who rob an older person of attributes of self-determination. It might be simple household chores. 'Let me do that for you' is a statement that requires careful analysis. Next time, when the helper is not available, it might be that little more arduous to perform the task oneself. It might be much more officious matters, like having a home help or meals-on-wheels, or any of a variety of *services*. The word services is deliberately emphasized, for that is precisely what they are, and those who provide them are the *servants* of the customers. Too often they parade as the masters, bestowing state alms and charities. If, for example, the service is at the wrong time or of the wrong shape, say so – politely but forcefully.

Too much provision for older people trades abysmally on the touching but unproductive deference and gratitude of the recipients. Older people must fight the notion that they are social casualties or patients. They are citizens and they are consumers, and their rights are as paramount as anyone else's. Unluckily, older people tend not to be militant consumers. A myth that abounds is that old folk grumble after the fashion of Mr Growser in *Toy-town*, who snorted of every incident that 'it ought not to be allowed'. Not true. Consumer surveys demonstrate that older people, on balance, are poor complainants. That has its pleasant side, for no one loves a whinger, but it can be overdone. It is necessary to balance the social budget, counting blessings on the credit side, and discounting resignation ('I can't grumble for my age') on the debit.

Questioning attitudes

It is all part of the attack on ageism, the standpoint that assesses people chronologically as other standpoints have previously judged by reference to gender, or race, or religion, or disability. As with all those other instances, the victims are usually part of the conspiracy. Old people play at being old people: taking the idea of retirement too literally has already been mooted as an instance of that. It is important that older people perceive ageism in themselves, as well as in others, and challenge it in both. When the dry cleaners offer a half-price deal for old age pensioners on Thursday afternoons, ask yourself whether that is not only patronizing but also offensive. It would, for instance, be illegal to offer such a bargain to Pakistanis or Irish people, given anti-racist legislation. Should old age pensioners be picked out in that divisive way?

When you are watching those 28 hours of television, keep an eye peeled for ageist attitudes. Scrutinize the fashion in which older people are used in advertising (brown bread and beer – never shower-gel and deodorants) or in comedy situations. Note the preconceptions that exist in the public mind that allow that to happen. In the first world war the Tommies used to play a little game with the stew. They used to whistle if they found a piece of meat. Whistle when you see an elderly, female news-presenter on television. It is important to develop that sensitivity to ageist indicators, and, preferably, to counter them when they arrive.

HOME-BASE

So much for attitudes and approaches to the older person as self. The next issue must be where and with whom all this occurs. Both accommodation and social relations are of huge import, and both are worthy of some analysis.

It might again be helpful in answering these questions personally to understand what the generality is like. Apropos housing, one in three of Britain's households now includes a pensioner. This means that three million pensioners are living quite alone, and another five and a half million pensioners live in wider family settings, often with their middle-aged children who, in many cases, are their carers.▶ Only 2 per cent of people over 65 live in houses with children in them. Many are amazed to learn that only 4 per cent – about 325,000 – of older people live in sheltered housing, nursing homes, residential care homes and so on. One hears so much about them that one assumes practically all old folk end up in an old folks' home. In fact, the nearest you can find to a generalization about older people is that nine out of ten live in their own home either alone or with one other old or near-old person.

Isolation is a mixed blessing. People bemoan the passing of a bygone and, by all accounts, somewhat fictional era when older people lived with their younger kin, and all was fine and dandy. We must be realistic about this. Many an elderly woman would prefer to live, and even struggle, alone, rather than share a kitchen with younger members of the family. Blood may be thicker than water, but it is also more damaging when spilt.

At home alone

However, solitude or, at most, twosomes, must be faced as the actuality of the age. That heralds one or two more statistics (mercifully the final ones), and these are about kith and kin. It is well-known that, in older age, women outnumber men by two to one, and that this is cumulative; so much so that, among over-85s, women outnumber men four to one. Three out of every eight older women are single, widowed or divorced; nearly one in two older women either never had or, in a number of cruel cases, have outlived their children.

Place these two factors alongside each other. They amount to one or two older persons, chiefly women, living in independent accommodation. In terms of life-style, and away from the practical and extremely important aspects of daily living, this indicates one special feature. Leisure, in its broadest and most positive sense, must be the motif of older age. Leisure is increasingly home-based for everybody; by that token, it is increasingly domestically oriented for older people. Collective leisure is dwindling. Society is becoming miniaturized. What used to be the cinema is stuck in the corner of the living-room, and, especially with videos and cable TV on tap, those hours spent gazing up at Greer Garson and Walter Pigeon in the raven-black of the Gaumont are a generation away. As Bob Hope cracked, with all the technical

SEE ALSO: ◀

THE CARERS'GUIDE:

What is a carer?   p. 166

Mr J. Mosley Turner, on the occasion of his 111th birthday, in the company of two of his daughters and other relatives. 5½ million pensioners live with their middle-aged or elderly relatives, many of whom are their carers.

nored this, chiefly because, for many, the house was a cross between a dosshouse and a kindergarten, a refuge from work and for children.

Sometimes people are surprised by these facts. They are astonished to think that they spend so much time not doing very much, or that they spend so much time in the house itself. It might be helpful, on a normal day, or over a normal week, to keep a quite factual log or diary. Map out a schedule in half hour or fifteen minute intervals, and, at the end of the day, just briefly write down a keyword or two about what you have actually done. Try and forget you're going to do exactly that, otherwise you might start filling the day to complete the log. Retain ordinariness as much as possible. Certainly many people, on examining this kind of record, have been startled at how humdrum the day or week has been, how lacking in forethought and in pertinent activity. One hastens to add that to be 'busy doing nothing', as Bing Crosby, Wallace Beery and Cedric Hardwicke once famously carolled, is fine – as long as, like that splendid trio, you acknowledge and glorify in the fact. The lesson here is for those who imagine they are utilizing their newfound freedom of time with verve and aplomb.

A QUESTION OF RELATIONSHIPS

Thus people, in ones and twos, face long stretches of home, sweet home. Here the new roles will be scripted and played out. A leading question concerns the relationship with one's family – if, of course, such a grouping exists. Politicians and advisers are wont to talk about your family helping, when, for many, there is no such opportunity for support or rapport. And, where family life is available, its format may have changed. There are many divorces, many remarriages and many single parents. The traditional four-seater family is no

advances in film, they'll soon be able to spray it on your eye-balls. The laundry has become the washing-machine, and the ice-stores the fridge. The concert hall has become the tape-deck.

Everyone encourages older people to get out and about. That is fair and honest enough, but one cannot duck the changes wrought personally or socially, by time. Going out is less congregated than it was: it is the family car, not the charabanc; it is the secluded meal out for three or four, not the hot pot supper with a cast of millions. Similarly, the home is central to leisure, and, in the past, architects and designers have ig-

longer the norm. You may have no grandchildren, or you may be – for some perplexed infant – one of eight grandparents.

Social mobility has often meant that families are, in any event, separated by distance. This has probably been overplayed. There was more mobility in the past than many now allow, and it is not quite such a novel phenomenon. Also, improved transport and communications help narrow the geographic gaps: the telephone is the great bridger of social chasm.

All 'last' generations have to or should adjust to such changes, perhaps this generation of older people more than some of their predecessors. Ideally, the 'last' generation should try not to be too dogmatic: it should relax and attempt, sensitively, to view these social alterations against a wider perspective. What happened 'in my day' is scarcely the finest opening to a recipe for dispensing wisdom. Relationships with one's children and one's grandchildren are about dialogue. The wise listen as much as they talk. Socrates is a good model. He proceeded by interrogation rather than by assertion. One gentle question to a recalcitrant grandchild is worth a hundred blurted and categoric statements.

Give and take

Balance is of the essence. Showing an interest may easily become interfering inquisitively; trying not to intervene may easily be interpreted as indifference. Old age is a useful testing-ground, not of whether all those years of experience have taught you about life, but whether they have taught you about yourself. Self-analysis, not analysis of others, is the key to good relationships. With children and with grandchildren, the ideal is for the blood-relationship, at times necessarily taut, to mature into friendship.

Marriage aforethought

Naturally, marriage remains the salient relationship for many, if by no means all, older people. It is well-rehearsed that more marriages end on the rocks than in previous generations, but perhaps we should ponder the huger miracle that so many remain intact, despite the operation of the law of averages. When one reckons how couples, for whatever complex of reasons, fall in love or court one another and are wedded, and how circumstance and other factors change perceptibly over time, then one must marvel at the resilience of humankind. Now marriages must undergo the additional stress of a lengthier period and that under totally varying conditions.

This does not address the matrimonial extremes, neither the idyllic bliss of that limited edition stamped 'made in heaven', nor the riven gloom of hellish linkages. It addresses, realistically, the vast majority of marriages, with their switchback of ups and downs, of acceptable companionship and affection, and generally on a decent and even keel. The norm will probably have been work and family, with traditionally, the mother taking greater responsibility for the latter than the former. Now both have vanished. Husband and wife are, in a new and un-saucy sense, 'living together' for the first time and for a long time.

It is all very well having one's husband snoring contentedly at one's side by night, but it is quite another matter for him to be permanently on the ration strength by day. For the first time in social history, couples are facing up to spending half their married lives without benefit of work or children. Joseph and Margaret Clare never managed it. Thousands now face it.

That doesn't mean it should be all yielding, giving and forgiving. It does require to be reciprocal, for personal relations have unwritten rights as well as unwritten responsibilities. Younger people, like older people, can be selfish and exploitive. Once more it is a matter of balance. The belief that grandmother dotes on the children leaves but a short step to dumping the kids on gran whenever, just as, conversely, older people, resentful of failing strength or power, can be equally manipulative of their children and grandchildren.

A useful analogy for guidance in these matters is the elastic band. Imagine that this piece of elastic is always in place, joining you and whosoever. It can mean an extremely close relation, or, according to need or mood, the distance apart can vary. In some circumstances, it may be drawn tight and long, especially, for instance, if you assess that you are being used or too much is being assumed. The trick, of course, is not to allow the band to snap. Year in, year out, a relationship may exist in a similar state of tension, taut or loose, although it is worth noting that most relationships do require some degree of moderating, closer here, wider apart there.

Thinking aloud
Relationships are, as the Duke of Wellington said of the Battle of Waterloo, 'hard pounding'. They require arduous work and profound thought. Perhaps a shade unluckily, words as well as acts are the chief currency of relationships; unlucky in the sense that not everyone is at ease with words. The older generation sometimes mistrust them, or have not had many opportunities to hone them. Do try and talk openly and fully at any level of any relationship. 'I wish you'd told me' is the epitaph inscribed on the tombstone of a million personal liaisons, collapsed and died.

It is difficult to advise; these are sensitive personal areas. What must be urged is that this is fully recognized, not as a problem, but as a question. New

guide-lines must be discussed candidly; new opportunities for sharing activities sought; and new directives for protecting separate experiences agreed. Whatever else, this requires deep thought and honest debate. It is one of the ramifications of new older age, little thought of, but likely to be as testing as other features. Marriage, thus far, has been principally about bread-winners and home-makers. Marriage, from now on, is also about leisure-seekers.

For some, there are few problems. Life together may have become humdrum, but at least it is not disruptive. Many people enjoy the sheer familiarity of the routine, even where, to the outsider, there may seem to be an unholy element of drabness or drudgery about it. When people talk about 'cementing' a relationship, they may be being more literal than they realize: the modes and mores of the partnership become set in concrete, and that is that.

For others, the routine may be too cloying or, where there has been change, it might have been too violent and disconcerting. It is evident that many marriages which have soldiered on, mildly and usefully enough through the years of work and family-rearing, become soured and acrid thereafter in retirement. It is partly that time takes its toll and partly that the marriage has a changed social base. Individuals react and change differently over time. A shared interest may wane for one and wax for the other. For example, the rate of interest in sexuality may, over time, vary considerably between men and women. ◄

To be tolerant, rather than irascible, in such changed circumstances, would be and is saintly. Many will feel, rightly according to their lights, that for the honour of the contract struck or, as the olde-tyme ballad beseeched, 'for the sake of the days gone by', the need to persevere is paramount.

SEE ALSO: ▷
A–Z OF HEALTH PROBLEMS:
Sexual difficulties   p. 196

Indeed, most people are more acutely realistic about these situations than some pundits might judge. One of the ways life is like a bowl of cherries is that it's full of stones: many acknowledge that nothing is ideal and that blessings must be counted. As ever, the ability, quietly and rationally, to talk out and over problems is a boon. Unfortunately, if it is a skill that has been left undeveloped during the Second Age, during the busy and distracting years of the marriage, it may not be too easy to sharpen later. But, in honesty, it is an attempt that should be made.

LOSS

Older age piles up losses like the team at the bottom of the fourth division. It is amazing how older people withstand them, for they sometimes fall like hammer-blows. You may lose your job, your spouse, your income or a substantial part of it, your house, your health, your friends. And you are expected to cope. If any one of those calamities was afflicted upon a 25-year-old, the world and his wife and his social worker would be running around headlessly trying to assist – but, for old people, they are seen more as natural and unavoidable disasters.

Which, of course, they are: and there is no point pretending otherwise. Although there are several comparisons among losing a job, a limb or a house, let us concentrate here on losing a spouse. There are, to voice a truism, two ways of losing a spouse. One is by death, and the other is by divorce or separation.

Divorce and separation

Apropos some of the previous discussion about the pressure of older age on marital composure, it is perhaps appropriate to mention marital break-down. Although only about 2 per cent of older age marriages are terminating in divorce, the figure was, until recently,

negligible and is growing with relative steepness. It might be argued, placing religious convictions to one side, that had social viability and cultural limitations been different in the past, then more of such marriages might have ended in divorce to a general increase in all-round happiness.

Where there is a mutual and satisfying agreement to part, then all may be as well as one could expect: a joint recognition that the members of a worthy partnership may now prosper more fruitfully apart. Where you are the partner taking the deep breath, and, having examined all the angles (social, economic, cultural . . .) are intent on breaking off the bondage of a difficult or intolerable relationship, then so be it. Neither of these are simple: they require enormous clarity of thought and courage of purpose. They carry their own brand of trauma.

Bereavement and grief

Imagine, then, the horror of being, as it were, deserted, cast aside, for obviously the longer the marriage, the more desperate the wrench. Although there is a self-evident distinction (you may want to kick his or her head in for treating you so badly) it is not unlike, in some degree, the loss of a spouse through death.

People try hard to offer counselling about and consolation in bereavement, and they are to be applauded. Unfortunately, and perhaps more than any other social distress, each bereavement is intensely unique. One may identify the portions of the loss, but it is a deeply private matter to apportion values to the parts.

Possibly the best advice to offer is: don't be surprised at any of your feelings. Some of them may seem eccentric, even unjust, but, if they are natural, they are the feelings to indulge. As with so many public social conditions, there is a model or prototype, that of the grieving widow, frowned upon if she abandons the weeds too early. . . . yet exhorted to pull up her socks if she mourns for too long.

Ignore the model. Do your own grieving thing, and hope to God your family, friends and neighbours will understand and support. For instance, it is apparent that grief is made manifest in some people in anger, an ire not unlike that felt for the errant spouse who has done a runner – a sense of having been left in the lurch. There may be guilt. There may be relief. There may be a startling reluctance to accept the truth of the bereavement. There may be a need to grieve volubly and over time and, as the vernacular teaches, 'get it out of your system'. There may be a need to pull down the shutters and turn swiftly to new opportunities.

So many conflicting and sequential emotions may be involved. Alarm, fear and anxiety may blur into anger or, in many cases, a searching for the person lost. Grief tends, perhaps, to occur in episodic pangs rather than in constant depressions, and the transitions into, through and out of these varying responses can themselves be alarming. Shutting out the memories may well vie with opening up to them. One can say little more than that grief is a proper form of reality, not to be ignored or underestimated by the bereaved or those around the bereaved.

If it is any cold comfort, society, in its wisdom, backs it both ways. Society tells you, at one and the same time, not to bottle it up and to try and forget about it. So be a natural mourner, and to hell with society. Society deserves what it gets, for society in all its manifestations has demonstrated fidgety unease in the presence of the bereaved spouse, somehow seeming to associate the loss directly with him or her. Thus loss can mean, sometimes imperceptibly, social and cultural losses, and it takes enor-

mous valour and determination to tackle these. One can do little more than post warning cones for the individual.

In practice, loss may be measured by lost roles. This is not meant disrespectfully or flippantly, but, however loving or compact a close relationship, it shows itself in social parts played. Thus a woman may lose not only a loved one per se, but one who exhibited his fondness and concern in the performance of tasks: a widow may have lost a gardener, a chauffeur and an accountant. In that life proceeds inexorably, these are often the immediately crippling aspects of loss. Then mourn the gardener, grieve for the chauffeur and weep over the lost accountant. Some feel it is unnatural, absurd or abnormal to miss someone for what he did rather than for what he was. What is real is what is missed, and that is the central truth.

Eventually, bereavement must or should be observed as opportunity. However deeply affectionate the relationship, and thus however acute the anguish, there must be some degree of dedicated energy freed for commitment elsewhere, in some new function, in some refreshing interest, or in some fresh person. What the hymn calls 'the ever rolling stream' of time, has in reality, no concept of the static. Ceaselessly, life journeys on, perhaps suggesting other chances of apt devotion or affection.

RETROSPECT

It is the last phase of life, and life-styles concern generations. Older people, self-evidently, are the last generation, irrespective of age, and that, it is sometimes forgotten, has its cultural appendages. Society is geared to a three-generation construct, child, parent and grandparent. Because of the demographic changes – in particular, the narrower range of the child-bearing years – this, too, is altering. Four and five generations are increasingly common, and already there are bewildering instances of an 'older' person who is someone's granny and someone else's grand-daughter at one and the same time. There may be a tension between the roles, seeking the solace of an elder's wisdom and sympathy one minute, being sought out for sagacity and support the next.

Being the last generation must mean that, however ambitious you remain about the future, much of life has been negotiated. It is this which gives a special and valued character to the last generation. The sorrow of youth is that it has no memories. Youth is more to do with prospects. Youth is concerned with the present or the yet to be. Older age, conversely, is a genuine time for retrospect. It is a time for memories, both good and bad. It is a time for coming to terms with life, and for guaranteeing personal identity. Older people are often elbowed by the young out of reminiscence. 'Stop rabbiting on about the past', they are sternly ordered, 'why don't you live in the present?' This is unfair and unhelpful. Life is more seamless than that, and should not be so compartmentalized.

Mastering the past

One's life-history is important in this connection, and is ripe for analysis. Everyone is an historical personage. With the help of oral reminiscence, the tape-recorder, visits and searches, photographs, plain old-fashioned writing, there is much to be gained by reconstructing one's self-history, in assessing the directions of advance or stagnation, and, in general, setting one's life against the prevailing canvas. In those who have accomplished this, one observes a measure of emotions and temper: nostalgia; buoyancy of confidence; self-awareness; contented relief and satisfaction; some pain, some honest pain;

mellow humour, and a dozen other traits. This older generation is, like other last generations but maybe more so, a repository of special memory. It is the final generation to know of a world pre-war, pre-television, pre-pop culture, pre-nuclear power, pre-common air travel, and so on. Perhaps there is a social duty, as well as an individual well-being, in retrospect.

Returning to roots

So much of what is written about older folk assumes that they are of British origin. It is true that the older echelon among ethnic minorities is not of the same proportion as in the indigenous population, for, obviously, it takes time for a recently migrant group to work through the process of ageing. But it is growing quickly, especially and currently among the European groups that have been in Britain many years, as well as British citizens from the New Commonwealth.

It has accurately been said of all these groups, ones that will soon grow in size, that they suffer a 'triple jeopardy', for, as well as the twin burdens of being old and often impoverished, they bear the additional strains of growing old in a second homeland. It is, and has been, the subject itself of a full book, and perhaps there is little one may do save exhort the elders within such groups that the pros and cons of the life-style of old age are as open to their interpretation as to anyone else.

The reason why this is an appropriate juncture to draw attention to that issue is because 'retrospect' is a really positive aspect. The past reminiscence of older people from overseas could contribute imaginatively to the total reckoning. That said, there is no denying the problems many of them face, and one hopes that all or much of the advice collated here will – on an individual basis – be seen as relevant.

Growing old in a second homeland has special considerations both for the elderly themselves, their families and the communities in which they live.

moodier consolation in a more Shakespearean view about the infinite finality of death, there must be few who do not suffer some pangs of ruefulness about the termination of a long life.

If there are styles of living, there are styles of dying, and, possibly out of retrospect, evolves an insistence that one leaves a mark, a memorial, in children well catered for or tasks well done on the mortal skein.

The hand that has dealt all these impactful changes in older age plays its final card, its ace of spades, by affecting the nature of the rites of passage at death. Put simply, death occurs more naturally and less sporadically. It is, happily, the lot of the great majority of people to live what we have come to interpret as a normal life-span. The relevant rites of passage – the burial or cremation ceremonial, for example of the Christian denominations – was mainly developed to heal rents in the social fabric when, as so often happened, death struck unheedingly. It is arguable, from a cultural, if not a theological, stance, that a different approach is appropriate.

The actual outcome of a conventional funeral is frequently the small and anonymous knot of uncomfortable mourners in the crematorium, somewhat guiltily playing through an inapt scenario. One hopes to give no offence, recognizing that, for some, the solace afforded is welcome and substantial. It is more about placing an alternative idea on the social agenda, one pleasingly exercised by several already, and one aimed at reinvigorating the rites of passage for the fresh mood of new old age.

It may be a proper comfort and pleasure to you, and will certainly be of considerable comfort and pleasure to those who survive, to plan (either over and beyond or instead of) the conventional ceremony. It could perhaps take

Signing off

At this level the reminiscence becomes more than the finding of self; it is a gift to the oncoming generations. The length of older age has been stressed, but although it may well be a third of life, it is, of course, the last third. Those negotiating it are, inevitably, nearer death. Whether one is cheerfully optimistic about eternal salvation or seeks a

the form of a memorial celebration of your life. It might be at or near a place you have found happiness; it might include music or readings or paintings that have given you especial pleasures or memories; it might include accounts or presentations of splendid family occasions; it might involve recordings or videos of favourite activities (your football team in action, for example, or a tape of the comedian you found funniest); it might call on relations, friends or neighbours to do their bit. The object would be that people would leave murmuring, 'George would have enjoyed that' or 'that exactly caught the nature of Gloria'. It would be a self-drawn and a living obituary. Above all, it should be shaped by your essence. The old comedian, Frank Randle, preferred funerals to weddings: 'Straight supping and no songs', he used to say. Help to endorse that positive attitude. Even if you do not wish to rise to the admittedly ornate business of prescribing your own ceremony, endeavour to make and leave a mark. We are told the universe is fifteen billion years old. By that measure, our three score and ten, or hopefully, four score seems puny and slight. All the more reason to ascertain that, as the song goes, your 'living has not been in vain'.

Coming to terms with death

Then there is death, the Reaper Himself. Let it be at once said that there is nothing wrong, weak or unusual about feeling apprehensive on the subject. Most people feel anxious about a visit to the dentist, so it's scarcely surprising that they might have more than a twinge or two about death. Fortunately there are philosophic positions to fall back upon, either of a religious or supernatural kind, or, for the humanist, the consolation that we have adequately filled our place and then vacated it, making way for the coming generation –

how selfish it would be to visualize a world of static immortality!

It does not help that death is not so open a theme as, say, it was in Victorian times. The Victorians were vigorously candid about death, and kept mum about sex. In the twentieth century we have shrieked about sex from the rooftops, and swept death under the carpet. Had Dickens written *The Old Curiosity Shop* today, Little Nell's central scene would have been a love-nest not a death-bed.

Like so many other topics addressed here, the preferred answer must be talk – talk to friends, your spouse, your family, your minister of religion, your doctor. . . . The point is that life and death alike must, for older people, become the subjects of more articulate and frank discussion. Too much has been kept under wraps. More than anything, we hope these thoughts and opinions will generate much franker discourse.

ENVOI

Older age, then, might be summed up as two negatives. It is not, assuredly, all beer and skittles. Equally, it is not all sackcloth and ashes. From the foggy recesses of mathematics lessons a myriad moons ago, the dim memory emerges that two minuses make a plus. It is a plus that allows and urges us to live well, and to yield gracefully, bequeathing a fond heritage. I was left my great grandfather's *A Pilgrim's Progress*, which has been valuable in recognizing the continuity of families and lives.

Even transferred to a mundane and everyday level, to the level of ordinary folk in ordinary situations, that analogy of the pilgrim in steadfast pursuit of a genuine and proper purpose is not a bad model. Boldness, tenacity, verve and imagination will and must be the virtues of the life-style of older age as we journey towards the third millenium.

MANAGING YOUR MONEY

SEE ALSO: ▷

MANAGING YOUR MONEY:
Earned income   p. 38

SEE ALSO: ▷

MANAGING YOUR MONEY:
Savings and investments
                 p. 41

The question of money is one which exercises most people approaching retirement – in fact nowadays the number of people enjoying the benefits of occupational pensions is expanding rapidly and people are being encouraged to think about the options at a much earlier age. On the whole, however, retirement means looking at income and expenditure differently from the way you have during your working life. Although many people receive a lump sum payment on retirement, and homeowners may well have paid off their mortgages, your net income will be less and you will need to take stock.

BUDGETING

Anyone who has never needed to budget before almost certainly will when they retire. Your whole lifestyle is changing, including the amount of money coming in and the things you need to spend it on. This is a good time to sit down and assess your financial situation. In fact, it is best to start organizing your finances well before you retire, if possible, even five years if you can manage it.

First, write down all the money you have coming in from whatever source. Then write a second list of all your outgoings, as shown opposite, above. When you deduct your outgoings from your income, you will see how much you have left over, or whether you are spending more money than is coming in. If that is the case, hopefully you can make adjustments by cutting back on less essential spending.

Planning while still at work

If you are doing this planning while you are still working, you could look for ways of boosting your income or releasing cash in retirement. These could include:

- putting more money into a pension scheme
- moving to a smaller house (the outgoings will be less, and if you own your home you could pay off the mortgage, if necessary, and invest any cash difference)
- buying a smaller car (which will be cheaper to run)
- looking for a part-time job to do after retirement ◀

If there is any spare money left over, you might want to save some of it. ◀ If you are still working and just coming up to retirement, it is sensible to put spare cash aside for later on. But remember that inflation will eat into your income to an extent, even when prices are not rising very fast. Four per cent inflation may be low, but it is still inflation! And when the cost of living is high, the effect is dramatic. For example, if inflation is running at 10 per cent a year, your nest egg will be halved every seven years.

Stretching your income

Once you have sorted out a household budget, you can look for ways of making your money last longer. You could delay paying bills until the very last moment, but you run the risk of leaving it a day too late so that your electricity or telephone is cut off. You then have to

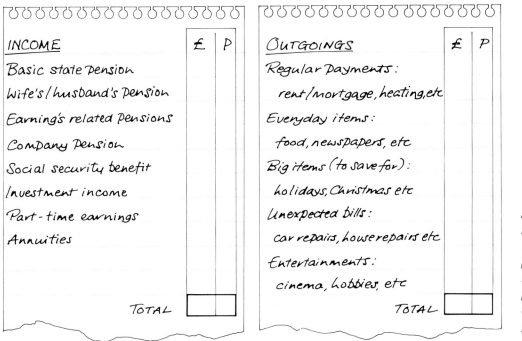

INCOME	£	P
Basic state pension		
Wife's / husband's pension		
Earning's related pensions		
Company pension		
Social security benefit		
Investment income		
Part-time earnings		
Annuities		
TOTAL		

OUTGOINGS	£	P
Regular payments:		
rent/mortgage, heating, etc		
Everyday items:		
food, newspapers, etc		
Big items (to save for):		
holidays, Christmas etc		
Unexpected bills:		
car repairs, house repairs etc		
Entertainments:		
cinema, hobbies, etc		
TOTAL		

Some typical entries to take into account when budgeting. You may not have all the possible sources of income on the left-hand side, but most people's outgoings are covered under the headings given on the right.

pay heavily to get them put back on again. A better way is to spread the cost throughout the year. This works to your advantage for most bills, except for car tax. If you buy a six-monthly licence instead of paying once a year, it costs an extra 10 per cent.

Local authorities will let you pay rates over 10 months of the year instead of all at one go at the beginning. Even if you had enough money to pay the whole rates bill at one go, it is better to keep that money in a savings account where it will earn interest and pay out a little month by month. When the community charge is introduced to replace the rates, ▶ you may be able to operate the same system.

Gas and electricity bills are obviously higher in winter than they are in summer. The gas and electricity companies usually have schemes which allow you to spread the burden out evenly by estimating how much you will owe for the whole year and dividing by twelve. You then pay the same amount each month, which makes the winter bills cheaper than they would have been, but the summer bills higher. If you start doing this just before the cold weather bills, you will benefit by paying the lower-than-average bills first.

The precise quarterly bills may not work out exactly the same as you are paying, so you can either settle the difference at the end of the year (they might owe you money) or carry it over to next year.

You can also buy savings stamps for gas, electricity, telephone bills and the TV licence. These are helpful for people who have difficulty meeting regular bills because they have a low income probably paid weekly in cash. You buy stamps as and when you have the money, for £1 or £5 each. This does mean you are paying the company in advance whereas if you wait until the bill arrives, you pay in arrears and hold on to your money for longer, but it can alleviate the worry of large lump sum bills coming at inconvenient times.

SEE ALSO: ◀

MANAGING YOUR MONEY:
The Community Charge
p. 49

Several banks will arrange a budget account for you to help spread your expenses evenly over the year. But you pay them a fee for doing this so it is better to save the money on a savings account and organize your own finances.

JOINT ACCOUNTS

There is a great advantage in husbands and wives having joint bank and building society accounts, because when a partner dies the surviving partner can simply continue using it. If the account is only in one partner's name, the other may not be able to draw money until probate has been granted.

GETTING THE BEST FROM BANKS AND BUILDING SOCIETIES

Almost everyone who wants to make the most of their money during their retirement will probably have contact with a bank or building society, and you may well want to go to them for financial advice. Budgeting is made a great deal easier with the services they offer – especially now that automatic tills have reduced queueing and don't necessarily confine you to banking hours. And a cheque account does reduce the worry of having to carry large quantities of cash about with you.

Banks and building societies are steadily growing more alike. The banks are copying the building societies' friendly, more informal approach, and many building societies now offer cheque accounts, personal loans, travellers cheques and have more flexible opening hours. Some banks even offer interest on current accounts in credit. It will increasingly be difficult to tell the difference between the two. However, this is good news for customers because it means banks and building societies are competing with each other to offer a better service, and puts the customer in a strong position to pick and choose.

You no longer need take the first offer you get, whether this is a savings account, loan or cheque account. By keeping an eye on what is around, you can switch from one to another. Banks and building societies now have to earn your loyalty and work hard to keep it. The days when a family stayed with the same branch of the same bank for generations have gone for good.

Financial advice

Another big change to these financial institutions came with the recent Financial Services Act which is designed to give greater protection to investors. Among other things, the Act states that anyone who sells investments, or advises about buying them, must choose between two positions. (The definition of 'investments' for this purpose is life assurance policies and pensions). Investment salesmen and advisers will either be 'tied', which means they sell only the products and services of one company, or they will be 'independent' and sell the best from a very wide range.

The Financial Services Act is designed to make sure that everyone handling investments is competent, solvent and acts in the best interest of the client at all times. Any insurance salesman must now make clear to you exactly what his situation is, whether he works for one particular insurance company or is independent and picks the best from a wide range. However, the rules do not affect everything the banks and building societies sell. The Act excludes ordinary deposit accounts, term assurance, loans and cheque accounts.

The smaller banks

As customers become more financially aware, and building societies move into banking services, all the big banks are sharpening themselves up. But the smaller ones are not being left behind. For example, Girobank at the Post Office now offers mortgages, overdrafts and cheque books. The Co-operative Bank has the advantage of thousands of outlets, through Co-op stores, which are open shop hours. The Yorkshire Bank still honours its commitment as the 'Penny Bank' and takes small deposits. The TSB (Trustee Savings Bank), the fifth largest of the banks, prides itself with being the most technologically advanced bank in the country.

Cheque accounts

Ever since they realized that building societies were about to move in on the market, banks have improved the facilities they offer on cheque accounts. Building societies now offer cheque accounts, too.

If you do not have such an account at the moment, you may wonder whether or not to get one. Since charges were abolished for accounts kept in credit, they are free and so there is a stronger case for having one. It means you can have less cash in the house, you can pay easily by cheque for goods and household bills and you can borrow without any trouble through an overdraft.

However you do not need to have an account with a bank to get bank services such as foreign currency and travellers cheques, a credit card, a mortgage or investment advice. You can get all these services from building societies and insurance salesmen without having a bank account as well.

Credit Cards

Credit cards also cut down on the amount of cash you need carry around. There are two sorts: Visa or Mastercard. All the banks and many building societies offer one or the other, although you can have as many as you like, provided your application is accepted. You do not have to open a bank account to have a credit card, but you do have to have a building society account to obtain one through a society.

Since you do not have to settle your whole credit card bill every month, only a minimum amount, the companies that run these cards make their money on the interest due on the balance. However there is then a danger of overspending and finding that you are never able to clear the debt.▶ But there is no reason why this should happen if your are careful – you do not have to use these cards for credit at all, but simply as an easy way to shop. Cheques can be quite limiting as the bank guarantee card system limits you to £50 per transaction. Although a few companies will accept a cheque for more than that with extra identification, on the whole they don't and the alternative, very unofficial, method is to write out more than one cheque. This can backfire because if your cheques do bounce, the bank will only guarantee one of them for a single transaction. With a credit card, all you have to do in the shop is to sign the voucher; you can then settle your credit card bill in full each month with a single cheque and you pay nothing extra in interest.

Debit cards

This is the new way of shopping. Debit cards are the plastic card equivalent of a cheque. Instead of writing out a cheque in the store, you hand a plastic card to the assistant who runs it through an authorization machine. The electronic stripe on the back holds all the information about your account, including an up-to-the-second balance. If you have enough money in your account, the cost of your purchase is immediately taken away and paid into the shop's bank account. If you do not have enough money, you cannot have the goods. This is a helpful system for people who do not like using credit cards because the transaction involves direct access to your current account. Again, it means you carry less cash and need keep less cash in the house.

Home banking

This is a comparatively new invention which enables you to keep track of your cheque account and pay bills from your own armchair. Three versions are available: one works through a television screen via Prestel; the second uses a small computer connected to your telephone; and the third – the simplest and

CREDIT CARDS

Remember that interest is charged on the outstanding balance of your credit card bill, so try to settle your bill in time to avoid paying more than you need for the goods you have bought.

SEE ALSO: ◀

MANAGING YOUR MONEY:
Repayment problems p. 41

HEALTH INSURANCE

People over the age of 60 are given tax relief on the premiums they pay for private health insurance from April 1990.

Health insurance will still be expensive for older people. But the tax will be allowed by charging lower premiums so even non tax-payers over 60 will benefit from lower premiums.

most effective – uses the ordinary telephone system. With this system, you can pay bills, check how much you have and move money from one account to another, at any time of the day or night. The only cost is for the telephone call.

If you already have a pulse telephone, one where the numbers make different sounds as you press them, you need no other equipment. If not, you can buy one of these telephones or use a pulse pad, which is very like a television remote control unit. By holding the pad over the telephone mouthpiece, you punch in the appropriate numbers for the information you want. A human voice answers, even to give you an up-to-the-minute balance, although this is a pre-programmed computer.

Home banking is extremely useful for anyone unable to leave the house. But it is also convenient for those who pay their bills at the very last moment and risk the post letting them down.

HELP FROM THE STATE

Whatever else people think about pensions and social security benefits, almost everyone agrees that older people should be entitled to help from the state – if they need it. It is worth stressing this because it should enable people to live their 'third age' – even their fourth and fifth – in dignity and comfort, and, perhaps most importantly, independence. Benefits are not hand-outs from charity: most older people either directly or indirectly will have contributed to them during their working lives through taxes or the National Insurance contributions they have paid. If you feel at all awkward about claiming benefits, contact someone from the Citizens' Advice Bureau or your local Social Services office, or ask the help of a friend or someone you trust, who can discuss your needs with you and support you in claiming what you are eligible for.

YOUR PENSION

Retirement is the time you finally cash in on the contributions you have made to a pension throughout your working life. It is too late now to make a different decision about buying a pension, but there is time to boost your eventual pension in the last few years leading up to retirement.

Broadly, there are two types of pension: state pensions and private, personal pensions.

State pensions

The state pension is made up of the basic pension which everyone receives plus, for those who paid in, the state earnings-related pension scheme (SERPS). (In practice, many company pension schemes are contracted out of SERPS). For those who were working between 1961 and 1975 there is also a small graduated pension.

Changes to SERPS

Changes are being made to SERPS, but they will not take full effect until after the year 2000. In between there are transitional arrangements based on a complicated formula so that no one loses out while the pension rules are changing. Existing pensioners are not affected by the new SERPS regulations, but those retiring after the end of the century will not receive as much from SERPS as those ending their working lives in the 1980s (see chart opposite).

Widows' pensions

The amount of widow's pension you receive depends on your age. You will get the full pension if:

- you are widowed at the age of 55 or older
- you are widowed under the age of 55 and have dependent children

You will get a reduced pension if:

CHANGES TO 'SERPS': WHAT THEY MEAN

NOW	LATER
SERPS is based on your best 20 years' salary	SERPS will be based on your lifetime earnings, including the years when your wages were low or even non-existent; this will make the total figure lower
The maximum you can receive is 25 per cent of your best 20 years' earnings	The maximum you will receive is 20 per cent of your earnings
When a pensioner dies his or her spouse continues to receive the full pension	When a pensioner dies, his or her spouse will receive only half the full pension

- you are widowed between the ages of 45 and 55. The pension is 7 per cent higher for each year over 45 (so, for example, a woman widowed at 47 will get 14 per cent more in pension than a woman widowed at 45). When a widow becomes 60, she can keep the widow's pension until she is 65, or change to the retirement pension.

Personal pensions

These have only recently come on to the market. They form part of a total shake-up of the pensions industry which gives far greater flexibility to men and women who want to make their own pension arrangements.

Older employees still in a company pension scheme should stay put; don't be tempted to leave it and buy a new personal pension. There will not be enough time before you retire to build up a good pension and if you change you will almost certainly lose your existing employer's contribution, so you would end up much worse off.

One big attraction of both company schemes and personal pensions is that you can take a tax-free lump sum when you retire as part of your pension. The only argument against this is that you then receive a smaller amount each month and have less to build annual increases on.

Many pension schemes also include an 'open market option', which means that, when you come to retire, you do not have to stay with the insurance company you have been paying into. At that point, you can if you prefer transfer your pension to another company giving better terms. Indeed, under the new pension rules a wider range of companies can sell pensions. Previously pensions were solely in the hands of insurance companies, but now banks, building societies and unit trust companies can all market their own pension schemes, so you can shop around.

Benefits for personal pension-holders

To encourage people to leave SERPS, the Government is giving rebates and

'SERPS' FACTS AND FIGURES

Who can claim?   Anyone who has made an average of 50 National Insurance contributions a year between the ages of 16 and retirement is eligible for a state pension.

People who have not made this number of contributions because of periods of full-time education, illness or unemployment receive credits instead, which entitle them to claim.

A married woman can claim a pension based on her husband's contributions. Until the changes in tax laws in 1990*, this pension will be taxed as part of her husband's income (see also 'Who forfeits'? below)

Divorced and widowed women over 60 can also claim on their ex- or late husbands' contributions.

Who forfeits?   Women who have stopped work to look after children, or who continued to work but paid the lower National Insurance stamp, receive no credits and so cannot claim a pension in their own right (see also 'Who can claim?' above)

People who have worked abroad receive no credit for these periods of absence, and so cannot claim.

When can you claim?   Women can claim between the ages of 60 and 65.

Men can claim between the ages of 65 and 70.

You must take your pension by the time you are 65 (for women) and 70 (for men) or you will lose it altogether

If you do delay taking your pension, you will increase the amount you eventually receive. A pension goes up by 7.5 per cent for every year it is unclaimed, even though you no longer have to pay National Insurance Contributions after normal retirement age.

*After the changes in the tax laws in 1990, a married woman who retires while her husband is still under 65 will, for the first time, be able to offset a pension based on her husband's contributions against her own tax allowance.

incentives to anyone coming out of the scheme to buy a personal pension. These sums of money can be contributed to a pension in addition to the usual maximum. This does make it more attractive to buy a personal pension but, even so, those over the age of 40 should think carefully before leaving a company scheme. And, as has been explained above, anyone over 50 should almost certainly stay where they are.

Boosting your company pension

The most you personally can contribute to a company pension is 15 per cent of your earnings (but there is no limit on your employer's contribution). If you are in a company scheme, there are several ways in which you can boost your pension. If the scheme is contracted into SERPS, you can take out a personal pension as well; alternatively, you can make Additional Voluntary Contributions (AVCs), which you can buy from your employer, an insurance broker or direct from the insurance company. The amount you put in is still restricted by the overall contribution limits, but it means that you can boost your pension by more than the company scheme allows.

As with ordinary pension contributions, there is tax relief on AVC payments but, unlike a personal pension, they will not enable you to take a tax-free lump sum.

OTHER STATE HELP

Pensions are the main form of State benefit for the over-60s, but there are several others which you may be entitled to but are not claiming – or which you may not even be aware exist! It is in your interest to know what all the benefits are, and to claim any that are yours by right.

Income support

This has replaced supplementary benefit and supplementary pension. It is intended for the unemployed, people over 60 who do not have enough money to live on, anyone too ill to work, and those staying at home to look after a

---

PERSONAL PENSION FACTS AND FIGURES

How much does it cost?

Anyone under 35 can put in a total of 17.5 per cent of earnings, including any contributions from their employer

Between 36 and 45, the limit is 20 per cent

Between 46 and 50, the limit is 25 per cent

Between 51 and 55, the limit is 30 per cent

Age 56 and over, the limit is 35 per cent

How soon can you claim?

You can retire and claim your personal pension at any time between the ages of 50 and 75, but of course the longer you go on contributing, the greater your pension will be.

How big a lump sum can you take on retirement?

The lump sum is limited to 25 per cent of your total pension contribution.

WIDOWS' BENEFITS

There are three social security benefits specifically for widows: widow's pension (see earlier), widow's payment and widowed mother's allowance. Your entitlement depends on your late husband's National Insurance contribution record.

Widowed mother's allowance is taxable and goes to someone receiving child benefit or who is pregnant when their husband died. Widows cannot claim both widowed mother's allowance and widow's pension at the same time.

Widow's payment is a single, tax-free, lump sum payment which goes to women who are under 60 when their husband died, or whose husband was under 65, or whose husband was over 65 but not getting a state pension.

SEE ALSO: ▶

HOME FROM HOME:

Housing benefit   p. 70

disabled relative. There is a set weekly rate, which is not taxable. Before October 1989, disabled people over 60 and all those over 80 get an extra premium which rises at age 75 and again at age 80. Disabled people over 60 get the same premium as those over 80. These new rates apply to couples even if only one partner reaches the required age or is disabled.

Anyone over 60 who is receiving income support will also have help from housing benefit. ◀ They automatically get free health prescriptions, dental treatment and travel to hospital for treatment.

Entitlement to income support is affected by the amount of savings you have. You can receive full income support with savings of up to £3000, but with savings of between £3000 and £6000 the amount is cut back. If you have savings of £6000 or more you will not be eligible for income support at all. Note, however, that if you own your own home its value is not counted as savings, and neither is the surrender value of any life assurance policy.

THE SOCIAL FUND

The Social Fund is the name given to the new scheme which gives loans, and occasionally grants, to people on income support. The loans have to be paid back, although there is no extra interest to pay. Whether you receive a loan or not depends on the local social security office. If you are turned down, you have no right of appeal, although you can ask them to look at your request again.

The Social Fund has three elements: budgeting loans; crisis loans; and community care grants. It can sometimes also help with the costs of a funeral.

Budgeting loans

These loans are intended to help spread the cost of buying essential items, such as a new cooker, clothing and bedding, over a longer period of time. But the Social Fund officers will only grant a loan if they believe you can afford to repay it, and any savings you have over £500 will affect the size of the loan.

Crisis loans

These loans are for emergencies; if your home caught fire, for example, you may get a crisis loan to replace basic items. Crisis loans are not restricted to people getting income support or any other social security benefit, but they still have to be paid back.

Community care grants

These grants are for people on income support who are returning to the community after being in some sort of residential care centre, and also for those who otherwise would have to go into care. This includes people coming out of hospital, nursing homes, hostels for the homeless, detention centres, and old people's homes. Savings over £500 will affect the size of the grant but at least it is not a loan and does not have to be repaid.

Funeral costs

These costs can partly be met with money from the Social Fund. But wherever possible the social security office will try to reclaim the money, from any savings over £500, from the estate of the dead person or from the insurance policies. If you need help like this you should claim before you start to arrange the funeral.

OTHER ALLOWANCES

Other allowances are available, too, for those with special needs. The following text explains those other allowances you may be entitled to, for example, if you are physically disabled.

Mobility allowance

This allowance is payable to those who become unable to walk before the age of 65 (the age is the same for men and women) and is an extra untaxed weekly allowance to help you get around. The money could be spent on taxis, for example, although you do not have to prove how you spend

the money. If you drive, or someone else mainly drives you around, you do not have to pay car tax. You can also apply for an orange car badge which allows you to park free.

Attendance allowance

This allowance is for people who need looking after during the day, at night, or both. They may be mentally or physically disabled. The money is paid weekly and is not taxable.

Invalid care allowance

This allowance goes to the carer looking after a disabled person, if they are unable to work because of the time spent with the invalid. ▶

Invalidity benefit and pension

If you fall ill while you are still working but are unable to work again, invalidity benefit replaces statutory sick pay or sickness benefit after 28 weeks.

If you first become unable to work at least five years before retirement age, you will also get an invalidity allowance. The younger you were when you became an invalid, the more you will receive. The amounts are small, but they are not taxable.

While you receive invalidity benefit, you are credited with National Insurance contributions, so you will still qualify for the basic state pension at retirement age. Meanwhile, you will receive a basic invalidity pension plus an additional pension.

Help with heating

The gas and electricity boards promise not to cut off the supply to any elderly people between the beginning of October and the end of March if they cannot pay the bills, but the money still has to be paid eventually.

SEE ALSO: ◀

THE CARERS' GUIDE:
Financial help   p. 173

THE TAX TRAP

If you continue to earn money after official retirement age, beware of the 'tax trap'. At present (1989–90), if you earn up to £11,400 a year, over the age of 65 you are allowed a much higher allowance before tax is deducted (the age allowance) than the rest of the population. However, if you earn even as little as £200 a year more you will have your age allowance reduced so that you are effectively being taxed at a higher rate than any employees under retirement age.

People on income support can go in 'fuel direct' if they already owe money for gas or electricity. It means that some of their benefit is automatically taken away each week to pay off the debt and pay for the current fuel they are using.

The Christmas Bonus

Pensioners have for many years received an extra £10 at Christmas. This may, or may not, continue.

EARNED INCOME AFTER RETIREMENT

People who continue working after retirement, whether full- or part-time, need to be alert to the tax-trap. This can make paid employment less worthwhile; it means you can pay a high rate of tax on a small amount of earnings.

The tax trap

The tax trap happens because of an arithmetic quirk in the tax allowance for older people, known as the age allowance. Those over 65 have a higher personal tax allowance than younger people; for those over 75, the allowance is higher still. The 65 and 75 age limits apply to both men and women.

If you are still working after 65, you can earn a modest amount (£11,400 per annum in 1989–90) and claim the age allowance. But once your earnings go above that amount, the age allowance is reduced by £1 for every £2 extra you earn – in other words, for every £200 of extra earnings, you lose £100 in age allowance. With independent taxation in 1990, husbands and wives will each be entitled to the earnings limit. Until then, the figure is the same for single people and couples.

The tax trap bites into earnings which are just a little over the limit. Compare the position of two people aged between 65 and 75 years; one earns £11,400 and the other earns £11,600 per year. The person with a salary of £11,600 has earned an extra £200 a

year, but has also had to pay an extra £75 in tax, and has only an extra £125 in take-home pay in the year. The reduction in age allowance which is caused by that simple £200 per year more, effectively means that, instead of the usual 25 per cent, the tax on the £200 is 37.5 per cent, when even the richest people in the country only pay tax at 40 per cent.

The earnings rule

This iniquitous rule was scrapped recently. It used to mean that in the first five years after retirement, anyone who continued working was penalised.

If you needed to draw your pension while working, your pension was cut once earnings were more than £75 a week and the state pension was completely taken away when they reached £79.

At the ages of 65 for women and 70 for men, however, the rule disappeared. But now it has been abolished for everyone and once you reach the official retirement age you can take the state pension and earn as much as you like without losing your pension.

However, if you can afford to live on your wages and delay taking the pension, it increases in value for the first five years.

National Insurance

Even if you do continue working after the normal retirement age, it is worth noting that you no longer pay National Insurance contributions on your earnings. This represents a significant gain to your net take-home pay.

BORROWING MONEY

The whole moral attitude to borrowing and buying on credit has changed. So much so, in fact, that people now boast about how much money they owe and how many credit cards they have.

Lending companies have reacted by making loans very easily available. You can walk into almost any high street store and come out with several hundred pounds' worth of goods, and you can borrow money with no questions asked from a wide range of sources. Banks are the traditional place for personal loans, but now building societies are also allowed to lend money for any purpose you like, such as going on holiday, buying a car or buying clothes. So it is more important than ever to know how much loans cost and what is involved. Borrowing small amounts of money requires a different approach to borrowing large sums if you are going to get the best value. A high interest rate on a loan makes borrowing less affordable.

Annual percentage rate (APR)

This is the key interest rate to look for. Usually advertisements show two rates of interest. One is the 'flat' rate and the other the 'true' rate of interest, or APR. The APR is always higher because it includes the hidden extra charges involved in borrowing money, such as an arrangement fee.

Bank loans

Banks have several different types of loan for various purposes. (Most have free leaflets describing the different types.) The simplest and most flexible is an overdraft.

Overdraft Provided you arrange an overdraft with the bank manager beforehand, you can write cheques on your current account even when you have no money left. You only pay interest when you are 'in the red' (i.e. overdrawn); as soon as your account is back in credit, perhaps when your pension is paid in, you stop paying interest.

But there is an expensive catch. Banks make no charges for current accounts as long as you stay in credit. But if you become overdrawn, *in addition* to the cost of borrowing, you will pay for every cheque that goes in and out of your account. This can make overdrafts quite expensive.

Personal loan Personal loans have a higher APR than overdrafts, but there

---

YOUR RIGHTS AS A BORROWER

Whenever you buy on credit, you are protected by the law against high pressure salesmen. But once you have signed an agreement you can only change your mind in very specific circumstances so it is important to be sure you understand what you are getting into before you sign. This means reading the small print.

Still you have to be careful because it is the last signature on the agreement that counts. So if a husband signed the form in the shop and then took it home for his wife to sign, you lose the right to cancel because the wife has never seen the salesman.

The only time you are allowed a cooling-off period is when you have had a face-to-face interview with the lender (a telephone conversation doesn't count) and you then sign the agreement in your own home. You must have done both of these to be allowed to change your mind.

The law also provides double protection if you buy faulty goods on credit. If you pay cash, you take up the matter with the retailer.

If you have bought on credit, you still go back to the shop in the first place but if they won't put it right you can then apply to the credit company for compensation.

However you must continue the payments while you sort out the problem. If you stop paying you have broken the agreement.

WHAT TO ASK BEFORE BORROWING

There are four key facts you should know before signing any credit agreement:

How much is the APR?

How much will you pay each month?

How many months will you pay for?

Can you miss one or two payments without penalty?

are no cheque charges. The loan is agreed to be paid back over a fixed period, say two years, and during that time the monthly repayments will never change. The rate of interest you pay when you start the loan continues unchanged, regardless of what happens to interest rates elsewhere. If you need to borrow the money for a large item, such as buying a car, you may well find this the most convenient, since you know your repayments are fixed throughout the loan period.

Revolving credit This pay-and-borrow scheme is a more expensive way to raise money. You pay the bank an agreed amount each month, say £20, into a separate cheque account. This allows you to borrow up to 30 times that figure at any one time. You could borrow £600 straightaway or let the money build up for a while. You pay quite high interest when you are in the red but you receive interest, at a lower rate, when in credit.

Building societies

Building societies are no longer restricted to lending only for house purchase. Many of them will now lend up to about £7500 for other purposes, too. Like a bank's personal loan, the interest rate does not change once the loan starts, and the rates are very similar to those of the banks.

The building societies that offer cheque accounts will also allow overdrafts and again these are very much in line with banks' terms.

Other sources of borrowing

As well as approaching your bank or building society, there are other ways of raising the money you need, but consider carefully before you do borrow – some methods are more risky than others.

Secured loans You will often see advertisements for secured loans in

popular newspapers. It is extremely important to understand what a secured loan involves, because it means that you put your house up as security. This is why secured loan advertisements say, 'Sorry, no tenants' or, 'Specially for homeowners'.

A mortgage is a secured loan. But banks and building societies are responsible lenders. Many of the other people advertising 'secured loans' do not have the same respectability and are more likely to throw you out of your home if you fail to pay.

Money shops These are high street outlets, similar to banks, but with a deliberately more approachable look. They are open office hours and on Saturdays and offer loans and savings accounts, but the interest rates on loans are more expensive than banks'.

Money brokers These are middle men who will negotiate a loan for you. There is no reason at all why you need use a moneybroker because credit is now so easily available.

If you are tempted to ask a broker because you have been turned down by a bank or building society, think very carefully first. The only reason a bank will not lend you money is if they think you cannot pay it back. So, if you have been turned down, it is probably better to wait before trying to borrow more.

Money lenders These people lend their own money to borrowers. Only very desperate people would go to money lenders, who charge very high interest rates indeed and waste no time demanding their money back forcefully if you are slow in paying.

Life assurance If you have an endowment life assurance policy, you can borrow against this. It is a cheap way of borrowing because you only repay the interest until the assurance policy matures. Then the capital sum is repaid from the pay out on the policy. However, this does mean that you will receive less than you otherwise would from the insurance policy when it matures.

Credit unions Credit unions deserve to be better known. They are formed by groups of people who have something in common – perhaps they belong to the same church, or work together, or live in the same area. Everyone in the group pays in a small amount of money each week, then those who need can borrow out of the pool. The maximum you can save is £2000 and the most you can borrow is £4000. The interest rate is fixed at 1 per cent a month, which is very cheap.

Buying on credit

Credit cards These plastic cards are an easy way to shop on credit. Thousands of stores accept them, whether Barclaycard, Access, Trustcard or another bank's Visa card. The danger is having this credit sitting in your pocket and being tempted to spend too much. But if you trust yourself to handle a credit card sensibly, it is a flexible and economic way of managing your money. ▶ You only start to pay interest when the bill is due, which is up to six weeks after you actually buy the goods. Then, if you pay the bill in full, there is no interest anyway.

Shops also offer their own credit cards, but they are usually more expensive than the banks' and you can only use them in one chain of stores.

Cards such as American Express or Diners Club are not credit cards – they are 'charge cards'. You can spend as much as you like with them, but you have to pay off the whole bill every month. And you have to pay an annual fee to have one of these cards.

Mail order Buying on mail order is not strictly credit because there are no interest charges, but you normally have an extended period in which to pay. Mail order catalogues are becoming more fashionable and the prices and range of goods more in line with chain stores, which makes mail order an economic way to shop.

Hire purchase (HP) This is now mainly used when buying cars or large items of furniture. HP terms vary enormously from company to company, so check what different companies offer before going ahead. Even if a salesman offers to arrange HP for you, you can still approach a finance company direct if you prefer.

Repayment problems

If ever you get into difficulty with debt problems, the one important rule is to face up to them straightaway. You will not make debt go away by ignoring it. If you offer to pay a little every week or each month to all the people you owe money to, they are more likely to give you longer to pay off your debt. But if you ignore their warning letters and do not get in touch, credit companies will assume you are deliberately trying to avoid payment.

Once you start getting into serious debt, it is very hard to climb out of it. You may feel the need for help if it is becoming a problem; the Citizens Advice Bureau can offer free, confidential advice so try to go and see them as soon as possible.

SAVINGS AND INVESTMENTS

Retirement is more often than not the time when you start cashing in on your investments, but advice on saving is still relevant if you want to set money aside for a specific occasion. If you are approaching retirement or decide to take up another job even though you have officially retired, you will probably want to make the best use of your money while you are still earning. Your choice of where to invest depends very largely on what you eventually want the money for and your temperament.

SEE ALSO: ◁

MANAGING YOUR MONEY:
Credit cards   p. 31

DEALING WITH DEBT

▶ Don't borrow more money than you can comfortably afford to pay back.

▶ If you do get into debt, contact your creditors immediately.

▶ If debt problems begin to pile up, contact your Citizens' Advice bureau for free, confidential advice.

Reasons for saving

The first thing to be clear about is what you are saving for: this will affect the type of investment or savings plan you choose.

For example, you may decide to put aside spare money for use in 10 or 15 years' time when you expect to spend more on health care or taxis. In this case, you need an investment which allows the capital sum to grow rather than one paying good interest: you want an investment that promises 'growth'. Unit trusts and investment trusts are an example.

If you are saving for next year's holiday, however, you need a short-term savings account, such as a building society's, which pays good interest, and allows you to take out the lump sum that you originally put in plus the interest it has accrued. This is an investment for 'income', but it need not be regular monthly income.

If you are investing to boost your pension, you should look for an investment paying a good rate of interest each month. With many accounts, you only receive interest twice a year or even annually.

The risk factor

There is an old saying which is very true: the greater the return, the greater the risk. The more interest an investment promises, the more likely you are to lose your money. With some investments, you could lose every penny you put in if they go badly wrong. Losses are not restricted to the interest you might have received.

While you are working, it is reasonable to take a higher risk if you can afford to lose some money. But in retirement, you most likely want to be more cautious. Only you can decide the degree of risk you want to take. Of course, if you have some spare money to gamble with and want to invest

SEE ALSO: ▷

MANAGING YOUR MONEY:
Income tax   p. 46

CHOOSING THE RIGHT KIND OF INVESTMENT

Here are some of the points to bear in mind before you start to save:

☐ Are you saving for the short or long term?

☐ Will you be saving regularly?

☐ Will you want to take your money out at short notice?

☐ Are you prepared to take a risk with your money?

☐ How will saving affect your tax situation?

---

for excitement, that is a different matter.

Period of notice

'Period of notice' refers to the time it takes to withdraw money you have invested, and you may not always be able to withdraw it as you like – you may even be penalized for withdrawing it too early.

Generally finance companies pay a higher rate of interest the longer you agree to leave your money with them. But this is sometimes waived if you have several thousand pounds invested.

Tax on investments

By law, tax on the interest payable on most investments is now automatically taken away *before* the interest is paid to you. In most cases, you cannot reclaim the tax, even if your income is low enough for you not to pay any tax normally. ◀

Non-reclaimable tax Banks and building societies pay out interest after deduction of tax which cannot be reclaimed, so non-tax payers should steer clear of these, unless the *net* interest rates (rates after tax has been deducted) are even better than the *gross* rates (rates before tax has been taken away) paid elsewhere.

Reclaimable tax Unit trusts and shares also pay dividends after deducting basic rate tax. But in this case you can ask the Inland Revenue to pay the tax back to you.

Gross payments The only place that pays out gross, without the bother of getting the tax back, is in National Savings investment accounts and various saving bonds.

Tax-free investments These are rare, but are useful to high-rate tax payers. They include National Savings certificates and Premium Bond prizes.

Starting to save

As soon as you have a little to save, you should start with an easy access bank or building society account. Once you have about £500 for emergencies, then you can think about other types of investments, or continue saving in the same account if you prefer.

There are many places now that take small, regular monthly contributions to a savings account. This is a good way to build up a pool of money without feeling the pinch, particularly if you want to save for a new coat or a holiday.

Banks and building societies have regular savings accounts. But so too do unit and investment trust companies, although these are not for short-term savings.

National Savings These are rock-solid, safe investments issued by the Government. Sometimes they pay a rate of interest competitive with other investments, sometimes they pay less. National Savings certificates and Yearly Plan are completely tax-free. All other National Savings Accounts pay

their interest gross, and are particularly useful for non-taxpayers.

Building society accounts Building societies now offer a wider range of savings accounts than they used to. Some sell unit trusts and others will even buy and sell shares for you. But the basic accounts are still available. The more you save and the longer you leave it untouched, the higher the rate of interest you will receive, and small building societies sometimes pay a better rate than the larger ones.

All interest is paid after basic rate tax has been deducted and you cannot claim the tax back. Building society investments are safe and you can buy them at any high street branch.

Bank accounts Banks have a similar range of accounts to building societies. If you have money sitting in an ordinary bank deposit account, this will be earning a very low rate of interest, but you can almost certainly move it to another account to earn more. You can walk into any bank branch and ask for information.

Stocks and shares This involves buying shares in companies which are quoted on the stock market. It is risky because share prices go down as well as up so you could invest £500 on Monday and see it fall to £250 by Thursday. But you stand to gain in two ways from owning shares. Over a longer period of time, the price of shares is more likely (although not guaranteed) to rise so you could take out more than you put in. Meanwhile, the shares should be paying dividends twice a year so you have a little income from them as well.

If you do buy shares directly in the stock market, you should buy into several different companies to spread your risk. It is not worth even thinking about unless you have at least £1000 to spare. Tax is deducted before dividends are paid but non-taxpayers can reclaim it.

Over the past few years, the Govern-

WITHDRAWING YOUR MONEY

Always watch out for time penalty clauses when thinking of withdrawing money from high-interest savings accounts. Sometimes you can only get your money back by forfeiting three months' interest, which could wipe out any gains you have made.

ment has been selling a number of nationalized industries back to private shareholders. For many people, this has been a first step in buying shares. But these privatization issues are not typical of buying shares, not least because most of them immediately rose sharply in price.

Conversely, others have been issued at a price far higher than their market value, so private investors have had to pay over the odds. There are no charges involved in buying any new issues whereas buying and selling through a bank or stockbroker costs about 5 or 6 per cent of your investment. However, if you do want to invest in stocks and shares other than the new 'privatization' issues, you can do so through a bank, some building societies, stockbrokers, or increasingly, through 'shares shops' such as those set up in larger branches of Debenham's department stores.

Unit trusts This is a less risky way of buying shares. Your money buys 'units' and your investment is combined with everyone else's in the same unit trust. A professional fund manager looks after all the money, which is large enough to invest in a wide range of companies. Hopefully, the manager is skilled enough to make your investment earn more than you could, although you cannot rely on this.

You have to pay to deal in unit trusts. There is an initial charge of about 5 per cent which is hidden in the difference between the buying and selling prices. Then there is an annual charge of around 1 per cent. You can buy unit trusts by replying to advertisements or contacting a company direct. You will find their names and addresses in most national newspapers as this is a competitive business and they advertise widely.

Investment trusts These are similar to unit trusts in that your money is pooled with others to spread the risk. But they have a wider scope. An investment trust company is itself quoted on the Stock Exchange and its sole business is buying and selling shares in other companies.

Many investment trust companies now have regular savings schemes which is a good way to start because this is the only way you can buy directly from the company. Otherwise you have you go through a stockbroker or bank. Charges are lower than for buying shares or unit trusts but they are not allowed to advertise individually in newspapers. To find an investment trust company, contact the Association of Investment Trust Companies. ◄

Investment trusts' big selling point is the 'discount'. Mostly the price you pay for an investment trust share is less than the total value of the investments the company itself owns. Of course this means that you sell at a discount too. If you are lucky, you can buy at a large discount and sell at a small one.

Personal equity plans (PEPs) This comparatively new type of investment enables you to buy shares and pay no tax on the profit. But the sums you can invest are very small and PEP managers usually restrict your choice of companies. Many banks and unit trust companies run PEP schemes.

Life assurance and annuities Life assurance is often sold for investment rather than protection purposes. It is a long-term investment with very severe penalties if you cash in early and this makes it unsuitable for older people. However, annuities are a different case. These involve giving a large lump sum of money to an insurance company, in return for receiving a regular income for the rest of your life.

The rate of interest is fixed when you sign the annuity and you can never get your money back. But, whatever happens, you will continue to receive an

SEE ALSO: ▷

RESOURCES & BACK-UP:
Savings and Investments
p. 217

income until you die. The older you are when you start, the better deal you get from an annuity. Alternatively you can buy a deferred annuity which does not pay out straightaway but at an agreed date in the future.

Older homeowners can mortgage their house to raise the money to buy an annuity. There is tax relief on the interest repayments. (See also Home Income Plans, below).

Where to go for advice

Where to go for advice on savings is the hardest question to answer. New legislation rules that everyone giving financial advice must be registered and must choose between selling the products of one particular company or from a wide range. This applies to all investments except bank and building society deposit accounts but includes life assurances and pensions. ▶

The only safe way of getting independent, unbiased advice is to pay a fee. Then you know your adviser has only you to please and does not need to earn commission. Even so, there are no examinations to prove how experienced or competent a financial adviser is, so whoever you go to, think carefully before committing yourself, and be careful not to set so much aside for savings that you leave yourself short of cash for everyday living expenses.

MAKING MONEY OUT OF YOUR HOME

One of the biggest problems for older homeowners is finding the money for repair bills. You may be sitting on a goldmine with the mortgage paid off and a house worth 100 times what you paid for it, but that is no help if you need £3000 for a new roof. There are several ways you can make money out of your house, but none is entirely satisfactory.

You could earn extra income by taking in lodgers, although there are obvious disadvantages in this for many people. You may be happy to sell the house and trade down to a cheaper one, which may be easier to look after (and you will keep all the money you make from the sale because the profits from selling a house are not taxable). Or you can stay put and use your house as security to raise the money you need, in the following ways.

Taking out a mortgage

This is a cheap way of borrowing a lump sum of money from a bank or building society. There are several types. An interest-only mortgage may suit you, because it is helpful for someone with a valuable property but not a large income. As the name suggests, you repay only the interest each month, and the capital borrowed is repaid after you die by selling the house. However, because of the complicated paperwork demanded by the Consumer Credit Act, many building societies have stopped this type of lending for loans under £15,000, so if you need only a small amount, you may have to consider another alternative. If you can afford the cost of the repayments, a conventional mortgage may be more suitable.

Home income plan

Under this scheme, you take out a loan on your house and use the money to buy an annuity. This is a type of pension which provides you with an income for the rest of your life. Once you have bought the annuity, you cannot get your money back. You must be at least 70 before you are eligible – insurance companies do not want you to be too young when you start, or they would have to pay out too much money over a long period of time.

Home reversion scheme

This provides a lump sum or an income for the rest of your life, but in this case you actually sell your house to a finance

SEE ALSO: ◀

MANAGING YOUR MONEY:
Financial advice   p. 30

company. You continue to live there as a tenant paying a nominal rent for the rest of your life.

If you do not want to renounce your entire interest in your property, you may be able to sell only half and keep an interest in the other half, but you will only receive half as much money.

Consider very carefully before opting for this way of raising money. You are selling your house to an outsider and, although you still live there, someone else owns it.

TAX IN RETIREMENT

It is not unusual for people to have direct contact with the Inland Revenue for the first time in their lives when they retire. Many on PAYE have never filled out a tax form, and most people with straightforward tax affairs are only sent a form every four or five years. Filling out tax forms is tedious but you might actually save yourself tax if you do it. By law you need not pay a penny more in tax than the absolute minimum. Inland Revenue staff will help you claim all the allowances you are due, if you ask for their help.

Types of taxation

There are two main types of tax: 'direct', such as income tax; and 'indirect', which includes the VAT you pay on almost everything you buy. There are various ways of cutting the direct tax you pay and it is quite legal to avoid tax. It is a different matter to 'evade' tax, which is a crime. But VAT is unavoidable for private individuals, whereas those who offer services or products can pass the cost of it on to clients or customers.

Income tax

Only those living on less than about £2000 a year pay no income tax. Even so, you do not have to pay tax on every pound you have. Everyone has a personal tax allowance, which is the amount of income they are allowed before starting to pay tax. Allowances are fixed every year by the Chancellor of the Exchequer and are announced at the Budget.

Married couples have two allowances: the married man's allowance and the wife's earned income allowance. At the age of 65, and again at 75, their allowances increase.

Single people have the single person's allowance. This is the same figure as that allowed to a married woman and like her allowance, it increases at the ages of 65 and 75.

A widow can claim a bereavement allowance (£1490) in the year her husband dies and the year after; from the day her husband dies, she can also claim the single person's allowance (the amount she can claim will depend on her age).

DIRECT TAXATION	
TYPE OF TAX	**WHEN PAYABLE**
Income tax	On all earnings over £2000 per year and on savings
Capital gains tax	On large profits from selling valuables
Inheritance tax	On some gifts during your lifetime, and possibly on your estate when you die

A widower continues to receive the married man's allowance in the year his wife dies; after that, he reverts to the single person's allowance. (With both allowances, the amount he can claim will depend on his age).

Single parents with dependent children receive an extra allowance (the same amount as the bereavement allowance). In addition, they can claim the single person's allowance.

Blind or partially sighted people receive a small extra allowance (currently £540), which they can claim in addition to any other allowances they may be entitled to. If both husband and wife are blind, they can claim twice the amount.

Tax relief

If you have certain regular outgoings, you are allowed an even greater amount of tax-free income: this extra allowance is known as tax relief. The two most common outgoings on which relief is given are the interest paid on mortgages of up to £30,000, and all contributions into a pension. The amounts you pay in interest, contributions or any other eligible outgoings are added to your other tax-free allowances, and you only pay tax on the income which is left.

Capital Gains Tax

You may have to pay capital gains tax if you sell a valuable object or make a large profit from investments. However, you can make a profit of several thousand pounds a year before paying tax and even then some gains are tax-free. For example, husbands and wives never have to pay on anything they give to each other. But even if you give a valuable object to another person such as a piece of jewellery or a painting you still may have to pay capital gains tax. This tax can be paid either by you as the giver, or the recipient. The taxman does not mind who pays.

You can make a profit out of some things without ever paying capital gains tax. Your house (but only one property) is the main one; others include a car, betting winnings, premium bond prizes and the proceeds of a life assurance policy.

If you run your own business and sell it when you retire, although you will have to pay some tax on the sale, you are taxed quite leniently on any profit you make.

Inheritance tax

Many people who now own a house could find their heirs paying inheritance tax when they die. If your assets, including your home, are worth around £100,000, then inheritance tax will bite into your estate.

There are various ways you can reduce this bill, mainly by giving away as much as you can during your lifetime. According to the 1989 figures, you are able to give away up to £118,000 without paying any inheritance tax at all, and this figure is expected to rise annually in line with the rate of inflation. In addition you can give away a further £3000 every year free of tax. This figure can be even more to a child or grandchild when they get married. But if you want to give away a larger and therefore potentially taxable sum, or its equivalent in, say, property or jewellery, then the 'seven year rule' applies. This means that provided you live for another seven years after the time of the gift, there is no tax to pay at all. In any case there will be less tax to pay even if you die before the end of the seven-year period. The only proviso is that you do not keep any interest in the assets you give away. This means that if you want to avoid tax, you cannot give the family home to your children and still live in it yourself.

You should not, however, get too carried away with the idea of saving tax.

SEE ALSO: ▷

MANAGING YOUR MONEY:
The tax trap   p. 38

Never give away so much during your lifetime that you leave yourself with insufficient to live on. Always keep enough money to pay the heating bills, buy good food and enjoy yourself.

Tax-free income

A few sources of income are completely tax-free. These include the Christmas bonus paid to pensioners, disablement pensions from the armed forces, and interest on National Savings certificates.

If you sell your home, you pay no tax at all on any profit from higher house prices. So, if you sold up and moved into a rented flat, you could pocket all the money you had from selling, apart from the expenses involved in moving.

If your only source of income is the basic state pension, then you will not have to pay tax because it is below your personal allowance. But if you have a company pension as well, then both pensions are taxed. In practice, all the tax is taken off your company pension by your ex-employer because the Departments of Health and of Social Security do not have the resources to take tax. The result is that the company pension looks very heavily taxed.

Querying a tax bill

Whenever the taxman sends you a bill or assessment that you disagree with you have the right to query it. If your affairs are quite complicated, then you need an accountant to help. But for most people needing advice, tax enquiry offices at PAYE Income Tax centres, or the Citizens Advice Bureaux, are fully able to help.

New tax rules

In 1990 many of these tax rules are being changed. The most significant change allows married women to look after their own tax matters for the first time. Older married women will qualify

for the higher age allowance. ◀ In their own right also for the first time; they will no longer have to wait until their husbands reach 65. Moreover, they can offset this allowance against any income, including a state pension based on their husband's National Insurance contributions. Until the tax changes take effect, these pensions are taxed as the husband's income and the wife cannot use her wife's earned income allowance to offset it, unless her pension is based on her own contributions.

Another change affects all elderly people, whether single or married. They will now qualify for a personal allowance based on their own age. But, it will also mean that married women will be taxed higher on their investment income. Until then, husbands pay tax on their wives' savings at the highest rate of tax they pay, even if the wife pays no tax at all, as the income from savings is simply added on to the husband's total income.

The community charge

Rates – which are a form of tax on property – are being replaced by the community charge, or poll tax. The changeover takes place in Scotland in 1989 and then England and Wales a year later. Instead of the tax being assessed on the property, poll tax is raised on the individuals living in the house.

Everyone over 18, including those on income support, will have to pay at least a contribution towards the poll tax. It is known as the 'poll tax' because the electoral register will be one source of information about the number of adults living in a house. Those receiving social security benefit will pay 20 per cent of the total. Otherwise, with only a few exceptions, everyone within a local council area pays the same amount of poll tax, regardless of the size of their home, whether they own or rent it, or who their landlord is. However, those living in old peoples' homes and long-stay hospital patients are among the very small minority who will not have to pay any poll tax.

Two adults living alone in a house will probably pay a similar amount in total poll tax as they do in rates. Poll tax probably benefits single people living alone as they should pay less in poll tax than in rates. Three or more adults in a house will probably be worse off because each will have to pay poll tax.

INSURANCE

Insurance is an important aspect of finance because the annual cost of premiums can often be overlooked when assessing the overall budget. Although life assurance premiums are generally fixed over a particular period, insurance premiums for property, personal belongings and cars have been climbing steeply in recent years, well ahead of inflation. However, this sort of insurance should not be something you skimp on if you can afford it.

Life assurance

The essential aim of life assurance is to provide a sum of money for your dependents when you die. But in recent years, the industry has switched more to selling life assurance as a form of investment. However, protection for your dependents, or anyone who would suffer financially from your death, is still important. There are various types of life assurance, suitable for different circumstances.

Term assurance This is the cheapest and most basic form. You buy term assurance for a fixed number of years and, if you die within that period, the insurance policy pays out. If you survive the period, your dependents receive nothing.

Term assurance can be used to protect a repayments mortgage until the loan is repaid, or to meet a potential inheritance tax bill if you have given possessions away to beat the seven-year rule. ▶

Family income policy This is similar to term assurance but pays a regular income to your family instead of a lump sum.

Whole life assurance This is more expensive but there is no time limit. The policy will pay money to your dependents whenever you die. You keep paying regular premiums until then.

You can, if you wish, stop the policy at any time and get a sum of money. This is the 'surrender value'. But you will get poor value for this, particularly if you want the money within a few years of taking out the policy. For the first couple of years, you will get less back than you have paid out. So only start a life assurance policy if you intend keeping it going.

Endowment policy This is the most expensive and combines the best of both worlds. The policy will pay out on a fixed date in, say, 10 or 20 years' time. But if you die before then, your dependents will get the money.

You can take out an endowment policy timed to mature when you know you have a big expense coming: for example, if you have planned an exotic holiday for when you retire, or a visit to relations overseas.

If you are paying a grandchild's school fees, you can take out a range of policies timed to mature year by year. Because of poor early surrender values, you should plan well ahead for this type of use and make sure the policies mature when you want them to.

With-profits or unit-linked Life assurance is invested in several ways, the most common being with-profits or unit-linked. With-profits, which are invested in shares, are safer but less likely to show a dramatic rise. This is because bonuses are not directly linked

SEE ALSO: ◀

MANAGING YOUR MONEY:

Inheritance tax   p. 47

to investment performance, so in poor years insurance companies can cushion the effect by taking money from their reserves. As a result there are no big highs – or lows – as with unit-linked assurance, and bonuses are guaranteed.

Premiums for a unit-linked policy buy units in a fund, like a unit trust. The result is more volatile than a with-profits so could be either better or worse, depending on how well the fund is performing when the policy matures, since the amount you get back depends on the value of the units on that particular day.

Non-life or general insurance

A general insurance policy will pay out when an agreed but expected event happens. You need to insure your house, your car and your holiday. You can also choose to insure a range of special items: your computer, your pets, your garden fête against rain, for example.

Types of insurance

House contents insurance You need this insurance whether you own your home or live in rented accommodation. It can be very expensive, however, particularly in city areas, but is essential if you want recompense after a burglary or fire damage. You can insure for the replacement of your possessions at their current value, that is their low secondhand value, or you can buy a more expensive 'new for old' policy which pays out the cost of buying a new replacement.

An 'all risk' policy is more expensive still but will pay for repairing accidental damage, say if you spill medicine on an armchair. And it will pay if you lose something outside your home, for instance if a precious stone fell out of a ring in the street.

Retired people can sometime negotiate cut-price contents insurance. Because they are around the home more than those at work, they are less likely to be burgled. Taking adequate precautions against burglary may also lessen your insurance premium.

Buildings insurance
This insures the fabric of your home against natural disasters such as flood, fire and earthquake, but it also includes some items inside the house, such as kitchen units. Roughly, anything that you can leave behind when you move house is covered by buildings insurance; the rest comes under house contents insurance. Buildings insurance is usually compulsory if your home is mortgaged.

Motor insurance
This is compulsory by law but there are various grades of car insurance. Only someone with a horrendously bad record would take the legal minimum motor insurance because it only covers the driver if someone is killed or injured on a public road.

More usually, car owners choose between comprehensive or third party, fire and theft. Third party, fire and theft pays for any damage you cause to another driver or car, and repair after fire or theft of your own car. Comprehensive insurance is the most expensive but pays for all this plus accidental damage to your own car.

The longer you go without making a claim, the larger 'no claims' discount or bonus you have up to a maximum of about 60 per cent. Nearly everyone has a no claims discount of some amount. Some policies include an extra premium to protect this discount even if you make a claim.

Motor insurance has recently been

getting very expensive, although it varies according to where you live. Older people can often negotiate cheaper premiums if they have a good driving record, and you can cut the cost by restricting driving to yourself or one other named driver and by paying the first £50 or whatever of any claim.

Health care insurance

Paying for private health insurance is expensive for anyone. For older people it is prohibitively expensive – a 70-year-old will pay twice as much as a 45-year-old. Even so, you may choose to pay privately rather than wait for an operation. The important section to watch in any health policy is the exclusion clauses. You may well find that the very treatment you need to claim for is excluded.

Private health companies, however, now keen to attract new customers, are introducing lower priced schemes with fewer benefits. One such is only activated if you have to wait more than six, sometimes 12, weeks for an NHS bed. Another, at up to 50 per cent below the standard price, covers seven common operations: hernia operations, varicose vein surgery, hip and joint replacements, tonsillectomies, cataract removal and medically essential sterilization. But if you already suffer from one of these complaints before taking out insurance, it will not pay up. In any of these schemes you can choose to go into a private hospital or an NHS pay bed.

Holiday insurance

The most important element of holiday insurance is for medical treatment. But it is important to know exactly what is included and excluded from the policy you buy. For example, if you have been to see your doctor just before taking out the insurance, the company may refuse to pay a claim, even if you suffered a completely different illness on holiday. And policies vary in what they cover you for in different countries of the world.

The policies sold at the back of holiday brochures tend to be standard, economic insurance. If your circumstances are slightly unusual, it is worth going direct to a company for holiday insurance tailored to your needs.

If you are visiting an EEC country, you may be entitled to free or cheaper medical treatment. Four weeks before you go, pick up a leaflet SA30 from a social security office which tells you how to claim.

Pet policies

A few specialist insurance companies will insure animals for vets' fees if they become ill. But they only take animals starting at a young age.

Pluvious insurance

If you are responsible for organizing a garden fête or any occasion that depends on good weather, you can insure against it raining. That should compensate you for a loss of money if people do not turn up.

IF YOU DIVORCE

Many people do divorce later in life either on or after retirement. Many more find that during retirement their children go through divorce and need their help and support, so a knowledge of the legal and financial implications is useful.

Seeing a solicitor

Most people are confused and upset

when a relationship breaks down. Divorce for elderly people can create particular problems financially as it may be harder to provide financial security for both parties. It is therefore very important that legal advice is sought straightaway. The Law Society can recommend a solicitor specializing in divorce in your locality. Alternatively, the Solicitors Family Law Association has a list of practising divorce solicitors who subscribe to a code of practice. ◄ They aim to deal sympathetically, with a view to finding a solution for both parties to avoid confrontation where possible.

Financial claims
You each have the same financial claims (known as ancillary relief) against each other for periodical payments (maintenance) a lump sum payment and a transfer of property order (ie an order that the house be transferred from both of you to one party, for example), and the Court has very wide powers to deal with the property. You can also ask the court to decide who should keep the contents of your home.

The Court will look at all the factors relevant to each case, for example, the age of the parties, length of the marriage, income, capital, earning potential, needs of the partners and any disability, illness or similar situation. The Court then looks at both partners' assets and the income available from all sources and tries to balance the needs and resources of both parties by making a fair division of assets and income.

Conduct
The Court does not try to establish who caused the breakdown of the marriage. It is possible for either party to ask for the other's conduct (behaviour or treatment of the other partner) to be taken into account in the financial settlement when deciding what is fair but that

conduct must be very bad indeed and it is rare for the Court to be asked to consider it.

Procedures for financial claims
If agreement cannot be reached by the parties or their solicitors as to who should have what then the Court will decide what is to happen to the parties' assets and money.

There is a full exchange of documents between the parties such as bank statements, credit card statements, building society account books and so on, so that each party knows precisely what the other has. If agreement has still not been reached then the matter will be put before the Court.

Paying the costs of divorce
There is no rule that one or other party should pay the costs. It is usual for the Petitioner to ask the Respondent to pay the costs of the divorce itself but the costs of an undefended divorce are fairly small (approximately £120). Anyone with a very small income and very limited capital can apply for Legal Assistance for the divorce itself under the Green Form Scheme. Always ask your solicitor if you are eligible under the scheme. For financial claims full Legal Aid is available if you have relatively little capital and a low income. If you receive more than £2,500 from your divorce settlement, however, you have to repay your Legal Aid costs but if you receive a house as part of the settlement then the Law Society will take a charge over the house instead of immediate payment and will only demand payment once the house is sold. The charge bears no interest.

Loss of legal rights upon divorce
Possible loss of legal rights is one reason why you should seek a solicitor's advice immediately upon separation and certainly as soon as you receive a Petition.

SEE ALSO: ▶
RESOURCES & BACK-UP:
Legal help   p. 210

GROUNDS FOR DIVORCE

Irretrievable breakdown of marriage is now the only ground for divorce, but it has to be backed by one of the following facts:

► Adultery which is intolerable to the other party
► Unreasonable behaviour by one party to another
► Desertion by one party for two years
► Separation for two years followed by divorce by mutual consent
► Separation for five years

If you are a wife you will cease to be entitled to a Widow's Pension upon your husband's death once Decree Absolute has been pronounced. Your solicitor will advise you as to how you can be compensated for this loss through the divorce settlement.

If you live together

If you have been living together but are not actually married (legally known as cohabiting), you do not acquire the rights of spouses however long you live together. It follows therefore that if you part company you will not be able to apply for maintenance from your cohabitee, although upon separation you will be entitled to keep your own assets. In rare circumstances, you can show that you are entitled to part of the other person's assets by reason of the contribution you have made to them. In general, however, a cohabitee derives no financial benefit from the relationship.

MAKING A WILL

As you grow older it is natural to want to be sure about what is going to happen to your assets and possessions after your death. It is not always essential to involve a solicitor, if your affairs are at all complicated it is a good idea to consult one. If you make a will you can be sure that you have controlled what will happen to your money and other possessions after your death. It will also enable you to protect those closest to you by providing for them and it may save you tax or delay payment of tax ▶ and, last, but not least, it makes life simpler for those who will have to sort out your affairs after your death.

If you don't make a will

If you don't make a will you are said to be intestate. Your estate (all your money, assets and possessions) will pass to your nearest relatives in a strictly laid

down order. However, you should not assume, for instance, that if you are married your spouse will receive everything, because if you have children, they will receive a share, even if they are grown-up and self-sufficient.

In addition, it may take months and sometimes years to sort out your affairs and in the meantime your nearest relatives and dependents can be without money to live on. At worst, ugly litigation (court action) can arise over who should receive what.

Seeing a solicitor

You can buy will forms at stationers' shops but solicitors charge a relatively small sum for drawing up a will. It is money well spent because it is important that your will is clearly worded and that you understand any tax implications arising from decisions you want to make. If you are leaving money to children under eighteen then your solicitor will explain to you that Trusts (ie the holding of assets on someone's behalf) will probably have to be set up on their behalf and you will need to consider what powers you would like the Trustees (ie those who hold the assets) to have in dealing with the children's money. Generally, unless your assets are very small and you and your spouse jointly own your home and wish to leave your shares in the house to each other, you are well advised to ask a solicitor to draw up a will for you. Always enquire about the firm's charges for making a Will.

It is sensible to draw up a list of all your possessions, cash and savings, and to mark against them what they are worth. This will help your solicitor to advise you on any tax implications. Draw up another list of the people you would like to leave money or possessions to, with their ages, full names and addresses and the names of two Executors.

DIVORCE PROCEDURE

▶ **The Petitioner files for divorce (a Petition)**

▶ **The Respondent acknowledges receipt of the Petition**

▶ **A Decree Nisi (provisional decree or divorce) is granted**

▶ **Six weeks and one day later the Petitioner applies for Decree Absolute**

▶ **If the Petitioner does not apply, the Respondent can apply for Decree Absolute three months later**

NOTE: These stages are usually activated by solicitors for each party.

SEE ALSO: ◄

MANAGING YOUR MONEY:
Inheritance tax   p. 47

- ▶ Consider dependents before others if they face financial difficulty after your death
- ▶ Remember that illegitimate grandchildren now automatically inherit from grandparents unless specifically excluded
- ▶ Inflation may make the residue of your estate (what is left over after specific legacies have been paid) much larger than you anticipated so update your will every few years

Executors

Executors are the people named in the Will to carry out your instructions in accordance with it. Upon your death, your executors will apply for a Grant of Probate which is a Court certificate enabling them to deal with your assets, selling and realizing them in the way you have set out in your will. It is usual to have at least two executors especially if there is a possibility of a trust arising in favour of a child. Some executors employ solicitors to apply for Probate and deal with the estate on their behalf.

Anyone can be an executor but it is sensible to choose people younger than yourself, who are going to be efficient but able to deal with any tricky aspects of your will sensitively. It is usual to let them know that you would like them to act in this way for you. An executor can also be a beneficiary and it is often a good idea to choose grown up children. Many people choose a professional executor such as a lawyer or accountant as one of the executors but you should be aware that a professional executor will charge for his or her services, and this will come out of the estate.

You must sign your will before two witnesses who are not named to benefit from it. They should then write their names, addresses and occupations beneath your signature.

Changing or renewing your will

A will is known as a 'revocable instrument', which means that you can always make additions to it or make a new one. It is a good idea to update your Will when circumstances change and you should certainly make a new Will upon divorce or remarriage because divorce may make part of your Will invalid, and remarriage revokes any Will made before marriage.

Simplifying your finances

The advice on page 28 outlines ways of simplifying your financial position on retirement, but you need to do this too with a view to making things easier for your executors. Remember that only items owned solely by you will fall into your Estate. Joint accounts and jointly owned property automatically becomes the property of the survivor unless you have taken steps to separate your joint interests in it. This means, for instance, that if you own a home with your spouse as 'joint tenants', your spouse need not sell it on your death, nor does it fall to your Estate, because it automatically becomes your spouse's possession. You may want to consider transferring the house into joint names for this reason.

Finally, don't be secretive about finances. Leave a letter with your cheque books or some appropriate place setting out a list of your accounts and assets to help your Executors, and if you haven't updated your Will recently at least keep a note of any changes of address of beneficiaries.

Contesting a will

It is possible to contest a will because it is not valid by showing that the testator (person who made the will) was not of sound mind, or the will was not properly executed. A will can also be contested if the wording is unclear.

Certain people, principally spouses, former spouses and dependents (either children or adults) can apply to make a claim against the Estate of a dead person if they have not been provided for in the Will or think they have been inadequately provided for in the Will. Any such application must be made within six months of probate being granted. You should consult a solicitor straight away if you find yourself in this position.

FUNERALS: PLANNING AHEAD

Facing up to the eventuality of your death, or that of your spouse, may not be easy or pleasant, but it is sensible to plan ahead. This will ensure that the wishes of the deceased are carried out, and will lessen the burden of responsibility on the bereaved. There is a substantial amount of detail to attend to at this difficult and stressful time, and costs can be high. Advance planning will make the whole procedure much easier.

Certification of death

Doctors are not allowed to charge for medical certificates and neither is there any charge for a death certificate. The white certificate and a green one releasing the body for burial or cremating are free of charge, but an extra one for granting probate or letters of administration costs £2. A certificate for releasing funds tied up in a bank, building society or insurance company costs £1.50. If the body is to be cremated, two further doctors' certificates are required, and each is entitled to a fee. It may also cost more to have a heart pacemaker removed before cremation.

Funeral costs

Now that the £30 death grant has been abolished, only the poorest are entitled to any help with the cost of a funeral. This comes under the provisions of the Social Fund described earlier in this chapter. Undertaker's charges vary so you should ideally try to compare prices before choosing a funeral director. This is difficult in reality, of course, because you will be extremely upset by the death of someone close to you especially if he or she has died suddenly and you have to make urgent arrangements for the body to be removed. You should at least ask for a quotation at the outset and ask to see the funeral director's price list, which they must provide under the terms of the National Association of Funeral Directors' code of practice. If at all possible, try to enlist the help of a sympathetic friend or relative who can be with you during these painful negotiations, otherwise you may find yourself facing an unacceptably high bill.

The cheapest, most basic funeral costs a couple of hundred pounds, but in many parts of the country, a funeral is simply not available at this price. Various factors affect the cost of a burial or a cremation and you should ask the undertaker exactly what is included in his estimate. There are extra charges – known as disbursements – for elements such as church services and burial or cremation. These are not part of the undertaker's own fees, but will increase his eventual bill substantially.

Saving for your funeral

Some people pay insurance premiums or join a friendly society during their lifetime to provide for their funeral expenses. A funeral director will ask if savings like these are available to cover the costs. The National Association of Funeral Directors has started a prepayment scheme for members. You can pay a lump sum, minimum £600, or make monthly contributions towards the cost of your own funeral, but putting money aside in a bank or building society account would probably be better.

A number of other organisations, of which you must be a member, arrange life assurance schemes for saving towards funeral expenses. Most Co-operative Societies have schemes and so does the Independent Order of Oddfellows. The charity, Age Concern, has arranged a scheme with Chosen Heritage for people who want to make their own funeral arrangements before they die. You pay for the funeral now, either by lump sum or over five years. Then, however much the cost of funerals has risen by the time you eventually die, there is no more to pay.

FUNERAL COSTS TO BEAR IN MIND

▶ Cemeteries may be council or privately run and fees vary widely.

▶ Crematoria are council or privately run and again fees vary, with many optional extras

▶ Tapered coffins are much cheaper than rectangular caskets

▶ There is a charge for a church service including the clergyman and organist, and also for having a minister at the graveside if there has been no previous religious service

▶ A funeral could cost double if it takes place outside the area where the deceased person lived, and even more if it means transporting the body from abroad

▶ Your funeral director can advise you on the cost of crematorium memorials or grave headstones

HOME FROM HOME

SEE ALSO: ▶

MANAGING YOUR MONEY:
Tax in retirement   p. 46

Everyone can use some advice about housing. There is plenty available for first-time buyers, but older people may be bewildered by the number of options that now stretch ahead. One thing is certain, your home takes on far more importance when you no longer leave it each day to go to work. Although you may have had to uproot the family in the past because of job changes, now you can make your own decision. For the first time in your life, you should be able to live exactly where you wish!

But first ask yourself if you really need to move at all? The once popular retirement dream of a cottage in the country or a bungalow by the sea may nowadays have been switched to a white-walled villa in the sun. If this is your goal, remember this type of move needs to be carefully planned and mistakes can be costly. And there is plenty of publicity around about the pitfalls of purpose-built retirement homes. Generally advertised for those over 55, would-be buyers might do well to meet residents and look over existing schemes, instead of viewing one labour-saving show flat. You will get a far better idea of what day-to-day living is like in a scheme that has been up some years. In addition, not everyone gives up work because of their age but through illness or disability. In this case a residential home with some sort of care may be what you should be looking for, rather than a retirement home.

All these moves need to be well thought out ahead. But whatever you choose, the whole point is to find a home in a place which feels and *is* comfortable, and is suitable for your needs. This chapter should help you choose what is best for you. But whether you stay put, or move on, be dictated by your own feelings. Although there are lots of people prepared to give you 'friendly' advice, be careful about taking it, for many will benefit by the decision you make.

STAYING PUT
Probably the first thing to be decided is whether you want to move at all. You may be quite happy where you live now, but being at home all day (and every day) will make you more aware of its limitations and drawbacks. Ask yourself the questions in the chart as they may help you plan better for the future. Apart from the expense of maintaining a house and garden and worrying that repairs may whittle away your capital, a home that is too large for your needs is exhausting to keep in good order. On the other hand, large properties appreciate faster in cash terms than smaller ones. Unless you really need to get your hands on capital at present locked up in your home, why not stay put and enjoy it?

You have probably invested much time and work on your home over the years. While it continues to increase in value, the bigger will be the profit if the time comes when you need to capitalize on it. Remember, unlike cash invested in a building society or unit trust, you pay no tax on profit from the sale of your own home. ◀

Preparing your home for retirement

If you decide not to move, it may be necessary to look over your home with a view to making it as comfortable and convenient as possible for the years ahead. This is a particularly profitable way to spend a lump sum, such as a maturing insurance policy or severance payment, if you don't feel the need to

A delightful country cottage might be your idea of a dream retirement home, but think about problems like isolation, heating, damp, repairs – and do you really want the work involved in maintaining that charming cottage garden?

REMAINING IN YOUR PRESENT HOME

- ☐ Is your home the right size for your needs or do you have extra rooms merely for visits from family or friends?

- ☐ Are stairs likely to prove a problem in the years ahead?

- ☐ Have you kept your home in decent repair so you won't have to worry about major outlays apart from routine maintenance?

- ☐ Is the heating system easily managed and efficient?

- ☐ Are there shops and public transport within easy reach if the time comes when you have to give up driving?

- ☐ Do you have good friends or family nearby?

- ☐ Are you involved with local activities which now occupy part of your leisure and may be more important when you can give them more time?

- ☐ Will the garden be too large to manage on your own in the years ahead or can it be converted into an easy-care plot with minimal work?

invest it for income. In any case, if you own your own home, using money to improve your home is a very safe investment in its own right, as it will increase the value of the property. ▶

Repairs involving roofs, rising damp, broken gutters or plumbing should not be delayed. Check with your local authority about improvement grants. ▶ Get into the habit of spotting trouble before it becomes a structural problem. Also bring in a reputable electrician to check your wiring and if necessary have extra power points installed. It is possible to raise them from the skirting to a more accessible level if required. If you don't have them already, have two-way switches put in on halls and landings to give you good lighting in danger spots, and it might be an idea to have an outside light installed by the front door on a time switch so that you don't have to come home to a dark house. Look, too, at flooring.

SEE ALSO: ◀
MANAGING YOUR MONEY:
Savings and investment
p. 41
HOME FROM HOME:
Grants and loans   p. 60

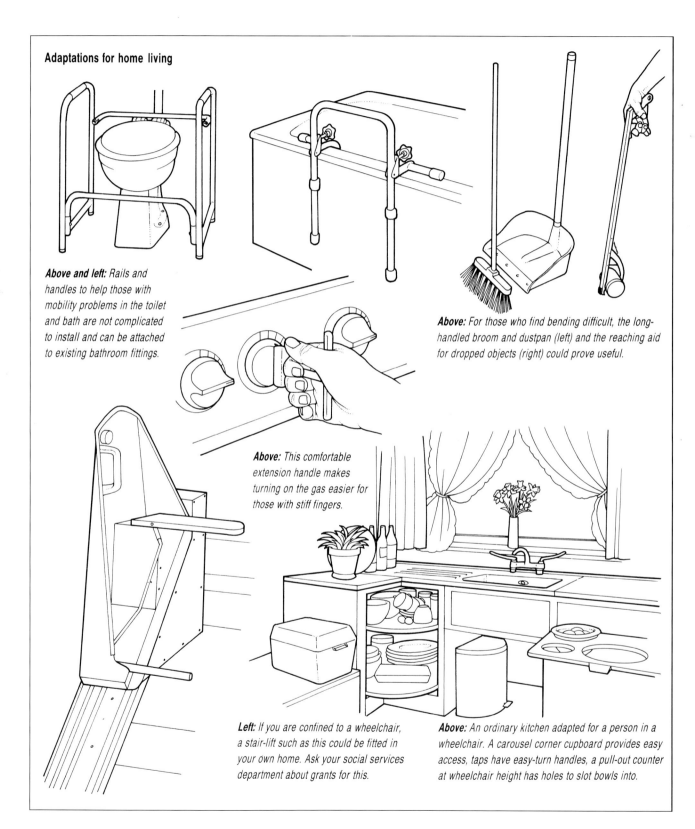

Adaptations for home living

Above and left: Rails and handles to help those with mobility problems in the toilet and bath are not complicated to install and can be attached to existing bathroom fittings.

Above: For those who find bending difficult, the long-handled broom and dustpan (left) and the reaching aid for dropped objects (right) could prove useful.

Above: This comfortable extension handle makes turning on the gas easier for those with stiff fingers.

Left: If you are confined to a wheelchair, a stair-lift such as this could be fitted in your own home. Ask your social services department about grants for this.

Above: An ordinary kitchen adapted for a person in a wheelchair. A carousel corner cupboard provides easy access, taps have easy-turn handles, a pull-out counter at wheelchair height has holes to slot bowls into.

Fitted carpets are expensive but good carpets are an investment. They are very warm and safe, too, as there isn't the danger of catching your foot in them. Rugs on polished floors are dangerous, as are loose stair carpets. Make sure these are securely fixed, using carpet tacks rather than stair rods, which can work loose.

Consider having a shower installed; it saves on hot water and is much easier to step in and out of. A plastic stool placed in the shower basin means you don't have to stand up to shower. A bath with handles helps, or have a hand rail fitted to help you get in and out. Even if you don't need it now, you may find you become less nimble in later years. Use a non-slip mat or install a new bath with a non-slip surface. ▶ You could have it sunk slightly into the floor, or have a raised step built along the bathside,

again to make it easier to get in and out of.

If you are not confident about your own abilities to spot problems with your home, the Royal Institution of Chartered Surveyors runs a voluntary service through most local Citizens Advice Bureaux and will generally advise on planning applications, repairs and housing grants.

If you don't know any good builders in your area, ask your neighbours and friends and see if they can recommend local firms. A twenty-year guarantee for damp-proofing and woodworm treatment means nothing if the firm goes out of business shortly after your work is completed. Look for guarantees backed by large professional bodies such as the National House Building Council, the Building Employers and the Federation of Master Builders.

SEE ALSO: ◀

THE CARERS' GUIDE:

Practical help   p. 173

PLANNING FOR BUILDING WORK

☐ Before you start – decide exactly what you want done. For larger jobs, consider getting advice from an architect or surveyor.

☐ Ask at the Planning Department of your local council whether you need planning permission or building regulations approval; this is especially important if your house is in a conservation area, is a 'listed building', or if the work involves changing the frontage.

☐ The Planning Department will also be able to tell you whether you can get a grant towards the work.

☐ Get estimates and quotations in writing from at least two firms. Find out as much as you can about them.

☐ Make sure that your contract is in writing and gives full details of prices, cancellation rights, guarantees and when the work will be started and finished. Check whether any subcontractors are to be used and who is liable if things go wrong.

☐ Be careful about parting with money in advance, especially if you are asked to pay large deposits. Always query any price increases and ask why they were not included in the original estimate.

☐ If you have a problem, act quickly and get advice from the Trading Standards (or Consumer Protection) Department of your local council or CAB.

DEALING WITH
DOORSTEP CALLERS

▶ Try to avoid
committing yourself to
anything you are not
sure of (see also page
71).

▶ If you do part with
money for goods or
services which you
don't really want, or
which are never
delivered, don't be
ashamed to report it
to the police or a
sympathetic friend or
neighbour. You may
help to bring about a
prosecution if the
caller is acting
illegally, and you
could help to stop
other people being
taken in.

Avoiding the cowboys

Your home may need improving or work carried out to make it suitable for you in later life. Unless you have been in touch with a reliable builder recently, bear in mind the seven golden rules in the chart on page 59, issued by the Office of Fair Trading.

The biggest danger can be doorstep callers. Always be cautious about workmen who say your neighbour is having work done, so can they do the same for you. A quick check may reveal that your neighbour hasn't even been approached.

Another old ploy of 'cowboy' builders is to claim that there are tiles off your roof and they will do you a favour in replacing them. If you have no reason to be worried about your roof, grab a pair of binoculars and see for yourself what, if anything, needs to be repaired.

Other questionable services on offer are wall-coatings and paints which never need repainting, and be very cautious of tarmac teams who offer to resurface your drive. There are plenty examples around of badly laid tarmac, now sprouting dandelions and thistles because the ground was badly prepared.

It pays not to be too trusting and this also applies to servicing and repairs. When a domestic appliance breaks down, try to establish where the fault lies. Check the fuse in the 13-amp plug first – a service engineer can charge as much as £20 for imparting just this information. If you don't have a service contract, always ask how much any repair or service will cost and the call-out charge involved. You can always get other quotes and compare.

Grants and loans

It is a long time since government money was readily available for house repairs and improvements. In some areas there is a four-year waiting time for local authority grants but if you or a member of your family is disabled you may be allowed a grant to provide extra aids and adaptions. Some very disabled people get help to have a downstairs toilet or stair-lift installed. More everyday items such as handrails or an extra bannister for the stairs can be supplied through the Social Services department of your local authority.

Discretionary grants can be made through the Social Fund scheme to certain priority groups on low incomes who get Income Support. Included in these groups are elderly people who need minor structural repairs to their homes. Ask at your local Social Security office for leaflet SB16, *A Guide to the Social Fund.*

The golden rule is not to start work or sign any contract with a builder until you have contacted the local authority officer who deals with grants in your area.

Local authorities can give grants of 90 per cent, up to a ceiling of £137 towards the cost of insulating lofts, lagging pipes and insulating hot water tanks. This is a valuable grant, since it helps to reduce heating bills and makes a house warmer. But these grants are restricted to older householders on Income Support or Housing Benefit. Some insulation salesmen operate from door to door, promising to organize the grant. Check with your local council before signing any contract, as help is now confined to those on low incomes and is not generally available.

An interest-only loan may be the simplest way of raising funds for repairs and improvements. Some banks and building societies are prepared to offer interest-only 'Maturity Loans' to older people to cover essential repairs. Interest rates fluctuate but repayments are not excessive and if such outgoings take you below the Income Support rate, you should be entitled to help from the Department of Social Security.

The loan itself is not repaid until the property is eventually sold. Although you may not like the idea of being in debt until your death, it is worth remembering that money spent on the house now, not only makes your home more comfortable, it can also increase its value, so your heirs don't miss out. Apply to local building societies and shop around.

If you are unlucky in raising money in this way, it may be possible to use the value of your home to get cash (and to increase your basic income) by taking out a Home Income Plan. ▶

A helping hand

In a number of areas there are specialist agencies to advise older home-owners on low incomes of help with repairs and improvements. Teams come under such titles as 'Staying Put' or 'Care and Repair' and are run by voluntary organizations, housing associations and some local authorities. The main aims are to modernize and to make homes more comfortable, but not to such an extent as to burden the owner with heavy debts. The teams survey the property, arrange builders, supervise work, raise the finance, and if necessary liaise with the Department of Social Security if the owner is on a low income.

Sadly these schemes are not available throughout the country. Check with your Citizens Advice Bureau or Housing Department to find out if there is a local one.

Housing associations and charities

If your home is too large for your requirement and you can't face builders and workmen yourself, Help the Aged has a 'Gifted House' scheme. You donate the house to the charity but eventually, after conversion, you return to live there without the responsibilities of ownership.

Later on, if you need care yourself, you can apply to move into accommodation with the Help the Aged Sheltered Housing Scheme. The Gifted House Plan booklet is available from Help the Aged's Housing Division. ▶

It is sometimes possible to sell your home to a housing association on the understanding that you live on in it without the responsibility of being an owner-occupier. The price paid by the housing association is not as much as if you sold it on the open market. This scheme allows you to stay on but gives you sufficient capital to carry out necessary repairs and improvements. However, it does mean that your heirs will not benefit from the property when you die.

FAMILY-SHARED HOMES

Sometimes after illness or the death of a dearly loved partner, a grandparent may be asked to share the home of one of the family for a short time. It may work out well and seem the obvious solution instead of moving into a residential home among strangers.

Everything depends on individual circumstances. Before making any long term plans, this sort of arrangement calls for a good deal of careful thought and discussion. Tact and tolerance are needed on both sides, so talk it over with your children *and* their partners.

When sharing a house, each group must respect the privacy of the other. Shared facilities, especially bathrooms and kitchens, must be worked out on some sort of timetable and payment of bills should be put on a businesslike basis.

Younger members of the family must understand that grandparents need rest and learn to be tolerant of their increasing frailty. Older people on the other hand have to accept that life in a busy household is no rest cure.

SEE ALSO: ◀

MANAGING YOUR MONEY:
Home income plan   p. 45
RESOURCES & BACK-UP:
Housing   p. 208

Ideally, if the home is large enough, it is best to create two separate units, with an annexe for the older person and enough space for the family and grandchildren not to feel cramped. The first step should be to apply for planning permission from the local council if major work is involved. If you as the older relative put up the money to pay for the annexe or alterations, or invest in the cost of the conversion, you should ensure that your rights are protected by having a legal agreement drawn up about ownership or tenancy.

Although it may be far from everyone's mind when planning this type of move, if at some future date your son or daughter were to split up with his or her spouse, or if the couple were obliged to move to another part of the country due to job changes, you should have some security of tenure or property rights. Admittedly, this is looking at the worst possible outcome. Countless generations of families have opened up their homes to grandparents, or even an older aunt or uncle in the past, and their company and support have been remembered with affection and love.

LETTING TO TENANTS
As long as there is a housing shortage, there will always be people looking for rooms and bedsitters in private homes. If you are a tenant you will need to check your rights to take in a lodger or sub-let any part of your property. This is not always an ideal way to add to your income. Apart from losing your peace and quiet you may also find that the rent paid to you by a tenant cancels out your entitlement to Income Support or Housing Benefit, or may affect your tax situation. ◀

Owner-occupiers may consider a conversion scheme that allows them to occupy the ground floor and rent out other parts of the house. It may be suggested to you by well-meaning friends or family as a way out of your problems. In fact it could add to them. Tenants are now fairly well protected and if, in the future, you wish to regain full possession of your home, you may find it necessary to go to law.

Unless it is a matter of offering a home to a very dear, lifelong friend, it can be difficult to get used to sharing even part of your home with someone else, although short-term lets to students might be a compromise. ◀

STAYING PUT IN COUNCIL HOUSING
Many older council tenants have devoted as much time and attention to their homes and gardens as have owner-occupiers of private properties. In recent years these tenants have been attracted to the 'Right to Buy' schemes, especially the high discounts after 30 years of tenancy.

Provided you can afford the mortgage repayments, building insurance and rates on your present income, you will probably have a soundly built, attractive property to add to your eventual estate. If you are thinking about this before retirement, however, you should bear in mind that when your income falls to pension level, it may be more difficult for you to find the money. Although at present the DSS support some owner-occupiers by meeting the interest part of the mortgage, this help may not always be available. A useful Government leaflet is *Your Right to Buy Your Home* which you can pick up at a CAB or Housing Advice Centre.

If you live in a sheltered scheme or council home restricted to people of retirement age or disablement, you may not have the right to buy. Councils consider it important to maintain stock of such homes for the future.

Repairs advice for tenants
Check your tenancy agreement and you will generally find that councils and

SEE ALSO: ▶
KEEPING BUSY:
Other ideas   p. 82

SEE ALSO: ▶
MANAGING YOUR MONEY:
Help from the state   p. 32
Tax in retirement   p. 46

housing associations are responsible for major repairs to your home. You may have to carry out minor repairs and decoration, but, under Section 11 of the Landlord and Tenant Act 1985, all landlords are responsible for repairs to the structure and to the services supplying water, gas, electricity and for sewage.

If your council home is overdue for repairs, contact the local authority Housing Department and then confirm your request in writing. If you are still waiting after a reasonable period, then get the Environmental Health Officer to inspect your home and put pressure on the council.

Similar rights belong to most private tenants. Again landlords are generally responsible for major repairs and your agreement should make this clear. Like council tenants, if you can't get the landlord to carry out necessary repairs contact the local Environmental Health Officer. You may need to get a solicitor to draft out a letter to the landlord, pointing out his responsibilities. This may ginger him up and then, hopefully, you won't actually have to take him to court, although this is always an option in extreme cases.

No landlords – council, housing association and private – are generally responsible for improvements, although some estates are now being modernized. You can carry out improvement work to your home with the landlord's consent. In every case, seek advice from a housing advice centre or CAB since there are a number of complicated steps to follow.

MOVING ON

There are some very obvious reasons to move in retirement. Perhaps you want to be near sons or daughters who live too far away, or to get back to your roots, or to be near friends. Then again, you may have always treasured a dream of a

cottage in the country or a bungalow by the sea.

However, rustic solitude is not for everyone and seaside resorts are often over-crowded in summer and deserted in winter, when heavy seas make even a walk along the prom a dangerous expedition. So if the area you are thinking of is unknown to you spend time there before coming to any decision. Over a few visits you will begin to know whether it is the right sort of place where you will be happy to settle down.

Check out the local library and see what sort of societies and clubs exist which you may like to join. Buy the local paper and a large-scale map of the area. If you are house-hunting from a different part of the country, you need to know how far you are from motorways,

Although a spectacular view of the bay may be tempting, if you decide to move to the coast, make sure your house is not separated from shops and local facilities by a literally breathtaking climb.

railways, coach and bus stations. You may feel confident about driving for many years to come, but there may come a time when frailty or illness means that the car has to be sold. It is then that public transport is essential. You also need to investigate local shop prices. Without a car you may not be able to get to cheaper supermarkets.

Many ideal places in the coastal zones already have large proportions of retired people and it is wise to check up on health services and local support social services.

Financing your move
Get an idea of current prices in different areas of the country by telephoning the New Homes Hotline. ◄ The New Homes Marketing Board will send a list of builders of retirement homes.

However, prices for older properties may vary from these prices, often being more expensive. It is a good idea to find out which is the most popular local paper for estate agents' property advertisements, and subscribing to this paper for a time.

If your home is too large for your present needs, it is tempting to 'trade down' in estate agents' jargon, by buying a smaller, cheaper home elsewhere and gaining a lump sum in the transaction. You may cash in quite handsomely if you choose to sell at the right time, but you may have difficulty if you want to move back to your original area. While in some parts of the country, house prices are on a rising spiral, in other areas they remain stable.

When counting the cost of moving, remember to build in estate agents' commission, which can be 2 per cent or more of the value of a property. Other extras, such as stamp duty, removal charges, insurance, VAT, solicitors' fees, not to mention new carpets and curtains, add up to a considerable figure.

SEE ALSO: ▶

RESOURCES & BACK-UP:
Housing   p. 208

As a cash buyer with probably a paid-up mortgage, you will not have to negotiate the hurdle of finding finance. But nor will you benefit from the survey conducted by a building society if you want a loan. If you are not buying a new home covered by a national guarantee certificate, you should engage a surveyor privately to carry out a full structural survey before committing yourself.

What sort of home do you want?
Retirement is going to give you more time to enjoy do-it-yourself activities, gardening, dressmaking and entertaining and you may not want to feel cramped in accommodation that is too small.

Compared to other homes of similar size, bungalows tend to be more expensive but there are many advantages. Everything is on one floor. There are no stairs to climb and there is easier access for exterior maintenance.

You may not have considered living in a flat in the past, but if you dislike gardening, find maintenance difficult and want a cheaper home (again on one floor) there are plenty for sale, usually on leases rather than freehold. Your solicitor should be able to spot any inconsistencies in the lease but steer clear of those which have relatively little time to run. They may be cheaper, but in the future they could prove to be unsaleable.

Ground rents are usually nominal but management and service charges have been contentious issues in the past as they could be very high and increased annually. Recent stronger protection through the Landlord and Tenant Act now gives residents rights of court action.

Mobile homes
You may be attracted to a mobile home. They are usually sited outside a small

town or village, within easy reach or on a public transport route.

Mobile homes started as just that – permanently sited caravans. But today's designs have improved so much that they look the same as small bungalows, often with a brick 'skirt' covering the wheel space. Usually they are bought on site, ready for immediate occupation with fitted carpets, curtains, even furniture if wanted. Interior decoration is minimal and they are as easily maintained outside as a bungalow. Happy owners can be found on most sites and many claim they feel far safer within the confines of the development than in conventional streets in towns and villages.

However, mobile homes are surprisingly expensive compared to small flats and houses in country areas and their value depreciates, whereas bricks and mortar rise in value all the time. Building societies do not give mortgages for them, although the manufacturers and developers of such homes can arrange financial loans and the interest can be offset against income tax.

When buying a mobile home watch out for re-sale restrictions. If you decide to sell your mobile home independently the site operator is usually entitled to a commission not exceeding 10 per cent.

The site operator will charge fees to cover maintenance of tarmac roads, disposal of sewage and upkeep. You are also responsible for rates and electricity bills. Some sites still charge more for electricity than the local Board. The Park Homes Residents' Guild ▶ will provide advice to would-be buyers.

SHELTERED HOUSING

Sheltered housing schemes are big business. Along with home computers, videos and personal stereos, they are among the success stories of the 1980s – for the developers. Today's sheltered home schemes are vastly different from the early basic blocks of flats, copied from those built by local authorities, who pioneered this type of accommodation. But although developers have branched out into building more sophisticated types of homes, they remain essentially developments for people aged 50-plus who prefer neighbours of similar age and circumstances and want the security of knowing there is someone on whom they can call for assistance at moments of difficulty. If you want to buy you can take your pick from cottage-style villages, up-market luxury flats (some with penthouses) and there are larger schemes incorporating residential homes for those who need permanent nursing care. Nowadays the communal facilities may include a library, snooker room, indoor bowls, gymnasium and restaurants. The warden may euphemistically be called a 'residential secretary' but it is still his or her job to keep a discreet eye on residents and be on call for help in an emergency.

Such success – and in the south-east in particular every vacant plot of land seems to be put to this use – is not without teething troubles. In the past, some developers have insisted that buyers, or their beneficiaries, sell back their homes to the building or management company at the original purchase price. So anyone considering this type of home should look carefully into re-sale conditions.

Other complaints have been over service and maintenance charges which have shot up without warning in some schemes, far higher than was anticipated in the original sales brochures. Together with changes in housing benefit, this has caused real hardship among owners on low incomes. It is therefore essential to find out how often the service charge is reviewed and what additional increases for future major repairs and maintenance are likely.

SEE ALSO: ◀

RESOURCES & BACK-UP:
Housing   p. 208

If you are buying a sheltered home as a straight cash purchase and have surplus capital over, great care should be taken when investing this money since it will be needed to cushion future increases in charges and running costs. Prospective buyers should also ask their solicitors to check if there is anything in the lease about being forced out if failing health meant you needed continual care.

Finding the cash

Not all buyers can afford the full price of a retirement home – there are parts of the country where the price of a detached house is a lot less than that of a sheltered home in the south-east! However, if you are not in the position to make a straight cash purchase, there are schemes around to help you buy a property which would otherwise be beyond your reach.

Some developers may offer a discount off the purchase price on the understanding that when you (or your heirs) sell the property, you only get back part of the value, proportionate to the original investment. Such schemes need to be looked at carefully and the conditions made clear. On the other hand, the Park Housing Association Sundowner scheme ◄ allows you to buy at a discount, pay rent on the outstanding lump sum, yet get full capital appreciation when you sell.

Some housing associations run Leasehold Schemes for the Elderly (LSE) which involve you buying a 70 per cent share of the lease, the remaining share being funded by a government subsidy. Like discount schemes you only get back a percentage of the property's current market value when it is resold.

Even more helpful for older buyers are Home for Life plans where it is possible to secure a home by paying around half the normal purchase price.

What happens is that anyone over 60 can acquire a 'life interest' in a property, rather than actual ownership. On death the property reverts to Home for Life and the older you are, the better the deal, pricewise. During your lifetime, you pay no interest, no rent nor ground rent.

Such a scheme is fine for people with no children, or who feel their heirs are already adequately provided for and won't need to benefit from the sale of property in the future. There are safeguards to protect capital during the early years of occupancy and anyone who surrenders their life interest gets cash compensation. Any sheltered housing development is eligible, provided it satisfies House Builders Federation design and other criteria and the management and maintenance requirement of Home for Life plc. ◄

Help with moving

Wanting to move is one thing, taking the plunge, especially if you are alone, and aren't happy coping with estate agents, solicitors and so on, is another. If you dislike dealing with people, can't bear the idea of strangers tramping through your home or the nail-biting problems of a 'chain' when one buyer can let eight or nine others down, then you can now turn to developers who have taken the pain out of buying and selling. When you are considering buying in to a sheltered housing scheme, it is worthwhile enquiring if these sort of facilities are offered by the developer, who will usually provide a prospectus with all services listed in it.

Some firms will buy customers' old homes at market value and then take over completely the responsibility of the sale, conveyancing and all paper work. Some firms also have an answer for the age-old problems of selling the old home before the new one is ready. They will lend a home from a pool of

SEE ALSO: ▶
RESOURCES & BACK-UP:
Housing   p. 209

BUYING SHELTERED HOUSING

FOR

- ☐ Your home is too large and difficult to maintain and you no longer want the responsibility for outside repairs, decoration and the garden.

- ☐ You have no one who calls in regularly and a warden/alarm system will enable help to be summoned quickly in an emergency.

- ☐ The scheme is built near shops and post office.

- ☐ You enjoy the company of others in the same age group.

- ☐ Fuel bills should be cheaper since the home is smaller and most schemes are well insulated.

AGAINST

- ☐ There will be service charges as well as rates and ground rent.

- ☐ You may have to get rid of a well-loved pet.

- ☐ You may miss the contact with neighbours of all ages and walks of life.

- ☐ You may find a sheltered flat cramped after a larger home. Show flats may look spacious but the furniture on show is kept to a minimum.

- ☐ There may be restrictions in the lease concerning the re-sale of the property, or your continued stay there if your health greatly deteriorated.

RENTING SHELTERED ACCOMMODATION

FOR

- ☐ There is a warden and/or alarm system to use in an emergency.

- ☐ Usually there are laundry facilities so you may no longer need a washing machine in the kitchen.

- ☐ Although small, it will be easy to run and many schemes have a guest room for overnight stays.

- ☐ If it is a members-only scheme (such as trade union, professional association or British Legion), you will probably be living among like-minded people.

AGAINST

- ☐ You may not share the interests of the other residents, yet the local authority is unlikely to rehouse you if this is the only reason you can give for wanting to move.

- ☐ You will probably not be allowed to keep a pet.

- ☐ The council's or association's policy may be to keep a balance between fit and active residents and frailer ones, but you may find yourself in the company of too many neighbours who need your help.

The best sheltered housing schemes, like this housing association one in the Liverpool area are purpose-built to provide attractive surroundings and privacy, but also to avoid isolation and provide immediate help in an emergency.

comfortable, unfurnished properties on their developments. Rent is nominal and the company will sometimes arrange your second removal to your new home free. When you are considering buying into a sheltered housing scheme, it is worthwhile enquiring if these sort of facilities are offered by the developer, who will usually provide a prospectus with all services listed in it.

There is more good news for those who prefer conventional methods of selling. Generally charges for conveyancing have come down in recent years and now that they are allowed to advertise, some solicitors are offering flat rate fees to handle any house. You should always negotiate a fee before you agree to engage a solicitor to act for you.

SHELTERED FLATS TO RENT
Local authorities and housing associations were the first to see the need for warden-controlled sheltered accommodation 20 or more years ago. Older tenants in private property were often badly housed and council tenants could be moved on to release larger homes for younger families.

You should apply to your local housing department for a place in rented sheltered accommodation in your area. If you are already a council tenant, ask about a transfer to a local scheme. But such is the demand it may be worthwhile thinking of moving to another part of the country as waiting times vary.

The council should tell you of any local Housing Association schemes you may apply for, and if you have links with a particular trade or profession, you may be fortunate enough to be considered for one restricted to members.

Many war veterans are rehoused by the Royal British Legion Housing Association in this way.

In fact there are about 2600 registered Housing Associations in the country and the Housing Corporation registers, promotes and supervises them. ▶ There are twelve regional offices which have details of local schemes and what is planned for the future. The National Federation of Housing Associations ▶ can also help with enquiries. Don't overlook the help given by the Citizens Advice Bureau where up-to-date information on local development is maintained.

Owners may want to sell their present home to the local council in return for being rehoused in sheltered accommodation. Not all councils operate these schemes but ask at your Housing Department. Bear in mind that almost always councils offer less than the market value of property and it could be as much as a third. Once you give up ownership, you won't be able to pick and choose where you would like to be rehoused, so it may be better to sell your property for its full value on the open market.

Residents may apply for a home help, and, if necessary, a district nurse for special needs. A warden cannot undertake any personal tasks such as shopping or cooking. This is where a fit, active resident may find him- or herself in demand.

COUNCIL HOUSING

It may be possible for older council tenants to move to be near relatives or children who will provide support. Some new towns and developments provide bungalows or special housing for their needs. The pressure on such council housing is less acute outside big cities but be prepared for long waiting lists in most parts of the country.

If you need to move to alternative council accommodation because of ill-health, you should ask your housing department for a 'medical priority form' and get your doctor to fill it in. The state of your present home and whether it meets your needs will be considered.

The National Mobility Scheme ▶ is a voluntary one agreed between most housing authorities in the UK to help council tenants move to a different area. Apply to your local housing department for details. It is not necessary to be a council tenant to be considered, but you can only seek a move if your council accepts your application. A leaflet explaining the scheme can be picked up from your housing department, CAB or direct from the National Mobility Scheme.

Some tenants achieve such a move by advertising in the local paper distributed in the area of their choice. You might be able to achieve an exchange this way. A private exchange bureau called Locatex also offers to help council and housing association tenants. All council tenants have the legal right to exchange their homes with their landlord's permission.

The options open to private tenants are few. Although in theory you are able to put your name down with the housing department for a place in a retirement scheme, you may face a longer wait than a council tenant vacating a large council house.

But, the more badly housed you are at present, the better chance you have of being rehoused by your council. If you are over retirement age and in poor health, the council has a duty to rehouse you, but you will always have to prove you have not made yourself homeless 'by intention'.

TIED HOUSING

If, like the Prime Minister, your home goes with the job, you may be worried

SEE ALSO: ◀
RESOURCES & BACK-UP:
Housing   pp. 208 & 209

SEE ALSO: ▶

RESOURCES & BACK-UP:
Housing   p. 208

about what happens on retirement. Check out the agreement you have with your employee/landlord. Some tied tenants have to move on retirement. If you are one of them and have not been offered, or been able to find somewhere else to live, contact your local council. Councils have a duty to provide accommodation for certain groups of people who may become homeless. If you are worried, get professional advice to be sure of your legal rights. Contact a local law centre or the nearest Citizens Advice Bureau.

ALMSHOUSES

The term 'almshouse' may conjure up a tiny, picturesque cottage with an Elizabethan chimney and hollyhocks at the door. But although many of the 30,000 units affiliated to by the National Association of Almshouses are centuries old, most have been modernized and many new sheltered housing schemes built.

The Association now has about 2500 groups and each charity or trust has its own qualifications for residence. It may depend on local residency, birth qualifications or your past working life. Again details of almshouses in a specific area

Well-established almshouses have long waiting lists, which is not surprising since they are often attractive buildings in pleasant surroundings.

may be obtained from the CAB or the Association itself. ◀

HOUSING BENEFIT

Wherever you live you may be able to get financial help with housing benefit. It works in a similar way to income support ◀ but savings up to £8,000 affect the amount you receive; if you have savings over £8,000 then you are not entitled to benefit.

Council tenants can get a rebate on their rent and rates which is worked out directly from their account. Private tenants are entitled to the same help but this may be paid to you by cheque.

Homeowners on income support may get help meeting the cost of interest on a mortgage, but there is no help paying the capital you owe, so if you are having financial problems, it is best to consult the bank or building society who gave you the mortgage as soon as possible. Even so, as long as the rating system continues you may be entitled to a rate rebate, especially if you are disabled and have had your house specially altered so you can continue to live there. Apply to your local authority housing department.

HOME SAFETY

Wherever you decide to live, unless you are moving into residential care, you are well-advised to look carefully at home safety, both from a security point of view and from the point of view of avoiding accidents.

Everyone wants to be safe in their own home. Elderly people can be the victims of any crime but they are, perhaps, particularly vunerable to crimes which take place in the home. Remember that the police will be prepared to call to anyone's home to provide advice as to how a home can be made safer to keep out intruders. Ring your local police station and ask to speak to the Crime Prevention Officer.

The doorstep code

Older people are often the target for bogus callers. Fit a door chain and viewer and ask the name of anyone you don't know. Generally speaking, entry upon another person's property without their consent is trespass and you can take legal action to prevent a person from entering your property. However, certain people are allowed to enter your premises without your consent. Briefly, these are as follows:-

- A landlord is allowed on to a property to inspect premises and to collect rent.

- An officer of the law, ie a policeman, is allowed to enter property to take goods he suspects are stolen or to arrest someone.

- A bailiff can enter property provided he has a court warrant enabling him to do this, and you should demand to see it.

- A gasman of British Gas plc can enter property to read a meter four times a year and also to inspect premises for a gas escape. He will have proof of identity which you should ask to see.

If the caller claims to be an official, ask for proof of identity and keep the chain in place. Take your time examining any card or document and when in doubt, ask strangers to come back later when you have had time to ring the department or company involved.

If the intruder is persistent, such as a salesman, then report his or her actions to the police. If the matter persists consider consulting a solicitor with a view to bringing an action in nuisance.

If you are putting property on the market, don't show any prospective buyers or tenants around on your own.

Insist that an estate agent's representative comes along or ask a friend or neighbour to be there. In the same way, it is unwise to place advertisements in shop windows or local newspapers which might attract suspect buyers.

In an emergency, a stranger may ask to use your telephone. Ask him or her to wait outside while *you* make the call.

At any time if you suspect a stranger, or if he or she is abusive or turns ugly, ring the police and give a detailed description. You may save some other householder who is far too trusting from being mugged. ▶

Unsolicited goods

Unsolicited goods and circulars are an increasing annoyance for everyone and can be a cause of worry. Unsolicited goods and mail are now covered by the Unsolicited Goods & Services Act 1971 and 1975. These Acts seeks to protect people to whom goods are sent or delivered without the goods being asked for.

If you receive unsolicited goods you may treat them as gifts and keep them, after six months, provided the sender does not ask for them to be returned. If a firm or person sending unsolicited goods or mail threatens to demand payment, threatens legal proceedings or threatens to place your name on a list of defaulters or debtors, then that firm or person is committing a criminal offence and you should inform the police of the threats and show the correspondence to them immediately.

Play safe

Considering the increased value of most homes in recent years and the cost of furnishing, carpeting and electrical equipment, home security is, sadly, often neglected. Strong locks are essential on all doors and windows, but the front door (usually the one by which you leave the house) is the most vulner-

SEE ALSO: ◀

HOME FROM HOME:

Avoiding the cowboys

p. 60

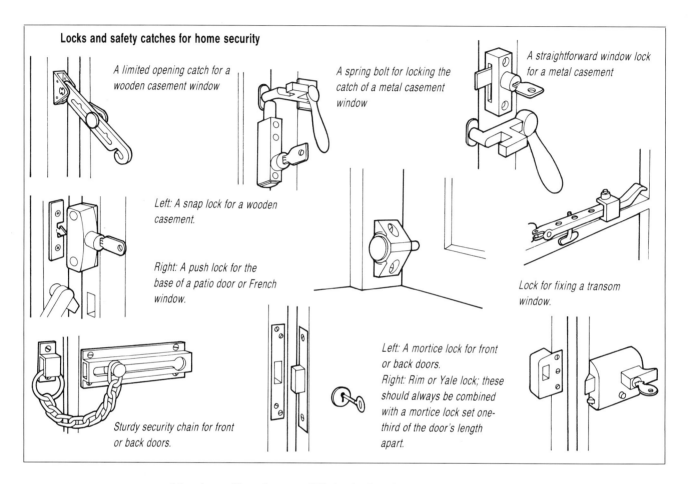

Locks and safety catches for home security

A limited opening catch for a wooden casement window

A spring bolt for locking the catch of a metal casement window

A straightforward window lock for a metal casement

Left: A snap lock for a wooden casement.

Right: A push lock for the base of a patio door or French window.

Lock for fixing a transom window.

Left: A mortice lock for front or back doors.
Right: Rim or Yale lock; these should always be combined with a mortice lock set one-third of the door's length apart.

Sturdy security chain for front or back doors.

Above: The Neighbourhood Watch scheme badge. Members of the scheme display this badge prominently as a deterrent to would-be intruders and as reassurance to other residents.

able. As well as the usual Yale, it should be fitted with a five-lever Mortice dead-lock. Spaced out, these two locks will withstand most intruders trying to force their way in.

Glazed doors add light to a dark hall, but the panels may be easy to smash. Today the emphasis is on heavier, stronger doors and a solid wooden one will withstand most attacks. The door frame is also important. Have a strip of metal fitted on the lock inside if it is weak. Doors which you can lock from the inside should have bolts at the top and bottom which are key-operated.

Fit security locks on ground floor windows and those near drainpipes and flat roofs. Keep ladders locked in a garage or outhouse and don't leave garden tools around which can be used

to aid a break-in.

Shut all windows, however small, when you leave home, even if it is only for a short walk. Nine out of ten burglaries are spontaneous and less than a quarter of an hour can elapse from the time of the break-in to the get-away, along with your treasured valuables.

Your local Crime Prevention Officer will willingly call round and carry out a security survey inside and outside your home, and give detailed advice on making it more secure. He will also recommend joining a Neighbourhood Watch Scheme if there is one in your area.

Protecting a small flat or house from intruders should not cost more than £100, even if you have to pay a workman for fitting locks and bolts. A five-lever mortise deadlock costs under £15 and window locks around £3 each. A number of insurance companies are now prepared to give discounts to householders whose homes are fitted with anti-theft locks or to those who belong to Neighbourhood Watch Schemes.

A light on a time-switch is a good idea for the front of your home, and can be put to good use when you are away on holiday. Keep garden shrubs well-trimmed so that your entrance is not concealed from the road. A side entrance and fence can be made more hazardous by planting hawthorns or training a rambling rose nearby. (The old-fashioned Albertine has enough thorns to deter most casual callers!) Draw your curtains at night so that passers-by don't get a free peep-show of your valuables and TV.

Burglar alarms are expensive. Some sophisticated systems can cost up to £1000, although there are DIY kits for under £100. For those living out in the country, it might be worth considering a telephone-based system linked to a central monitoring point. Cheapest of all is to buy a dog and keep yourself fit and active as well by exercising it every day.

Steer clear of accidents

Although you may be as fit as a fiddle when you retire, it is a sad fact that the likelihood of having an accident in the home increases with age. Loss of balance and falls account for thousands of deaths and there are nearly 200,000 accidents on stairs in this country each year. Far too many older people are incapacitated by broken hips and limbs and never recover full movement again. Below is a check-list of accident-preventing tips.

Emergency alarms

In recent years, emergency alarm systems similar to those provided in sheltered housing schemes, have been offered to private residents. The most sensible type for older people are those which can be worn around neck or wrist so that the alarm button is easy to push.

One of a number of different types of private personal alarm system, which may be reassuring for those who live by themselves.

ADVICE ON HOME SAFETY

• All stairs should have a handrail along the wall for extra support. If one of your household is handicapped and has difficulty moving around, the local Social Services department may provide an extra bannister and grab rail.

• Cheap aids such as a suction-type bath mat and a strong bath seat are helpful for getting in and out of the bath. Consider having a shower installed as they are more economical, as well as being safer. Using soap on a rope or liquid soap means you are less likely to slip in soapy water.

• Fires resulting from furniture upholstered in polyurethane foam are now so numerous that its use is forbidden now by law, apart from a new, flame-retardant type. When buying, look for a label, indicating that the covers are flame resistant.

• RoSPA, the Royal Society for the Prevention of Accidents, advocates the installation of smoke alarms which are easily fitted and relatively cheap.

• Chip pans soon blaze away if left unattended and it's worth investing in a glass fibre fire smothering cloth, kept within easy reach of the hob.

• Gas fires and other appliances should be regularly serviced and air vents must never be blocked up. A free safety check on gas appliances is available to anyone over 65 or any disabled person living alone.

• Try getting into the habit of pulling out plugs when you have finished using an appliance.

• Electric blankets should be regularly checked in accordance with the manufacturers' instructions.

CRIME PREVENTION TIPS FOR YOUR HOME

▶ Change the locks when you move into a new home and replace them immediately if your keys are lost or stolen.

▶ Ring the police at any time if you think that someone is breaking in.

▶ Don't think 'it can't happen to me'; too often it can – and it does!

SEE ALSO: ▶

RESOURCES & BACK-UP:

Housing   p. 208

It is also possible to have pull cords fitted in your home, or push a button on the alarm unit itself.

INSURANCE

As well as being sensible about home security, your next line of defence is adequate insurance. Even though you are already insured, it is worth looking over your present policy and comparing it with what's on offer, as the market is now highly competitive.

In the past, many building societies expected borrowers to insure with the company of their choice, on the implied understanding that it was all part of the terms of the home loan. Fortunately this has now changed, and in any case, by the time most people reach retirement age, mortgages have often been paid off. So now is the time to look around for insurance bargains.

A number of companies, Royal Insurance, Norwich Union and Legal and General among them, are prepared to give premium discounts to 'low-risk' householders who fit special locks on doors and windows, or who belong to a Neighbourhood Watch Scheme. Others offer cheaper policies to older householders who are likely to be at home most of the day. Hill House Hammond Ltd have a Retired Householders department and they also offer reduced home and contents policies for dog-owners. Many an attempted burglary has been stopped because a dog barked and even a small terrier can alert the neighbours that someone is about.

Age Concern and North London Reliance have also considered the needs of people in sheltered flats and smaller homes who have pared down possessions and no longer need expensive cover. The minimum amount for home contents insured by Age Concern is £4000, the maximum £15,000.

Two companies have launched bargain rates for property-only insurance.

In arrangement with Lloyds of London, the Scarborough Building Society has undercut other rates by offering a rate of 13.5p per £100 insured. This is a significant saving for home owners when the average property insurance is around 18p for £100. A similar bargain is offered by Zurich at 14p per £100 insured, but this company have a proviso that your house was built after 1919 and is not in a known area of flooding or chronic subsidence. These two companies also offer low-cost contents cover.

In recent years, property prices in some parts of the country have trebled, and you must be certain that you have your home adequately insured. Don't try and save on this very necessary expense. Under-insurance can lead to the company refusing to meet your claim in full and the market value of your property and its contents may prove to be inadequate when put to the test. The Association of British Insurers will send you their free leaflets, *Building Insurance for Home Owners* and *A Guide to Home Contents Insurance*, which are useful when re-assessing cover. ◀

It is important that anyone planning to move into a flat or maisonette converted from a larger property should check out that insurance on the structure of the whole building is adequate. It is not sufficient to insure your own accommodation: the roof, entrance hall and other shared parts must be covered under a collective policy.

MOVING ABROAD

Many people's retirement dream is to move abroad, where the climate is reliable and the cost of living is cheap. But it is not enough to spend a fortnight every year acquiring a sun-tan in a favourite resort to decide to put down roots there. You need to live there out of season for at least three months, and to talk to other ex-patriates who have settled there. Ask about local taxes and charges and what happens when they need medical care.

Many residential schemes now being built around the Mediterranean are within easy reach of the sea, but are not always on public transport routes to the local markets or hospitals. You must bear in mind the cost of regular taxi trips if you later give up your car.

Basic costs of property overseas may be half that of similar sized houses or flats over here, but there are often additional charges for connecting water and electricity, landscaping gardens, and for cleaning and maintenance. You have to think about furnishing too, either taking what the developer provides, or paying for the removal and shipping out your own furniture.

A number of British firms are now building properties overseas, the Prudential Property Services, Bovis and Taylor Woodrow among them. There are even some sheltered flat schemes. Reputable UK firms work in association with reliable foreign-based agents but any prospective buyer needs to consult an independent lawyer who also has contacts with lawyers in the country in question.

Apart from the obvious need to ensure that the vendor is the legal owner of the property, the code given in the margin, right, should be followed.

If all this sounds common sense, it will save you from falling into the trap that has turned one British couple's retirement dream into a nightmare. Having sunk all their capital into a flat in Spain, they found out that the agents who sold it did not actually own it. Then they discovered that the property had a number of charges set against it. These charges are debts run up by previous occupants, including unpaid builders' fees and even mortgages. The unlucky couple may have their home sold over

their heads while legal complications and costs mount up, and they may well end up homeless.

Useful reading before taking an irrevocable step is *Living and Retiring Abroad* by Michael Furnell. Would-be buyers should contact the Federation of Overseas Property Developers, Agents and Consultants. ► FOPDAC will advise if builders are members of the Federation and will be able to put prospective purchasers in touch with solicitors specializing in overseas property sales who understand foreign property laws.

Health and wealth abroad

By retiring abroad you will not escape income tax altogether, but you can avoid the double blow of paying twice over if the country of your choice has a bilateral agreement with the UK to cover this eventuality. It may take three years to acquire non-resident status and the Inland Revenue have to ensure that you are not just having a prolonged holiday abroad. To satisfy the taxman that you are settling abroad for life, you will have to dispose of all property in this country, and a long period of residence overseas is not sufficient evidence. The Inland Revenue office will send you useful leaflets on this subject which give full information and a list of countries with taxation agreements with the UK.

Although the state retirement pension can be paid throughout the world, you may lose the regular inflation-proof increases if the country you choose has no reciprocal agreement with the UK. Contact the DSS overseas office in Newcastle for more details. You should, however, get the increases in a country belonging to the EEC. It is well to remember however that this proofing is only against UK inflation, and not the inflation rate of your adopted country.

Health schemes in operation abroad

COMMONSENSE SAFEGUARDS BEFORE BUYING ABROAD

► **Before even considering living abroad read all you can about the country and take advice from impartial experts.**
► **Don't sign anything you don't understand.**
► **Discuss management charges and on-going costs.**
► **Don't take anything on trust.**
► **Demand to be given the title of the property when paying the bulk of the money, *not* afterwards.**

SEE ALSO: ◄
RESOURCES & BACK-UP:
Housing   p. 208

are not the same as the NHS and it is wise to look into private health care insurance before you think of settling elsewhere. Two firms which specialize in overseas health care and accept older age groups are the Exeter Hospital Aid Society and Kent Insurance & Securities Services (Overseas) Ltd. ◄

SEE ALSO: ▶

RESOURCES & BACK-UP:
Health insurance   p. 210

MOVING INTO CARE

It is not easy to admit that you are no longer capable of living alone. But, if you don't want to give up your independence entirely, a number of sheltered housing developments are beginning to include extra care facilities. They really represent half-way houses between ordinary sheltered housing and residential care. Sometimes they are known as *very* sheltered housing. They may include a dining room with midday meals, design features which lead to continued mobility, or extra domestic support, as well as round-the-clock housekeeping. They may be provided by commercial developers or by the associated groups of the major Housing Associations in the field such as Anchor or Hanover.

The Abbeyfield Society, with houses throughout the country, sets out to provide community living in a family atmosphere. Each of their houses (usually ordinary homes in ordinary streets) provides residents with a bed-sitting room of their own, but a resident housekeeper serves one meal a day, which is eaten together as a family. Unlike most residential homes, the Abbeyfield Society allows you to furnish your own room and this type of accommodation is often preferred by those who are still able to get out and about but find cooking a problem. Fees are reasonable, and around 40 per cent of Abbeyfield's residents are helped with fees by the DSS. Such schemes inevitably have long waiting lists.

Residential care

Given the choice, most people would prefer to remain in their own home for as long as possible. But, for some people, residential care with services provided and relief from household chores may turn out to be a blessing in disguise. Residential Care Homes may be provided by the local authorities, by charities or by private proprietors.

The local authorities are responsible for inspecting these homes to ensure that they offer reasonable standards of care, and in a number of cases private proprietors are now coming together in associations to protect themselves and their residents from some of the abuses which have marred the past in a fast growing market. In much the same way nursing homes are the responsibility of the local health authorities. Some homes have dual registration.

Every local authority has a number of residential care homes (sometimes called Part III accommodation in Social Services jargon). Unfortunately, such is the demand that most authorities have long waiting lists and you will need to consult your GP and social worker.

All meals are provided in communal dining rooms and it is not always possible to have a room of your own. Nurs-

Even long-stay care in hospital can be made homely in schemes such as this one at the Bolingbroke Hospital in South London, which provides a choice of wallpapers and furnishings and enables people to bring their own belongings and favourite ornaments.

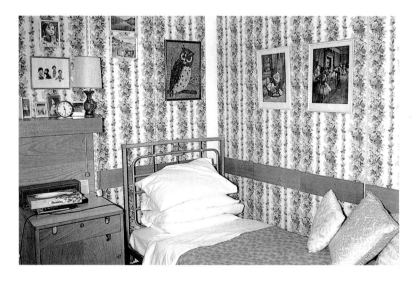

ing care is not included and if a resident becomes increasingly infirm, a transfer to hospital is usually arranged.

There are also residential homes run by charities, religious bodies or trade unions. To be accepted you may have to satisfy certain rules or criteria and you may have to attend a personal interview before the management organization.

Such homes are well run, and usually residents have more in common than those which come under local councils. Again the local Social Services Department or Counsel and Care for the Elderly can help. ▶

Privately run homes
The real increase in places can be found in the private sector where the number of residential homes has trebled in recent years. Standards of care vary although they must be registered with the local authority if they provide a home for more than three people.

You should never consider a home that is not registered, nor one that you have not visited personally. A trial stay of at least a month would enable you to make up your mind on whether or not to make such a move. It would also give you some idea of the other residents, the staff (although these may change fairly regularly) and whether you would feel at home there. Help is on hand in such homes for washing, dressing and having a bath, but if a resident needs full nursing care, then a transfer to a nursing home has to be arranged.

Any extra charges that may be imposed on top of basic fees should be sorted out before you move in. If charges for residential accommodation exceed the maximum limits supplied by the DSS and neither you, nor the family can cover the shortfall, it may be possible to get help from a trade association or local charity. Fees for both residential and nursing homes vary enormously and fact sheets are available from both

Age Concern and Counsel and Care for the Elderly.

If you decide to apply for a place in a local authority home, your social worker will need full details of your income and savings in order to work out how much you can afford to pay. If you own your own home and live alone in it, the value will be taken into account in assessing your income. If your spouse or carer lives in your home, the local authority can use its discretion but your spouse may be expected to contribute towards your upkeep. Behind this ruling is the principle that local authority accommodation is subsidized by the ratepayer, and residents should be expected to draw on their capital assets as well as their income.

In the same way, if you are thinking of moving into a private or voluntary new home, the value of any property owned will be taken into account when your savings and income are assessed. Should your home have to be sold to help pay the fees, its value can be ignored for a period long enough to allow the sale to be completed.

If you do not own any property and your income will not meet the fees in a private home, you can claim Income Support from the Department of Social Security. ▶ But there are maximum limits on this type of support and although you must have a certain sum for personal expenses, it is often found that the difference has to be met by relatives, friends or from charity.

Whichever you choose, a local authority, a voluntary or charitable home, or one run for profit by a commercial company, there are nearly always waiting lists. You are allowed time to come to terms with living communally and have the right to a trial period and although the weekly fees may seem very high, there is usually some form of help from the State. (A useful book is *At Home In A Home* by Pat Young.)

SEE ALSO: ◀

RESOURCES & BACK-UP:
Companions and help in the home   p. 201

MANAGING YOUR MONEY:
Help from the state   p. 32

KEEPING BUSY

The concept of retirement has changed dramatically in recent years. Although you may have 'retired' from traditional paid employment, and may have reached the rather arbitrary age at which you are entitled to draw your pension, it does not mean that you automatically retire from normal life. On the contrary, 'retirement' is often a time of opportunity and there is a wealth of ideas, activities and schemes on offer for you to take up just at the moment when you have enough time to do them properly. They may be work, hobbies, educational courses or holidays – or combinations of all of these. They merge naturally in a way that rarely happens during working years. If, for instance, you want to go on a short residential course about bee-keeping and as a result of what you have learned, set up your own hives, selling off the excess to friends or even local shops – does this constitute a holiday, a hobby or a new business? The answer of course is all three; the lines of demarcation between work and play become blurred. With a little planning, and proper consultation with partners, parents, children and anyone else whose life will be affected, it is possible to work out how to use those newly found hours of freedom to maximum effect, doing exactly what *you* want. This perhaps is the key to a happy retirement.

CONTINUING TO WORK

If you really want to continue with paid work, ask yourself exactly why. If the answer is money, read the chapter on finance before proceeding. In some cases you might find you are actually worse off by continuing with full-time employment, although a small amount of part-time work could be cost-effective. If, on the other hand, you feel you would be lost without some definite routine each day, think you will miss the companionship of other people or like the idea of having an interest outside the home – then the world really can be your oyster, and there are plenty of options open other than paid employment.

Many of those who are keenest to continue full-time work are those who, for one reason or another, were forced through 'early retirement' schemes to abandon their jobs in the first place. With generous severance payments or good occupational pensions, it is often not the need for money, but the hurt of rejection that motivates them; a desire to prove they still 'have what it takes' and that their employers made a huge mistake in letting them go. Trying to re-write history in this way is usually a thankless task. A bitter person, whose confidence has just taken a gigantic knock, may not be best placed in his or her later years to impress a new employer.

It is very sad that after perhaps 40 years or so of happy working, some people do end up feeling, quite wrongly, that they are somehow to blame for their job loss, but if this should happen to you, try to look at the situation from as detached a viewpoint as possible. Perhaps the factory closure or company take-over had been on the

One of the main benefits of increased leisure time in retirement is that it enables you to concentrate on acquiring or perfecting creative skills like pottery-making. Leaving behind the responsibilities of a job or family means that you can take advantage of day-time and residential courses and by selling your work you could even turn an enjoyable hobby into profit.

cards for years or new technology simply meant fewer skilled jobs. Whatever the specifics of the situation, instead of letting those final few months leave a nasty taste to taint your retirement, rather rejoice that you have gained some extra years in which to recapture that feeling of achievement, through something you enjoy doing – and you certainly do not need your old job back for that.

Paid work

How you go about finding a new job, and how successful you will be in your search, will to some extent depend on where you live, your previous job and whether or not you want to continue in the same line of work. At some time during their working lives most people consider a change of career, even if they never do anything about it for good

practical reasons – maybe it is not as well paid, is insecure or requires long training. This is a good time to take another look at those earlier aspirations, to see if they cannot be fulfilled after official retirement, at least in adapted form. This applies equally to paid and voluntary work. Imagine, for instance, the woman who wanted to become a doctor at 20. Perhaps her parents could not afford it, so she became a secretary instead, giving that up eventually to raise a family. Certainly her dreams of becoming a surgeon are gone forever, but a job as a secretary in a busy doctors' practice might prove rewarding for the very reasons – a desire to care for people's health – she was drawn to medicine in the first place. With the added experience gained by bringing up her own family, she could be of great help. In the voluntary sector, training as

Bookshops or charity organizations will be glad to take on older people with relevant skills in part-time employment, either on a temporary or permanent basis. Your years of work experience will be valuable and if you are prepared to work flexible hours this will enable full-time staff to be released for breaks, holidays or training sessions. This type of job will also give you plenty of contact with people, which can be very rewarding.

a first-aider or helping in an old people's home could bring the same sort of satisfaction.

Amongst the generation now retiring, anyone who was fortunate enough to get a good education was encouraged to find a job that made full use of it. It is a bit different today, when you may find that the chap who has come to build the new garden wall went to university, but simply prefers work that involves using his hands. Look at your own personal skills to see if that interest cannot somehow be translated into paid work of some kind, whether it is cooking, gardening, photography, carpentry or some other craft.

Looking for work

Whatever sort of work you are looking for, the first thing to do is to let everyone around you know that you are interested in continuing to work. At the time retirement approaches, friends may well be strongly placed to help, not as a favour but because they will be well aware of your capabilities. It is as well to work out beforehand what sort of job you are prepared to do, and to let others know too. For instance, if perhaps you recently retired as company secretary, it might be assumed that a couple of days' work a week as a book-keeper would be too lowly a role even to offer. On the other hand, if all you are looking for is part-time work to finance a holiday or a hobby, or simply to make yourself useful, your availability could be a godsend to a small new enterprise that desperately needs help, but cannot yet afford more full-time staff.

You may have overlooked the local Jobcentre as a source of employment opportunities. It can be a pretty variable feast, but certainly worth exploring further. Those taking early retirement may also find the 'PER Register' useful. This is the shortened form of the Professional and Executive Recruitment Service, a Government-run organization offering employment in the professional, executive, scientific and technical fields. They publish *Executive Post* each week, listing job vacancies.

There are a few commercial organizations that specialize in finding work for older people. Success After Sixty, for instance, has branches in Central London and Croydon and specializes in all types of office work, although you do not have to be 60 to register with them. Executive Stand-By, with branches in Northwich (Cheshire), London and Bristol, specializes in finding short-term contracts particularly for people working in the petro-chemical industry.

Some local groups of Age Concern will also have details of jobs available. These tend to be part-time work, much of it unskilled, but could be interesting for people who want to turn their hand to something completely different – and do not know where to start. You may also find helpful a free pamphlet called *Work in Retirement* (published by the Pre-Retirement Association) that lists agencies and other organizations that may be useful in finding work. ▶

It also makes sense to scour the local and national papers, not just for their advertisements but for news that might provide some sort of opening for you, such as a new company opening up. In addition it may be worth contacting the local Chamber of Commerce and any professional body that you belong to who may have heard of something useful on their grapevine. Talking to people generally – perhaps in the pub or the Club – may give you access to useful inside information.

Writing away

When writing away to a prospective employer, you will need to attach a record of your previous employment (curriculum vitae or CV) and it is worth

SEE ALSO: ◀

RESOURCES & BACK-UP:
Retirement
preparation   p. 216

spending some time working on a basic application letter which can then be modified from time to time according to who you are writing to. If you have not had to do this for some years there are several good careers books which give advice on this – although most are geared towards young people and school-leavers. In fact your own grand-children will almost certainly have received careers guidance on this so if you get on well with them, they might be able to help. A few points worth remembering: include all relevant experience, but avoid an over-lengthy chronicle. If relevant, mention that you would be prepared to work part-time and include any other useful information which helps build up a good all-round picture – hobbies, interests, personal circumstances and so on. Your CV should of course include the names of people to whom prospective employers can apply for references. If you are approaching retirement, it might be possible to obtain an open reference from your employer; this is helpful if you would rather your previous employer did not know you were applying for a part-time job at his arch competitor down the road! But personal references are usually just as good, especially if you are moving into a completely new area of enterprise. It's as well to ask the person or people first, but anyone who has known you for a while and knows your personality and capabilities will be suitable, and most people are only too glad to oblige.

Do not be put off by the idea of taking work on a temporary basis. This gives both parties a chance to find out how things are working, and the opportunity to retire with honour if need be. Sometimes a temporary job can turn into something more permanent, particularly with office jobs, but do not set too much store by this: most jobs are what they claim to be – temporary.

Learn to spot those employers who see your retirement and willingness to work as a way of subsidizing their business. Their ads may claim a position 'would suit pensioner'. But why? Is it because they are looking for someone mature, reliable and experienced – in which case why don't they say so? Or is it because they are paying half the going rate? It may well be that the job in question is something you would genuinely enjoy doing or that there are perks attached, so don't dismiss it out of hand, but find out exactly what is expected and if the terms are unacceptable leave well alone. Scrooges do not usually improve on closer acquaintance.

Other ideas

There may be a source of employment that you have not even thought about that lies in your own life experience and personal skills. Do you play the piano or speak another language fluently? If so, what about giving tuition on an informal basis? Could your experience in your previous job be put to use in some sort of consultancy capacity – to enable a small business to benefit from your know-how? Are there extra rooms in your house that could be let? While the very idea of having strangers in the house is abhorrent to some, for others they could provide welcome company in addition to the financial gain.

Of course, taking in lodgers on a permanent basis may affect your entitlement to housing benefit, if relevant, and then there is the new Community Charge, too, which is made on the number of adults living in a particular house; although in theory it is up to each individual to pay his or her own Community Charge, you may feel that it is too much responsibility to be worrying about whether or not your lodger has paid up! Consult the chapter on housing to assess your rights and responsibilities in this area. ◀ A good way of 'testing the

SEE ALSO: ▶

HOME FROM HOME:

Letting to tenants   p. 62

water' of room letting is to take in students on short-term lets – the accommodations officer of the institution nearest to you will be able to advise you on this, and if you live near a university town there are often students coming for short periods from overseas for language courses who need accommodation for perhaps two or three months, usually with breakfast and evening meal. Alternatively you could try offering traditional bed-and-breakfast accommodation – the local tourist information centre would be able to advise you about rates, advertising, safety requirements etc.

Other skills like gardening, cooking or domestic work are likely to be much in demand by those without the time to do the work themselves. (Find out in advance the going rate per hour for this type of work in your area.) Word of mouth, or the response to a card posted in the newsagent's window (or similar notice-board, such as the church, library or post office) will give a good idea how much in demand your services are likely to be. This type of work also has the benefit that you are in control of how much or how little you do – rather than the other way round. This is ideal if you want to go off on an extended holiday or are needed at home or to help with grandchildren.

Two other organizations which deserve mention here are Homesitters and Universal Aunts. Both organize homesitters – people who are prepared to go and live in someone else's house for a while, looking after it for them, in return for a small fee – which can vary between £25 and £65 plus expenses. Anyone interested should apply well in advance as it takes a while to check out references, and homesitters are expected to do several short stints each year – so it's not just a cheap way of getting a fortnight's holiday. Universal Aunts also employ people as short-term

companions. They also provide nannies and babysitters; if you have worked with children before this may well be an area you could look at especially on a temporary rather than permanent basis. Many people who have acted as foster parents, childminders or nannies go on doing so well past official retirement age – their experience in this field makes them invaluable both to their employers and to the children in their charge. Some people also feel able to look after their own grandchildren as well, but others prefer not to have the permanent responsibility of children – even if they are dearly loved grandchildren – so it is worth thinking very carefully about this before committing yourself.

WORKING FOR YOURSELF

There are lots of ways of working for

Even if it is difficult for you to leave the house very much, if you have a teaching skill, such as a musical instrument, which you can pass on to others, you could still work a few hours a week by taking on pupils in your own home.

yourself – self-employment is becoming more and more common. Many people earn their living working from home or offering their services on a freelance basis to a number of different employers, or even setting up their own businesses. It may be that you simply want to augment your income a little by selling the proceeds of a skill or hobby, like pottery, garden produce or hand-knitting. There are thousands of people augmenting their incomes in this enjoyable way, but it is a good idea to approach it in a fairly businesslike manner, costing your materials or ingredients and time on a realistic basis. Many people are a little diffident about selling their wares, and yet if you look around you can find many quite large enterprises which mushroomed from small beginnings like this. It is too easy, however, to underprice things. Costed honestly, it may be that your profit only comes at a pound or so an hour, but that's probably fine if you're enjoying yourself and it is less likely to interfere with your tax situation or entitlement to benefits. But it is also important to make sure you are not actually subsidizing your customers by selling, say, home-made fudge for less than it costs you to produce it in the first place!

Setting up in business

If you feel your enterprise has more scope than simply producing pin money, you may consider setting up your own business. This may not mean actually forming a limited company – you can act as a sole trader or set up a partnership initially if the turnover is likely to be fairly small – but either way it is very important to give it serious thought before embarking. There is something very seductive in the idea of becoming one's own boss and of those who succeed, most say they would not have it any other way. However, failed businesses, and thus to some degree

failed dreams, are thick on the ground, so before proceeding look at the chart opposite and give some thought to the points it raises. It will help you decide whether you are prepared to accept the challenge of your enterprise, or whether it is perhaps too risky.

If the answers to these questions are mainly positive, and you are still determined, there are a number of organizations to help: The Small Firms Advisory Service, run by the Department of Trade and Industry is one and CoSIRA, The Council for Small Industries in Rural Areas, is another, The Manpower Services Commission run a number of courses, through existing colleges, and some of them are specifically designed to help the new entrepreneur. Some are part-time or held over a succession of weekends to make the timing easier for those still in paid employment. The Hotel and Catering Training Board run a variety of courses that might prove useful and also publish several booklets. There are also many specialist books available through your public library.

Make contact with the local Chamber of Commerce whose address you will be able to get from the National Chamber of Trade or, in Scotland, the Scottish Retail Federation. And look at the chapter on personal finance to assess the likely effect on your own financial position. ◄

Other enterprises

Running the village post office and general store is another popular retirement dream. Every week newspaper small-ads offer sub-post offices as businesses for sale which do sound tempting for the retired couple. Do be careful: new legislation means that in future hours of opening will be strictly regulated and this could adversely affect your chances of making a profit as the Post Office side of the business has

SEE ALSO: ▶

MANAGING YOUR MONEY:
Earned income after
retirement   p. 38

RESOURCES & BACK-UP:
Work   p. 221

SPOT-CHECK BEFORE STARTING YOUR OWN BUSINESS

☐ If you are married, discuss it with your husband or wife, who *will* become involved, at the very least with extra chores on the home front, if not as an active business partner. Running a small business can be very lonely, so you will need moral support and someone on your side.

☐ Be realistic about whether your health is up to it. With a paid job or voluntary work, you can always opt out if your health, or that of the family, demands it. This is not as easy when running a business.

☐ If it is a totally new line of business for you, have you been able to gain some experience first in someone else's establishment, even if you are not paid for it?

☐ Do you have a proper business plan, and enough financial backing to cover the 'start-up' costs? There are various agencies who can help here – the Citizens Advice Bureau, Chamber of Commerce or Manpower Services Commission will be able to give you advice. A good accountant can also help to draw up a business plan, showing overall outlay and how soon you are likely to go into profit. You'll also need to gain the confidence of a sympathetic bank manager. Remember that you will be expected to give a personal guarantee to underwrite a loan or overdraft facility and for most people this means using property as collateral. This is another reason for a married couple to be absolutely clear about the implications, and you should consult a solicitor from the start.

☐ Think about marketing and sales: do you plan to sell directly to the public and if so, who are your rivals? How do your prices compare? Is it possible to test the market in a small way perhaps by selling your wares at a craft fair or on a market stall? A hard lesson learned here might save you thousands later.

☐ Are you prepared for the fact that you may well be going from a five-day week to a seven-day week, including working in the evenings, as this is what most small businessmen find themselves doing, at least to begin with?

☐ Do you know how to keep your account books up-to-date and to keep an eye on cash flow? Once again an accountant can help – and they often save you more in the area of tax in the long run than you pay out in fees. An accountant will also advise about the possibility of having to register for VAT, something that does increase the paperwork. And don't forget National Insurance contributions, especially if you are employing any full-time workers.

☐ Have you looked at what training courses might be available to help in the new venture? These could range from simple book-keeping through to marketing techniques, to use of computers.

Working for yourself does not necessarily mean setting up a fully-fledged limited company. As with this garden trug-making workshop, you may find that an old-fashioned skill could provide you with the basis for a small business, as well as preserving a useful craft for the next generation.

SEE ALSO: ▶

RESOURCES & BACK-UP:

Work   p. 221

until now provided the *guaranteed* income. It could become a very quick way of getting through the retirement nest egg.

Franchises are another popular choice, particularly those where only a modest outlay, perhaps a few thousand pounds, is required to set them up. Franchises can work superbly – Benetton, Wimpy Bars and Budget Rent-A-Car have proved that – but for anyone with no experience of retailing or who falls prey to an unscrupulous operator (and there are some about) the result will be a nightmare. Before proceeding check with the British Franchise Association and *always* get your solicitor to go over the small print with you, particularly clauses relating to the sale of the franchise. ◀

VOLUNTARY WORK

It is one of the happier facts of life that voluntary work means radically different things to different people. Were it otherwise hospital patients would be

---

CHOOSING VOLUNTARY WORK

☐ Do I want to help by doing something similar to my normal paid work – or would a complete change make more sense?

☐ Are there any causes I feel passionately about or do I have a few prejudices or lack of sympathy with others?

☐ Do I want a regular commitment, to give some sort of routine to life? Or, realistically, will I only be able to help out from time to time?

☐ After years of telling other people what to do, do I want to let others now take the lead, or will I be best used organizing their efforts?

awash with the tea provided by friendly helpers and there would be nobody to do the disc-jockeying, build the dry-stone wall or embark on expenses-paid trips to the other side of the world. Believe it or not these are actual examples of the work done by bona-fide helpers who have chosen different ways of doing their bit, and in most cases find they are loving every minute of it.

Nowadays there is no shortage of good causes which rely on voluntary help. It would be impossible to give a definitive list in the space provided here, but there are several 'umbrella' organizations that will be able to help. However, before rushing off to join up or sign on, it is a better idea to sit down and do a little 'personal homework', giving honest answers to the questions in the table set out below, opposite.

Once you have answered these questions a clearer picture should emerge as to what type of voluntary work might suit you best. The other golden rule is start in a small way and get a clear understanding from the beginning just what is expected, as you would do if you were taking on paid employment. If you enjoy it, there will be plenty of opportunity to take on more work, but if you find that the work (or the people involved with it) do not suit you, then resign and look for something else. The idea of being in a paid job you dislike is bad enough, but the idea of doing voluntary work you do not enjoy is sheer lunacy, both for the volunteer and the unfortunate recipients of your energies. It breeds resentment and ill-will in a situation which depends on good-will.

Where to start

REACH stands for Retired Executives Action Clearing House, a registered charity which specializes in matching up retired people, with their mass of different skills, with a number of interesting organizations that desperately

The range of possibilities for voluntary work is very wide. It could mean anything from helping children with reading at school (above), to delivering meals to the housebound (left), when bad weather means that there is no possibility for them to get out and about.

need help but cannot afford to pay. Through them, a former senior executive of a large construction company undertook to co-ordinate the efforts of a local community group who had taken on the task of making the disused neighbourhood baths into a community centre. Although the job was small fry compared to the type of contracts he was used to he said afterwards that he found it more of a challenge, particularly knowing the effort that had gone into raising the necessary funds.

The Citizens Advice Bureau will be only too pleased to give you information about what groups in the area need help (the CAB number will be in the local telephone book) and many towns now have a Volunteer Bureau which will also be able to put you in the picture as to just what help is needed where. They also publish a Volunteer Bureaux Directory which you could borrow from the local library or get from the National Association of Volunteer Bureaux, price £3.50. Other useful organizations are listed in 'Resources & Back-up'. ◄

SEE ALSO: ▷

RESOURCES & BACK-UP:
Volunteering   p. 220

It goes without saying, of course, that voluntary work does not need to be 'organized' in any way. Shopping for a housebound neighbour, or looking after a sick or handicapped child to give his or her parents a break, are every bit as valuable as waving a collecting tin. Another aspect of voluntary work is that it gives you the opportunity to do something about some aspect of your life which irritates you – be it government policy towards pensioners, conservation, lack of literacy in schoolchildren or cruelty to animals. You now have more time and opportunity to stand up and be counted, by joining a pressure group, a charity, even a political party, or helping out in your local school.

There is plenty of voluntary work to be done overseas as well. BESO stands for British Executive Service Overseas,

an independent organization initiated by the Institute of Directors, with some government help, to provide consultants with management, professional or technical expertise to help in developing countries. Assignments last on average two to six months, volunteers can take their partners, with air fares and living expenses paid. Successful postings in the past have included a master-butcher from Hertfordshire who went to advise the Tanzanians on setting up a meat-processing plant and a factory administrator who flew to Jamaica to train instructors.

It is also worth noting that Voluntary Service Overseas, International Voluntary Service, the Catholic Institute for International Relations and the United Nations Associations also have similar assignments, although most last two years or more and some require that, with a married couple, both partners must have relevant skills.

FURTHER EDUCATION
No doubt some readers will be familiar with the wealth of educational opportunities presently on offer because they have already been attending classes or courses before retirement age. However, for others the idea of returning to studies can be daunting, particularly for those who were forced for financial or family reasons to leave school early. Don't be put off, however. Teaching methods are much more relaxed than they used to be, especially in adult education. Classes can be fun as well as instructive and can be extremely good value. Whether your interest is philosophy or philately, Chinese cooking or chair upholstering, there are ways of pursuing it, even though there are cut-backs in further education in most places. Learning a new skill can not only be stimulating and useful, but it will also give you the chance to get to know people you might not otherwise meet.

Continuing your education in older age can be very rewarding and there are now many excellent residential courses where like-minded people can gather to study their particular interest in convivial surroundings.

Short courses and evening classes

The local adult education institute is the source of most weekly courses. As AEIs are administered by the local education authority the variety and cost of courses will, to some degree, reflect the spending of the local authority as a whole, and it may be irritating to find that you have to pay full fees in one area, while your retired friends living a cou-ple of miles away under a different authority get concessions, or in some cases, free classes. However, all classes are heavily subsidized and usually offer a fairly wide choice. You will normally be able to choose between day and evening classes (the former preferred by some people because it saves a walk or bus ride home in the dark) and also choose between those for people of all

There is no reason why older age should prevent you from acquiring a modern 'high tech' skill such as computing or word-processing, which could lead to new opportunities for paid work.

ages and those designed specifically for retired people. There are benefits in both. For some people the pleasure lies in being with a mixed group, while the advantage of a class specifically aimed at older people might encourage them to enrol for a class they might otherwise avoid, such as computer studies for beginners or keep fit classes. AEIs also run accredited GCSE and A-level courses.

If you are worried about your ability to derive enjoyment from further education, you might try enrolling for just one term to study a subject you already know something about. There would be no question of feeling out of your depth – and you might find that, having got the taste for it, you wanted more.

For those who cannot find the course they want offered locally by their adult educational institute, remember the curriculum is not sacrosanct. If you can find a number of people, say 15 or so, who are as interested as you in pursuing a subject not presently catered for, there is nothing to stop you approaching the local education authority and asking for that class to be laid on, backing up your request with your findings. Alternatively, if that falls on stony ground, but you are really serious, why not gather together and set up your own?

The local town hall, library or CAB will be able to give details of the nearest adult education institute. Enrolment is normally around the beginning of September and most publish a list of classes on offer in advance. It pays to enrol early because the most popular classes get booked up very quickly. Conversely, less popular classes may actually be cancelled if there are not enough students to make them viable.

The Workers' Educational Association (WEA) has been providing day and evening classes for years in a wide variety of subjects. They also organize a number of summer schools and study tours both in Britain and abroad.

For those who prefer to study at home through correspondence courses, the Council for the Accreditation of Correspondence Colleges will be able to provide a list of colleges and give general advice on correspondence courses. The National Extension College has a series of courses specially designed for adults who left school at an early age and have not done any studying since, and they also offer special rates to older people.

Two rather less formal ways of learning are through the National Adult School Organization and The University of the Third Age. The former is open to all ages and is composed of small groups who either follow a national study syllabus or a course of their own choice. Instead of a classroom, they meet in members' homes and they also have a number of social activities connected with their 'Friendship Through Study' groups.

The University of the Third Age is something that originated in France and has been adapted slightly over here. It consists of a small network of self-help groups in which older people educate themselves by sharing their experience and knowledge. Not only do the groups avoid the competitive spirit sometimes associated with conventional learning but the whole idea is that the classes can evolve according to the interests of the members. Some groups, however, opt for fairly conventional subjects like art or French but the advantage is that each group has a great deal of autonomy, including how much to charge to cover their costs.

Few people with a television set can be unaware of the existence of the Open University. Its major purpose is to provide university degree courses for which students study at home, using workbooks backed up by television and radio talks and lectures, mainly given on BBC 2 and Radio 3 and a postal tutor to mark essays and projects. Less well known is the OU's Associate Student Programme, consisting of nearly 200 'pack' courses which contain written information and an audio or video cassette. These cover a wide range of topics from jazz to retirement planning and are designed for people who 'want a challenge but not a degree'. ▶

A more recent arrival on the television screen has been the Open College. This operates in a similar way to the Open University except the emphasis is on technical skills rather than academic knowledge. Many of the programmes are intended to train young people in a particular field such as catering or retailing. However, some are of a more general nature – on using a computer or managing your time more effectively. The Open College transmits between 1 and 2pm Monday to Friday on Channel 4 and there is extensive back-up material to accompany each course.

The more adventurous might also consider going back into full time further education to study for a degree. Even if you went on to higher education as a young person after school, there is no reason why you should not enrol again to study in depth perhaps a subject which has become interesting to you later in life, or you might discover a course which was not available at all at the time when you went to university. There are colleges which cater specifically for mature students (Birkbeck College, London, and Lucy Cavendish College, Cambridge, are two university colleges offering undergraduate and post-graduate courses), and many other universities, polytechnics and colleges of higher education are happy to accom-

SEE ALSO: ◀

RESOURCES & BACK-UP:

Leisure   p. 211

Fitness   p. 203

Learning a new language, or taking a refresher course in one you learned years ago, make visits to the country where that language is spoken much more interesting.

point was the former perfume salesman who left school at 14, but on retirement joined one of these courses at the local polytechnic. He enjoyed it very much and found studying easier than he had imagined it would be. Eventually he went on successfully to do a BA Honours degree course where he found himself with students of all ages.

One of the nicest ways to learn is away from home (and distraction) on a residential course. It is often difficult to decide where education stops and holidays begin these days, so some suggestions and organizations covering these courses are included in the section on holidays, later.

PASTIMES AND INTERESTS

'Hobbies' seems to be a rather feeble word for the many activities, pastimes, interests, passions and obsessions, collections and classes that most people have to fill their leisure time. Retirement is a time to indulge your particular interest to the full, or to take on a new one. Most people will have a few thoughts of their own on the subject, so the following are really just a few scattered ideas to be digested alongside the opportunities mentioned in other sections of this chapter.

It makes sense to have a good mix of hobbies: something physical, like bowling, walking or tap dancing, alongside some mental activity, like learning a foreign language or studying philosophy. It also makes sense to have a free, or almost-free, hobby like Scrabble or whist alongside one which requires outlay on materials, like photography or pottery or wine-making. If something in the latter category takes your fancy, but you fear that the cost of materials will be ruinous, make sure everyone close to you knows about your new interest – just before your next birthday or Christmas. Your family and friends will be glad to provide paintbrushes or

modate mature students on their degree courses. Two useful reference books are *The Directory of First Degree Courses* published by CNAA, and *The Compendium of University Entry Requirements*, both of which will be available at the public library.

You will probably have to finance yourself during your time at college. Although local education authorities do offer a certain number of discretionary grants, these are harder to come by in this time of financial stringency and will probably only be given to younger people returning to college to study basically vocational courses. Finding a course and college which will take you may mean living away from home during term time, so you need to assess your personal needs and financial situation quite carefully beforehand.

You may also be put off from applying because you are not confident about your ability to study properly. It might be worth looking for a college that runs a 'Return to Learning' course, some of which may be residential. A good case in

modelling tools or maybe even a tripod or new photographic lens.

The English Tourist Board publishes a booklet entitled 'Hobby Holidays' which gives details of residential holiday courses that offer tuition in a wide range of subjects. It is not a bad idea to start a new hobby this way as there will be expert advice on hand, everybody will be in more or less the same boat, and by devoting yourself wholeheartedly to a particular subject for a week or so you should see some progress. You may also be able to borrow equipment, saving the cost of buying your own until you have decided whether or not this really is for you. Evening and day classes have the same advantage and although some people prefer to follow a book and study at home, it is nice to strike up new friendships with people who, by defini-

tion, will have at least one interest in common with you.

If you are interested in the arts you might well consider becoming 'A Friend of . . .' a particular theatre or company. Many theatre, opera and ballet companies as well as museums, art galleries and even churches and cathedrals have formed these groups. 'Friends' are usually able to enjoy privileged booking, occasional invitations to special shows previews and receive a regular newsletter.

Collecting is getting increasingly popular and if you travel a lot it can be fun to collect a small souvenir wherever you go – even if it is only books of matches. It is best to choose something small and inexpensive – spoons or thimbles for example, or a hand-painted patterned tile.

Rambling or hill-walking are excellent pastimes in that they combine personal enjoyment with physical fitness, thereby improving your all-round health and well-being.

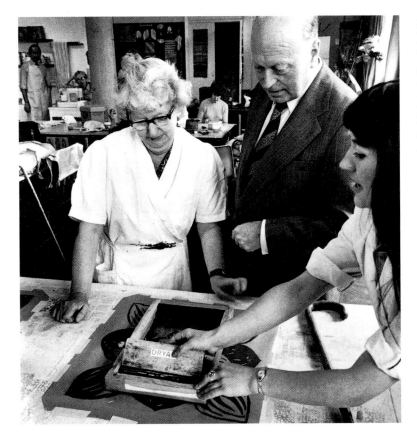

Screen-printing is only one of many crafts which you could pursue as a hobby, either at classes or at home, depending on the amount of equipment required.

SEE ALSO: ▷

RESOURCES & BACK-UP:
Leisure   p. 211
Fitness   p. 203

Anyone interested in pursuing a craft will find the Crafts Council a mine of useful information. ◀ In addition to the successful exhibitions they mount from time to time, they will be able to provide details of courses, names of suppliers and factsheets on every conceivable craft.

Most people get some exercise in the course of their job, even just going to and from work, so on retirement you need to make an effort, if the extra inches are not going to pile up quickly on the waistline. The Sports Council has become aware of this and is actively promoting fitness for the over-50s. If you contact the Sports Council they will be able to give you details of facilities available in your particular area. The range is vast – from windsurfing to diving, bowls and canoeing to hockey and swimming. If you have always been

involved in a particular sport, but no longer feel up to taking an active part, there is no need to abandon your old club or team altogether – there are other ways of maintaining your involvement. By offering much needed help, like making the sandwiches or handling administration, you can continue to enjoy the convivial atmosphere and contribute to its continuing success. ◀

The public library will have details posted on their board about local activities and classes in addition to those run by the local authority. If you like the idea of pursuing an interest and having a holiday at the same time, the Holiday Care Service and the National Institute of Continuing Adult Education, mentioned earlier, will have details of short residential courses and holiday breaks relating to a mass of different interests and hobbies.

HOLIDAYS

The opportunity to travel is one of the most positive aspects of retirement. Older people from all walks of life are venturing further afield than they ever thought possible in their youth when it may have taken a war for them to see the world. With holidays in Spain costing a little as £5 a day, you no longer have to be fabulously rich to get away. And there are many concessions offered to older people in the UK as well as foreign holidays.

Best known are the specialist holidays for older people. Saga Holidays were the pioneers in this field, but other tour operators, like Intasun's Golden Days or Thomsons' Young At Heart have been quick to join the market. The key to it is that retired people can take their holidays when they choose and many prefer to go off-season when resorts and transport are less crowded. In return hoteliers, coach operators and airlines are only too pleased to offer large discounts, knowing that otherwise their hotels or coaches might well stand empty. There are several good reasons for taking a holiday through one of these operators: the competitive prices, the presence of couriers who are trained to look after the needs of older travellers, and in some cases inclusive insurance premiums. They also offer a vast range of 'special interest' holidays covering subjects as diverse as archaeology, dancing, painting or retirement planning. While they are working most people go on holiday exhausted, looking for a relaxing break to recharge the batteries. In retirement, you are less likely to be taking a holiday for this reason, and activity holidays have extra appeal. All the tour operators offer different extras, from the promise of no night flights, to free tea each afternoon or perhaps most useful of all, no 'single room supplements' at certain times of the year. Even if you do not like the idea of being part of a group and prefer to maintain at heart some degree of inde-

pendence, you can still take advantage of the savings made by an 'all-in' holiday to travel to and from the destination, going off to do your thing as you would on any other package tour.

Truly independent travellers will no doubt have sorted out their own 'tips and wrinkles' by now, but it is worth mentioning that at any age it pays to shop around for air travel bargains in the 'bucket shops', usually found in newspaper small ads, and compare these prices with the cost of a package.

Travel concessions
British Rail offer good reductions with their Senior Citizen's Railcard and these are the greatest bargain of all in November each year when, to encourage further card sales, fares are slashed, and it is often possible to travel from one end of Britain to the other for a fraction of the normal cost. The prices and conditions vary each year, but it is worthwhile planning your longest do-

Remaining physically active in older age is essential for good health, and there are many fitness classes and groups available specifically designed for the older person.

Older age should not deter you from trying adventurous holidays abroad. In fact, if you can afford it and you are physically fit, this is when you can plan to visit those exotic places you never had time to explore before.

mestic trips around this time. Holders of the British Rail card are entitled to purchase, for a further £5, the Rail Europe Senior Card which will give discounts of 30–50 per cent on rail journeys taken in Europe.

British Airways offer concessions of up to 30 per cent to retired people on domestic flights, including the Channel Islands.

Bus companies may offer concessions or certain special deals for lower cost fares on regular bus routes. However this varies widely from area to area, so check at the depot or garage. Coach fares are now so competitive – and therefore cheap – especially between certain popular cities or resorts that they may not offer extra concessions for retired people but again it is always worth checking.

It is also worth pointing out that almost all museums, stately homes, country parks, zoos and so on that charge entry fees offer reductions to the over-60s or pensioners, as do many theatres, concert halls and cinemas. If you want to know before you visit ask at the local Tourist Information Centre. As a general rule, the National Trust does not offer any concessionary entrance fees, but if you take out life membership of the Trust you do not have worry about entry fees or further annual subscriptions.

Educational holidays
Many public schools, residential colleges and campus-based universities open their doors to holiday-makers each year. At their Summer Schools you can follow a wide range of different activities and it can be ideal for husbands and wives who want to holiday together but pursue different interests.

The National Institute for Continuing Education publishes a brochure of weekend breaks and short residential courses where you can study just about anything – from pottery to an examination of Rodgers and Hart musicals. An additional bonus is that many of them are held in beautiful old houses and have a lively social atmosphere.

The Field Studies Council publishes an index of the courses they organize in Britain and overseas. Prices are very

Holidays can now be very productive – there are more and more specialist holidays being provided both at home and abroad which combine comfort, good company and the opportunity to pursue a particular interest such as drawing or painting in beautiful surroundings.

reasonable (around £135 including board, lodging and tuition for a week's stay.) The subjects on offer include natural history, painting, drawing and photography. Their overseas holidays take a specialist theme, for example, spring birds of Majorca or flowers and painting in Andalucia.

Holiday care

Finally a word about an excellent organization that could be extremely useful in planning your holiday, whatever you decide to do. It is the Holiday Care Service, a registered charity whose brief it is to provide information on holidays and travel, particularly for those who might not otherwise be able to take a break for reasons of age, disability, poor health or lack of funds. They have dozens of leaflets on every conceivable area of holidaying, from exotic round-the-world cruises, to skiing for disabled people, to working holidays for single mums and farmhouse accommodation – and lots more. The service is free, although all voluntary contributions are gratefully accepted.▶

They have recently set up a new scheme called 'Holiday Helpers'. These are volunteers who will accompany someone who is perhaps blind or disabled on holiday and although the volunteer is not paid a salary, their travel and accommodation is free. They are always looking for more volunteer-escorts and anyone with nursing experience is especially welcome. For those without, simple training can be given, so if you would like to know more about the scheme contact them about it.

The Holiday Care Service is sometimes able to help with the cost of a holiday. Although they do not have funds themselves, they can put people in touch with relevant organizations who may be able to help. Certain benevolent societies earmark holiday funds for particular sections of the community; it is a case of knowing where to look. For instance, some organizations will help former servicemen, another a former trade union member. Many people are unaware that some

SEE ALSO: ◀

RESOURCES & BACK-UP:
Holidays   p. 207

Disability or financial difficulty do not necessarily mean you can never get away. There are several schemes to help those who are disabled or disadvantaged to have real holidays among friendly and helpful people.

local councils will provide either a small grant towards a holiday or in some cases a stay at the Council's own holiday home within the UK, usually somewhere beside the sea.

To make life a little easier for people with special needs, the Service publishes a series of guides to different parts of Britain containing useful information such as which hotels have a ramp or can cope with a special diet.

PETS AND GARDENING

Keeping a pet and tending the garden are two of the pastimes most associated with retirement. It is not really surprising since, as enthusiasts will agree, few activities could bring more pleasure.

Pets and wildlife

The criteria applied to choosing and obtaining a pet will be the same as at any other time of life – personal preference, space and cost. Some some people are put off having a pet by the fact that they

want to feel free at last to come and go as they please without the responsibility of caring for a pet. One solution is to organize an animal-sitting rota with friends who also have pets so that you can take it in turns, and there are various aids available to allow pets to be left alone at least for a day or so. Your local pet shop should be able to offer advice.

Sadly, some sheltered housing units will not allow cats or dogs, so what are the other options? Fish are wonderfully relaxing and much more fun than most people realize, while others feel the same way about canaries or budgerigars. If you have a garden or live in a rural area, you could try to 'adopt' a wild bird or animal. These will never be 'pets' in the normal sense of the word but they can provide you with endless hours of pleasure and in many cases may even depend on you for their existence. For instance, the saucer of milk you leave out each evening could be vital to a hedgehog whose normal diet has been depleted by the use of pesticides. Squirrels can become remarkably tame, and a regular source of food on a well-positioned bird table will attract more interesting birds than just sparrows.

The Royal Society for the Protection of Birds has a wide choice of birdfeeders, some in clear plastic which fit up against the window on suction pads, giving a wonderful armchair view of the birds feeding. They also have nesting boxes for different species and even bat boxes for another endangered species that you might want to encourage in your garden.

Gardening

One of the saddest things that can happen to the dedicated gardener on retirement is that after perhaps half a lifetime cultivating the plot, it becomes difficult to cope with the work. Some couples have even upped and sold their houses purely on this basis, but not without a lot of heartbreak.

Yet it is possible to adapt a fairly large garden, up to half an acre certainly, into something that can be easily managed, if you are prepared to put a little thought and money into it. The thought is needed for some ruthless decision-making about what can go and what you treasure most. Low-maintenance gardening techniques have become popular in the last few years, not just for older people, but they do entail replacing annual bedding with perennials and shrubs that require a lot less work, and in some cases replacing lawn with hard surfaces. If you have a fairly large garden, it may be worthwhile beginning the changeover to a more labour-saving garden design before retirement, so that the new plantings are beginning to mature by the time you actually retire.

Careful planning can save the spirit of the garden. For instance, if roses are your pride and joy, accept that you will be spending quite a bit of time on them

and cut back on bedding elsewhere. If, on the other hand, you believe colourful summer bedding is what a garden is all about, perhaps the lawn or part of it could be replaced with one of the attractive hard surface materials now on the market – York stone, real or simulated, or bricks laid herringbone-fashion, perhaps. Or have raised beds built so you can continue to use bedding plants without too much bending. Even if the lawn is your greatest pleasure, sinking mowing stones round the edge will save on time-consuming trimming, and modern, electric mowers are much lighter to use than petrol-driven motor mowers or hand mowers. There are a number of excellent books around on garden design which will provide further inspiration. Professionals say that for some reason people are reluctant to spend money on having their garden landscaped, but investing perhaps £2000 on getting the garden right could mean you are saved from a move – and far greater upheaval and expense.

The British Association of Landscape Industries will be able to advise on a list of their members who could do the work (and having chosen one, ask if you can have a look at other gardens he or she has done, or some photographs if

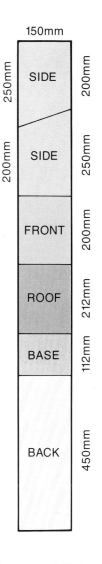

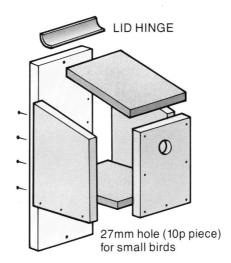

LID HINGE

27mm hole (10p piece) for small birds

Encouraging wildlife in your own garden is a delightful and worthwhile hobby. The Royal Society for the Protection of Birds provides the plan for this simple nesting box which you can make yourself using a plank 150mm wide and 15mm thick. Simply cut the plank into pieces as shown above and assemble, as left. Apply a coat of wood preservative, not creosote. Place the box 3–5 metres up to be safe from cats.

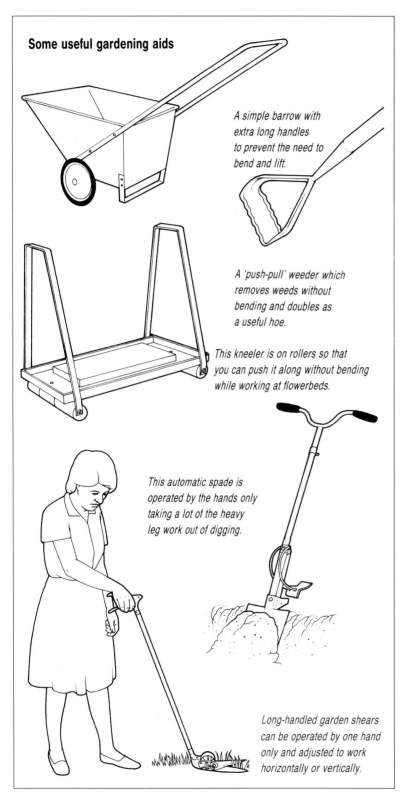

Some useful gardening aids

A simple barrow with extra long handles to prevent the need to bend and lift.

A 'push-pull' weeder which removes weeds without bending and doubles as a useful hoe.

This kneeler is on rollers so that you can push it along without bending while working at flowerbeds.

This automatic spade is operated by the hands only taking a lot of the heavy leg work out of digging.

Long-handled garden shears can be operated by one hand only and adjusted to work horizontally or vertically.

a visit is impractical.) Gardening is a very personal thing and you must be happy with the end result.

Well worth reading are *The Low-Maintenance Garden* by Graham Rose and *Equipment for the Disabled: Leisure and Gardening* by Andrew White. You certainly do not need to be disabled to benefit from the many ideas and gadgets which will make life easier – like pruners with long handles to avoid a precarious balancing act on the steps for instance, and the book also has some good ideas for 'home-made' gadgets.

'IT'S SOMETHING I'VE BEEN MEANING TO DO FOR YEARS . . .'

Many people look forward to retirement to 'put their house in order' in a way that time, and possibly money has not allowed for previously.

Family reunions

Going to visit children (and perhaps unseen grandchildren) in a far flung corner of the world is particularly popular. Some companies offer very competitive rates on reunion flights to Canada, Australia, New Zealand and South Africa, which have the added advantage of a courier available to help at each stage of the journey. Your travel agent will have details of other packages but it is also worth considering buying a round-the-world ticket which will not cost much more and will enable you to do the journey in easy stages, stopping-over en route in some of the most exciting cities in the world. A magazine called *Business Traveller* gives good up-to-the minute information on comparative air faires. Again, look around and check the bucket shop prices.

Personal histories

Even if you do not feel up to writing a fully fledged book, it is nice to be able to hand down some family history to the next generation and there are two ways of doing this. One way is to write a series of simple anecdotes about your family and things you remember from childhood – the price of sweets (or lack of them) schooldays, being ill, Christmas and so on. The world is changing so quickly that these personal glimpses of life will be treasured by your grandchildren, when they are old enough to appreciate them, and even more by their great-grandchildren.

Another way of bringing the past to life is by tracing the family tree. There are now a wealth of courses, short-break holidays and books on this fascinating subject. You should start by writing down all you know, and asking other members of the family to contribute their knowledge. The Society of Genealogists will be able to help you further and membership of their Society will give you access to their library plus a quarterly newsletter and magazine. ▶

Photographs and other memorabilia, of schooldays, the armed forces and so on, are also fine heirlooms – provided there is some way of knowing what is what! There is nothing more intriguing – or frustrating – than finding an old sepia photograph of someone who bears a definite likeness to other family members, yet no-one knows who it is. Marking up some of those old photos in the attic will be much appreciated. If, like many people, you are a hoarder you may end up with mementoes you really do not know what to do with. If you have a collection of wartime mementoes, before throwing them away, offer it to the Imperial War Museum who are interested in acquiring material relating to the First and Second World Wars.

Home movie buffs can now get their old films transferred to video-tape for between £30–50. They are far easier to watch on your television, without the paraphernalia of projector and screen. It also means the originals will not get worn. The various companies operating

this service will also put your colour slides on to tape and even add a 'voice-over' commentary or music if required. The local paper or a good photographic shop should have further details of this movie-to-video service.

Above: *If gardening is important to you it is worth investing in the construction of raised beds which reduce the amount of bending and heavy work involved.*

SEE ALSO: ◀

RESOURCES & BACK-UP:
Gardening   p. 204
Leisure   p. 211

Left: *Growing your own produce is enormously satisfying, can save you money and gives the benefit of regular exercise.*

GOOD HEALTH

Good health can be a very subjective thing, especially as people grow older. A simple definition of health is that it is the absence of disease, but few people use this definition, because of course it is much more than that. Health has as much to do with the way you feel as with the way your body is working – after all, when you reach the age of 70 or 80, you may well have a disease, such as arthritis, but you can still be healthy. Good health is related to your ability to do what you want to do; if your body is functioning as well as possible, it will allow you to get about, to see friends, to look after yourself and to enjoy life in the way that you want.

Inevitably, the concepts of good health and ageing become inextricably entwined. There is a popular assumption that poor health is the inevitable result of ageing, even though there are thousands of active older people, some well into their 80s, who enjoy very good health.

WHAT IS AGEING?

Ageing is a normal biological process, or more probably, a set of biological processes. It is not something that suddenly begins when an individual reaches 40 or 50 or some other arbitrary age – on the contrary, it starts as soon as normal growth and development have been completed, after adolescence. The causes of ageing are not known, but there is almost certainly some in-built process taking place which means that people age even if they live in the perfect environment. Recently there has been a claim that the rate of biological ageing can be slowed by adopting a certain lifestyle and by the consumption of large amounts of vitamins, but these conclusions are disputed.

One of the reasons why so little is known about ageing is that it is very difficult to know which of the changes that can be observed in a group of older people, for example a group of people aged 75, are due to the cumulative effects of the ageing process or to having lived a certain lifestyle or in a certain environment for 75 years. For example, shortness of breath and cough is so common in some areas that it is regarded as normal, but a detailed investigation of many older people reveals that the shortness of breath and cough that they suffer is not due to ageing but to factors such as air pollution, cigarette smoking and, for men, exposure to dust at work. Similarly it is hard to know how many of the changes that are seen in the skin are due to ageing alone and how many are due to prolonged exposure to sunlight.

The effects of ageing

Before considering the effects of ageing on specific parts of the body it is useful to try to give a general definition of the effects of ageing on the body. Some experts believe that the best definition of the effects of ageing is that ageing reduces the body's ability to cope with 'health challenges'. For instance three common 'challenges' to the body are:

- A marked drop in temperature during a cold snap

- Dehydration of the body as a result of infection
- Immobility due to the need for bed rest during a severe illness

All human beings are affected by these challenges but the older you are, the more serious is the impact of these changes on your body. In all of these circumstances the human body reacts to try to compensate. However, the more you are affected by the ageing process, the more slowly you react to challenges; some very elderly people may not react at all to changes in environmental temperature. In addition the response to the challenge is less accurate, and the effect of the challenge is greater simply because of the body's failure to react.

In other words, ageing does not cause many problems if you are sitting quietly but when asked to cope with any of the hundreds and thousands of everyday decisions or challenges you are faced with, which may range from making decisions about the on-coming traffic to recovering balance following a stumble, the more you are affected by ageing the slower and less appropriate is the response.

Can ageing be slowed down?

Although some people believe that the rate of ageing can be slowed most scientists do not believe that ageing – that is the normal biological process of ageing – can be influenced by diet, chemicals, or any other means.

There is, however, great agreement that ageing by itself does not cause serious problems until people are well into their 80s or 90s. There is plenty of scope for preventing the three factors that are responsible for most of the loss of ability that takes place as people grow older – namely disease, loss of fitness, and social problems.

The painter Rembrandt's many self-portraits illustrated his own ageing with remarkable honesty. Far left: Rembrandt at 34 – smooth-skinned and hopeful.
Left: *Thirty years later, his skin is wrinkled, his beard and moustache predictably greying, but above all his face shows the world-weariness that comes from years of struggling with money problems – a good example of how outside influences can affect the ageing process.*

A family party for much-loved grandparents emphasizes the imperceptible but continuous progress of change from youth to old age.

COPING WITH AGEING
As has already been emphasized, ageing is a normal biological process with no significant change in the way in which your body works, and the effects of ageing alone will not cause problems in looking after yourself or enjoying life to the full until you are very old. People who have problems before their late 80s have them because of the development of disease or because of loss of fitness, or both. Changes in your sleep pattern or the way your bowels work or the way you feel in different temperatures should not occur to a noticeable degree as a result of ageing.

Regulating your life
The general effects of the ageing process are to reduce the body's ability to cope with challenges and strains, so it is important for you to think about the rhythm of your life and to try to make sure that it is regular. For instance, while one member of a couple is at work a rhythm is imposed on life. Retirement brings an end to that particular rhythm and, of course, this brings freedom from the need to have the rhythm of your life dictated by your employer. However, a regular rhythm has advantages as well as disadvantages, and once the first six months of retirement are over you will probably find that you have settled into a new rhythm, a rhythm of sleeping and walking, of exercise and resting, of taking up new activities and enjoying familiar ones.

Changes that signal disease
Ageing is a process that takes place slowly and almost imperceptibly. You probably only notice yourself ageing month by month, or year by year. If, however, you notice a fairly sudden change in yourself, for example increasing breathlessness, which takes place over a period of only a few weeks or months, this may not be the result of normal ageing but the sign that something is going wrong as a result of the development of a disease, and you should seek the advice of a general practitioner.

If you notice a similar change in someone else, it may be helpful to point this out to them because sometimes the last person to notice the development of a disease is the person affected. It takes place day by day and they hardly notice the change, whereas you who see them only once a month or once every few months can notice a significant change in their appearance or abilities.

SOME SPECIFIC EFFECTS OF AGEING
Ageing does have an effect on specific parts of the body and some of these effects can clearly be seen.

The hair
Going grey or white One of the effects of ageing is that the cells in the scalp which make human hair no longer produce pigmented hair but produce

colourless, or white, hair. This is a normal biological change which takes place earlier in some people than in others, usually for genetic reasons. Keeping your hair well-looked after by regular visits to the hairdresser can be a great morale booster if it is going grey or thinning a bit, and for women a short-ish, neat haircut is easier to maintain anyway. There are many hairdressers who offer a home service now that styling techniques often only involve the use of scissors and high-powered hand dryer. Look in your Yellow Pages or local newspaper for hairdressers offering this facility, or ask around the neighbourhood. It is particularly helpful for the housebound; it enables you to keep looking your best and to have a welcome visitor now and then.

Baldness Baldness is a condition which is inherited. In this aspect of ageing the cells which make hair simply stop the production process and when hair falls out it is not replaced. There is a strong family tendency to baldness, demonstrating that this is passed from one generation to another genetically. Like almost all genetically-based changes, however, it may appear in someone with no family history of baldness and vice versa. There is no effective means of preventing baldness.

These normal ageing changes can of course be masked either by dyeing the hair which appears to do little long term harm if well done, or, in the case of baldness, by hair transplantation. However it is worth thinking about why you might want to mask hair changes – neither is anything to be ashamed of.

Hair loss in women Changes in the hair illustrate that normal ageing affects men and women in a different way, for hair loss in women is usually a sign of some underlying disease, for example thyroid deficiency, and is therefore an indication that a doctor should be consulted.

HELPING THE
HARD OF HEARING

- If the person finds it hard to admit that he or she is not hearing very well, it is important to try to be patient – that way you are more likely to coax him or her into agreeing to a check-up.

- Don't shout – speak slowly and clearly and make sure the person is sitting where he or she can see you.

- Limit background noise, such as the television or radio, while talking to someone who is hard of hearing.

- If there are a lot of people around, for instance at a social gathering, find a quiet place for the person hard of hearing to talk to people on a one-to-one basis.

Changes in hearing

As part of normal ageing some loss of ability to hear high notes occurs, which makes it difficult for some people to hear sounds such as the telephone ringing. Nothing can be done to slow the basic ageing process, but if your hearing loss is to such a degree that it affects your quality of life, for example by affecting your ability to carry on conversations, you should see your general practitioner for advice. If someone close to you, for instance your partner, seems to be suffering hearing loss, perhaps by requiring the television or radio sound to be turned up so that it is uncomfortably loud for you, it may be sensible to suggest as tactfully as possible that he or she visits the doctor to have a hearing test. After all the loss of

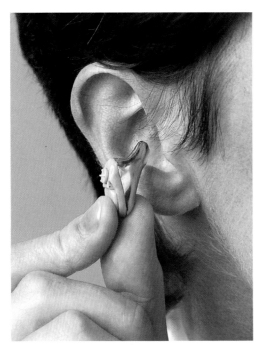

Although hearing can be affected by ageing, modern micro-technology has developed hearing aids which are so small and discreet that they are scarcely noticeable when worn.

SEE ALSO: ▶

A–Z of HEALTH
PROBLEMS:
Deafness   p. 191

SEE ALSO: ▶

MANAGING YOUR MONEY:
Income support   p. 35

SEE ALSO: ▶

FOOD AND COOKING:
The basics of healthy
eating   p. 126

hearing may simply be due to a build up of wax which is further impairing the normal hearing loss due to ageing, and a simple syringeing by the doctor can remove it.

Deafness

Genuine deafness is due to disease, not ageing, and your general practitioner will refer you to a specialist at the hospital if your hearing loss is substantial. ◀ It may be suggested that you use a hearing aid – these are now very discreet and can really make a difference. There are also aids that you can have fitted at home, for instance to the telephone or doorbell; the hospital specialist, health visitor or Citizens Advice Bureau can advise you about this.

Changes to eyesight

Ageing does affect your eyesight, mainly because the lens of the eye loses its elasticity. Some types of visual problem actually improve with age precisely because of this decreased elasticity. Lens elasticity affects how quickly the

eye responds to change in light strength and focus – when this is reduced your optician may recommend bifocal spectacles.

There is a charge for eye tests, but you are exempt from this charge if you are on income support. ◀ Eye tests are carried out at an optician or specialist shop. Remember that these latter are commercial organizations whose main business is to sell frames, so you may come under some quite strong pressure to get a new pair of spectacles even if you don't really need them. There is no need to stop wearing contact lenses simply on grounds of age, but obviously you need to be able to handle them, which could be difficult for someone whose hand and finger joints are affected by arthritis.

Sense of smell

Unfortunately, the sense of smell is also one of the senses which diminishes with age, and with it the sense of taste, so sometimes older people begin to lose interest in food. This is sad, and can be detrimental to health if it stops you from eating a balanced diet simply because it is boring. The advice given in 'Food and Cooking' can help here. ◀

More importantly, from the safety point of view, is that it may affect your ability to smell smoke or gas, or food that has gone bad. If you suspect that your sense of smell is becoming less keen, double check gas taps, avoid having open fires or make sure they are adequately guarded, and check fresh food stocks frequently.

Changes in the gums and teeth

Many people now enter retirement with their own teeth. There may be one or two missing or they may have had major work done on them, but they are still their own teeth. The main cause of tooth loss in youth is dental disease, that is disease of the teeth themselves; the main cause of tooth loss in older age groups is gum disease, known as gingivitis.

You may have observed that the gums recede with age but this is not by itself gingivitis. Gingivitis is inflammation of the gums due to infection, but it can be prevented in a number of ways.

PREVENTING GUM DISEASE

- Brush your teeth correctly using a soft toothbrush in vertical movements ensuring that the brush sweeps above teeth and gums.

- Use dental floss to remove large pieces of food from between the teeth.

- Where you have a large gap between teeth, buy a small pointed toothbrush which can be used to brush the teeth surfaces facing one another and the gum which forms a roof or floor to that space.

- Use a small wooden dental toothpick between those teeth which have small spaces between them to help to keep the gums healthy.

When you lose a tooth, the bone in the gum where the tooth was formerly set thins and is reduced, wasting away because it is not being used. This is another good reason for trying to keep your teeth into old age by adopting the measures given above and by visiting the dentist regularly, about every six months. There is a charge for a dental check-up, and you have to pay about 75 per cent of any complete course of treatment. However, if you are on a low income you may have these charges reduced or be exempt altogether – ask your dentist, health visitor, local Social Services office or pick up a leaflet about dental charges from the Post Office or Citizens Advice Bureau. ▶

When you visit the dentist, he or she may recommend that your teeth are scaled and polished and may show you ways of keeping your gums healthy. If the dentist does not have time to do this personally, he or she may suggest you see the dental hygienist attached to the practice, or you could ask to see her yourself. Many health centres offer the services of a dental hygienist as well.

Denture care

Although more people are reaching retirement age with most of their own teeth intact, there are of course many others who do have complete or partial dentures to care for. If you are fitted with dentures the first set may not fit for long because the gums change in size and shape quite quickly after the removal of teeth. Dentures should not be painful to wear and if you do experience persistent pain or a sore on the gums which takes time to heal, consult your dentist. Continue to visit the dentist regularly for check-ups and clean your dentures carefully as instructed.

Changes in the skin

Skin changes occur in everybody but in some people they occur to a greater degree than in others. It is very difficult, however, to tell which skin changes are due to normal ageing and which are due to decades of exposure to sun, wind and water.

Skin changes that can be seen may include loss of elasticity, roughness of the skin surface, dryness, folds and wrinkles, and changes in pigmentation, with large brown spots becoming obvi-

SEE ALSO: ◀

MANAGING YOUR MONEY:
Income support   p. 35

CHARGES FOR EYE TESTS AND DENTAL CHECKS

There is now a charge for eye tests and dental checks so let the optician or dentist know if you are on income support so that you can be exempted from payment.

HAIRDRESSING AT HOME

If you find it difficult to get out, employing the services of a home hairdresser and/or manicurist is both practical and a boost to morale.

SEE ALSO: ▶

A–Z OF HEALTH PROBLEMS:

Sexual difficulties   p. 196

GUIDELINES FOR SKIN CARE

- Do not rely on creams which claim a 'rejuvenating effect'. Certain types of bland cream can help keep the skin moist but at present there is no strong evidence that certain types of expensive skin preparations can actually slow down the rate of ageing. Although there are no magic formulae for rejuvenation, using a lanolin cream on your hands does help to avoid chapping and rough skin especially during the winter. Wear rubber gloves as much as possible when doing housework and keep the nails short and neat. If you find this difficult you could try a home manicurist (some home hairdressers also offer this service.) If you are being visited by a District Nurse anyway, ask her to help with your nails.

- Avoid direct powerful sunlight as much as possible. Use a hat, apply sun cream or lotion with a good blocking factor. Be particularly careful when you are by the sea or in snow because these can reflect sunlight.

- Use make-up carefully. Try to choose make-up and skin preparations which have as few different chemicals as possible; one of the things that occurs in old age is that the skin becomes more sensitive to different types of chemicals and the fewer the chemicals you use the less likely is it that you will develop sensitivity or reactions.

ous in some people more than in others.

It does seem that many of these changes are due to ill treatment, for example extensive sunbathing, and if you wish to keep a youthful appearance the following guidelines for skin care are suggested.

Sex in older age

Although some people may think sexual activity in older age is either inappropriate or impossible, neither case is of course true and the existence of sexual activity between a couple is a sign of good health. If problems occur they are often of a psychological nature, just as they are between younger couples. ◀

By retirement age women have passed the menopause and indeed may find this very liberating, especially if the menopausal years have been at all trying. However dryness and shrinkage of the vagina can cause some difficulty and a lubricant may be necessary to make things easier. Men have no actual 'change of life' but their male hormones decline very gradually as the years pass which may lead to less frequent intercourse. However, since sexual satisfaction does not necessarily mean full penetration a happy and fulfilling sex life can continue well into old age.

Foot care

Many older people suffer from painful feet, but this can be avoided if you make sure your shoes offer strong support. Don't wear slippers for long periods as they allow the muscles of the feet to weaken and the feet to spread, with consequent discomfort when less pliant footwear is worn. On the other hand, socks, stockings, tights or shoes should not be so tight that they constrict the circulation.

Poor circulation in the feet means that they may feel cold and become red and painful, but don't be tempted to warm them suddenly with a hot water bottle or putting them against a radiator. Keeping your whole body warm is much better. Foot exercises ▶ help the circulation and maintain the tone of foot muscles.

Problems with feet such as bunions or hard skin ▶ can be helped by a chiropodist. These are provided free by the National Health Service, but they are often over-stretched, so you might have to go to a private practitioner. Ask your doctor or health visitor, or at the local health centre. A chiropodist can advise you on foot care so that you can prevent foot problems developing.

IMPROVING YOUR HEALTH

One of the great advantages of retirement is that it can provide the opportunity actually to improve your health and fitness. As is being constantly stressed throughout this book, retirement age only means the age at which you stop paid work and become pensionable – a strictly economic concept! And stopping work means that you cease to be subject to the stress of the workplace, and you have the leisure time available to concentrate on doing those things which are both enjoyable and good for you. One of the first steps is to find out how healthy you think you are.

How healthy are you?

There is a very simple scale with which to measure your own assessment of your health. Decide whether your health is excellent, good, fair, poor.

Excellent If you estimate that your health is excellent you need to concentrate on the sections of the book—on food and exercise—that help you stay healthy. However, even though you think your health is excellent it might become even more excellent if you were to take a little more exercise or stop smoking or undertake some of the changes in lifestyle suggested in the

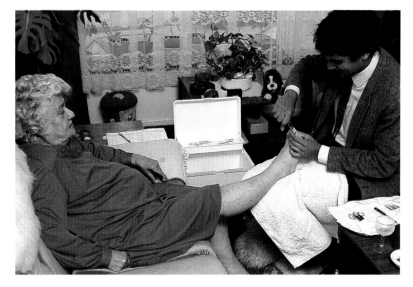

chapter on 'Keeping Busy'.

Good If your health is good you need to identify the reasons why your health is not excellent and see if you can tackle them, as well as taking steps that are important in preventing disease and disability.

Fair In the same way, if your health is only fair it is essential for you to try to identify those health problems which stop you having good health (see below).

Poor If you feel your health is poor you either need to see a doctor, or if you are in regular touch with a doctor or a hospital service, you need to consider whether there are ways in which the treatment you have been given could be more effective and therefore improve the way you feel or the way you function. You may also have to consider the way in which you adapt to disease. ▶

How well do you function?

Following your own assessment of your health, apply the same criteria to how you function. How would you rate your ability to look after yourself, your house or the ability to get about inside and outside the house, on the same simple scale of excellent, good, fair, or poor.

Regular visits to a chiropodist can help prevent or alleviate some of the painful foot problems that older people all too often experience.

SEE ALSO: ◀

MOVEMENT AND EXERCISE:

Foot exercises   p. 159

RESOURCES & BACK-UP:

Foot care   p. 202

PROBLEMS WITH HEALTH:

Adapting to the challenge of illness   p. 179

In assessing this aspect of your health it is, of course, important to think about the standards that you are using to judge your state of health.

Are you comparing yourself with the healthiest person of your age that you know, or the average person, or simply with what you think is normal for your own age? A person in his late 80s who has been lucky enough not to develop a disease and has kept himself reasonably fit will be able to use a bus and the telephone, dress himself, bath, wash all over, get to the toilet in time, read a newspaper, have a drink and generally enjoy life reasonably well. However, there are some people in their 80s who think it is normal not to be able to go out of the house or even to be incontinent. With these contrasts in mind, it is sensible to think of the fittest person you know of your own age, or if you have developed a disease, to think of the fittest person you know who has the same disease as you. If you are really the fittest person, congratulations, but you may surprise yourself and be able to get a little bit more fit even though you have a disabling disease.

The common disabling diseases in old age are arthritis, stroke, heart disease, bronchitis and Parkinson's disease. Tips on coping with each of these common health problems are outlined in the chapter on common health challenges. ◄

THE IMPORTANCE OF FITNESS

It is helpful to understand the importance of physical fitness when planning your campaign for better health. Perhaps the simplest way to understand what is going on is to think about the changes in ability which take place as people grow older. At birth everyone has certain abilities, which increase with development. However, there comes a point of maximum ability, and from this point, which may last a year or so, there is a steady decline. This decline in ability becomes serious when it drops below the threshold which is needed to perform a certain task, for instance being able to walk half a mile. For a person who lives half a mile from the shops dropping below this threshold of ability is therefore very important because when he or she drops below it, the individual is seriously disadvantaged and becomes dependent on other people. Maintaining fitness helps to extend the time before which this threshold of ability is crossed, enabling you to remain independent much longer.

What is fitness?

A person's fitness is measured by the way in which their body responds to a physical challenge. If you were to look at ten people sitting in a room it would not be all that easy to determine their levels of fitness. If, on the other hand, you made them climb up five flights of stairs, you would see their relative levels of fitness very quickly. Some people would be very much more distressed than others and would take much longer to recover from the exercise they had taken.

A person's fitness is important not when they are sitting quietly but when they are required to do something over and above the demands of daily life. For young people this is not particularly important except if they want to play sport, but for someone in their 60s, 70s or 80s fitness becomes very important because it is the reserves of fitness that an individual calls on when he or she has to do something like climbing a flight of stairs or walking a mile or recovering balance after tripping up. The fitter someone is the more able he or she is to meet these challenges.

The four fitness factors

There are four different aspects of fit-

SEE ALSO: ▷

A–Z OF HEALTH

PROBLEMS   p. 188

ness, (all beginning with the letter S): strength, stamina, suppleness, and skill.

The most encouraging message is that all these aspects of fitness can be improved in old age. By changing their lifestyle older people can improve their physical ability and regain lost abilities by taking up the types of exercise outlined in the section of this book on exercise and fitness. ▶

Fitness and disease

It is an unfortunate fact that disease becomes more common in older age groups. The reason for this is not that disease is caused by ageing but that most diseases are caused by environmental factors and the longer you live the longer you have been exposed to these factors. Obviously when someone gets a disabling disease such as arthritis their best possible rate of decline changes due to the combined effect of ageing *and* disease.

For many people what happens after the onset of disease is not only due to the effects of the disease itself, but also due to the fact that they lose fitness even more quickly than someone who does not have a disabling disease. There are two reasons for this. Any disease that reduces your activity levels reduces your fitness level with a consequent loss of strength, stamina, suppleness and skill. In addition, other people often do not allow a disabled person to do what he or she can and wants to do, and this type of 'helping', which is often well intentioned, can actually make the person's problem worse by leading to a loss of fitness. (See diagram, far right.)

HEALTH BUILDING BLOCKS

Before starting to think about ways in which you could improve your health, take a look backwards and think how you have arrived at your present position. Health is like a journey which starts before you are born with your

Maintaining physical fitness can bring personal satisfaction too, as Mr Jack Watkin (left) found when, at 80, he was the oldest competitor in a 'Fun Run'.

SEE ALSO: ◀

MOVEMENT AND
EXERCISE   p. 142

parents. Wise but unhelpful advice is to choose your parents carefully, and there is no doubt that some people are genetically at risk of disease so that from the moment of conception their health is influenced in certain ways. Sometimes they may be born with a congenital disease; others are born with a predisposition, or a tendency, to develop diseases which is greater than average. However, in general you should not worry too much about family history. If your parents lived to a good old age then you should hope to live to a good old age too, but if your parents died early it was more likely something to do with their lifestyle or the environment in which they lived than any genetic pattern, and

**LOSS OF ACTIVITY
DUE TO
DISABLING DISEASE**

↓

LOSS OF FITNESS

↓

**LOSS OF ACTIVITY
DUE TO
LOSS OF FITNESS**

↓

**FURTHER LOSS
OF FITNESS**

Swimming is one of the best forms of exercise. Many public pools offer lessons for adult beginners, and it is never too late to start learning to swim.

you should not assume that you are also going to die early.

Once you have set out on the road, the direction you take, and how far you go, is determined by a number of potential dangers that lie along the route namely:

- Your lifestyle
- Your working environment
- The place in which you live or have lived
- The health service you receive
- The beliefs and attitudes of the people that you have lived and worked with
- Luck

However, you cannot influence your luck, and if you have retired it is obviously irrelevant to try to change the working environment; that is something which has had an influence on you

but will no longer continue to do so.

Thus to improve your health in future you need to try to influence the following factors, which are subtly different from the factors which influence health earlier in life:

- Your lifestyle
- The environment you live in
- The health service you receive
- Your income
- The beliefs and attitudes of other people

Of course, you yourself have considerable control over some of these factors, while over others you have much less control. For example, you have much more control over the amount of exercise you take than over the level of your pension. In theory you do have an ability to influence your pension by the way you vote and how politically active you become, but in practice your influence on your own level of pension is relatively limited and what most people have to try to do is to make their money go further rather than take direct action which can increase income.

Changing your lifestyle

Elsewhere in this book there are many ideas about changing your lifestyle.

The word 'lifestyle' is vague, meaning different things to different people. In this context it means ways in which you can change what you do to improve your health or reduce the risks of disease.

Taking exercise

Almost everyone could be fitter than they are, and exercise and movement are helpful in achieving this. However, there are a number of questions which need answering in this context.

The risks of exercise In general the benefits of exercise greatly outweigh the risks. If, however, you are very unfit and overweight or suffer from a chronic disease for which you take medicine, or

WHAT EXERCISE TO AVOID

- Exercise which involves great effort while holding your breath, like pushing a car or moving furniture

- Exercise which involves very high bursts of activity particularly in a competitive field such as squash.

- Exercise which subjects your joints to banging; for example swimming is better for older people than running.

REDUCING THE RISK TO MUSCLES OR JOINTS

- Slowly build up the amount of exercise you take over a period of six months or a year.

- Concentrate on ways to improve your suppleness, for example by taking up Yoga.

- Warm up slowly before each exercise session; warming up involves stretching all the muscles and joints that you will be using very slowly and carefully ten or twenty times before you actually start taking exercise. ▶

are worried about taking up some new form of exercise you should ask the advice of your general practitioner.

The best type of exercise

As is emphasized in the later chapter on 'Movement and Exercise',▶ the only golden rule about exercise is that it should be something that you enjoy. However you can ask yourself which of the various aspects of fitness will be improved by the type of exercise you are considering. Housework and gardening are good for building up strength and stamina providing you remember one simple rule and that is that you must keep going for a minute or two after the moment you first feel you want to stop if you are to improve your fitness. This is the basis of training whether you are Steve Cram or a 75-year-old woman. The benefits of training are obtained when your body is doing that bit of work more than it finds it can do without effort. Imagine you are cutting the grass and you feel that you're breathing quickly and that your pulse is going a little bit faster than normal. You always feel this way when you have a job half finished. If you stop and take five minutes break then your fitness will not improve. If on the other hand you keep going then your body will benefit from responding to the challenge you have given it.

If you experience pain

Remember that exercise should cause minor discomfort but not pain. If you feel pain then stop. If you feel chest pain when taking exercise then stop and phone your doctor or the local ambulance station right away because chest pain coming on during exercise can be a symptom of heart attack and should be treated as an emergency.

Exercise for suppleness

Because things like housework and gardening can improve strength and stamina it is important to think of types of exercise that will also improve your suppleness and skill. Improving your skills also stimulates the brain and the nervous system. Learning new dance steps is obviously one way of improving skill as is learning new Yoga movements

ASPECTS OF YOUR LIFESTYLE THAT AFFECT HEALTH

- ▶ The amount of exercise you take
- ▶ What you eat
- ▶ The amount of alcohol you drink
- ▶ Whether you smoke or not
- ▶ How much time you spend with other people and how well you get on with them.

SEE ALSO: ◀

MOVEMENT AND EXERCISE:

'Warming up' and 'warming down'   p. 144

or painting or craftwork.

If you suffer from a disabling disease and are attending an Outpatient Clinic ask the physiotherapist, occupational therapist or doctor for advice on exercise and classes particularly suited to people like yourself.

GIVING UP SMOKING

Cigarette smoking is a relatively recent phenomenon among the mass of the population. It became common among men during and after the First World War and among women during and after the Second World War. The effects of these changing habits can now be seen in the changes which have taken place in the diseases affecting men and women during the twentieth century.

There is now no doubt that cigarette smoking is a major cause of cancer, heart disease, narrowing of the arteries of the leg, and chronic bronchitis and emphysema. In addition cigarette smoking aggravates or contributes to a number of other diseases such as peptic

---

TIPS TO HELP GIVE UP SMOKING

- Ask your general practitioner's opinion; no matter how strongly you yourself believe something, the opinion of your medical adviser that this is a good thing for you will often reinforce your desire to stop smoking.

- Set yourself a date some time in advance and tell people when you are going to give up.

- Use the money you save to put towards some project or holiday that you long for, or get yourself sponsored to raise money for a charity.

- Stay away from cigarette smokers after you have given up; during the first week or two after giving up the smell of cigarette smoke may make you long to have another cigarette.

- If you have tried all these things and still find difficulty giving up then you may find it helpful to try nicotine chewing gum. Ask your general practitioner about this.

- Some people find hypnosis or acupuncture helpful. Try something new if you have tried to give up before and were not able to by yourself, but remember people give up after smoking for 30 or 40 years and 30 or 40 or more a day. Try once more and surprise yourself.

- Think about doing without cigarettes on a daily basis, don't try to think months ahead as this can be too daunting.

- One final tip: try to link the change in cigarette smoking with some other change in your lifestyle, particularly one which will improve your health, for example swimming or taking up a new hobby or the arrival of a grandchild. There is very good evidence that the health of children is adversely affected by adults who smoke in the same house, so the arrival of a new grandchild whom you want to see frequently may give you that final stimulus to stop smoking for the sake of your grandchild's health and your own.

---

ulceration. For these reasons stopping smoking is one of the most important things a person can do to improve his or her health and reduce the risk of disease.

Is it too late to stop?

Some people ask if it is too late to stop smoking when they have been smoking cigarettes for 30 or 40 years. The answer is, unequivocally, NO! Obviously the sooner people stop the better because the longer you take in the chemicals in the cigarette smoke which cause harm, the greater will be the risk. In addition you may have sustained some irreversible damage, for example damage to the lining of your bronchial tree and respiratory passages as a result of prolonged cigarette smoking. Nevertheless the evidence is clear, so do it now.

Stopping altogether or cutting down

People who find it difficult to stop sometimes cut down the number of cigarettes smoked, but cutting down is much less effective than stopping altogether for two reasons. The first is that harm continues to be done, even when you are smoking small numbers of cigarettes. The second, and more important, reason is that if you continue to smoke even a small number, the numbers you smoke will probably start to creep up again. The best way to stop is to stop completely—anything else will ultimately be useless.

Giving up cigarettes

A number of people reading this book will have tried to stop smoking before. For them there is one important message. Research shows that many people give up successfully on the third, fourth, fifth, sixth or seventh – or even greater – time of trying.

Pipes and cigars

Pipe and cigar smoke is less harmful to the smoker than cigarette smoke. However, some people who stop smoking cigarettes and change to pipes or cigars do not achieve the benefit they should because they continue to inhale the pipe or cigar smoke. The best thing to do is to stop smoking altogether.

WATCHING YOUR ALCOHOL INTAKE

The easiest way to assess what you drink is to think of a glass of wine or a half pint of beer, a small sherry or a measure of spirits as one unit of alcohol, and to count up how many units of alcohol you drink in a week.

If you drink less than 20 you are probably not suffering any adverse effects from alcohol, providing you don't drink and drive, but if you are consuming more than 20 units of alcohol your health could improve if you cut back.

There are, however, other signs that you could think about when measuring your alcohol intake. Consider the questions in the list that follow:

- Are you drinking more than you did five years ago?
- Do you find yourself taking a drink more than once a week because you feel sad or unhappy?
- Do you find that you feel you need a drink to help you go out to a party or social event?

These are some of the early signs of problems and it would be wise to discuss your drinking with your general practitioner because it may be that you drink because you are anxious or depressed, and there may be more effective ways of dealing with your anxiety or depression which your doctor could help you find. ▶

HEALTHIER EATING

The word 'diet' is sometimes used to mean a weight-reducing diet but the word by itself simply means the food we eat. A healthy diet is one which contains at least enough of what you need for

THINKING ABOUT SMOKING

No matter how long you have been smoking, you can still benefit from giving it up.

No matter how often you have tried to stop smoking before, try again!

SEE ALSO: ◀
A–Z OF HEALTH
PROBLEMS:
Depression   p. 191

FOOD THAT CAN HARM YOU

What you eat can actually harm your health
* *by giving you too much fat in the diet*
* *by providing you with more energy than you need.*

Get your energy balance right   If you are taking in more energy than you need ◀ you will put on weight, and a weight control strategy is discussed in the section on obesity. ◀

Being careful about fats   There is no doubt now that animal fats, if eaten in excess, increase the risk of heart disease by increasing the level of blood cholesterol.

However, there is not much evidence at the moment about the benefits of reducing the amount of cholesterol you eat after the age of 65. This is simply because this topic has not been studied by research workers, most of whose work has been done with younger people. However, reducing the amount of fat that you eat will not do you any harm and may well be beneficial both in helping your arteries keep healthy – you may have another 30 years of life ahead of you – and in helping you control your weight, because fats are energy rich foods.

SEE ALSO: ▷

FOOD & COOKING:
Calories   p. 126

A–Z OF HEALTH PROBLEMS
Obesity   p. 195

survival and health, and does not contain too much of those foodstuffs which cause harm if eaten excessively. The human diet provides a large number of different types of foodstuff and the diet of most older people in Britain contains enough different types of foodstuffs for healthy living. Advice on food, cooking and nutrition is given in the chapter on 'Food and Cooking', especially on how to increase the main deficiencies in most modern diets, namely fibre, vitamins and minerals. This advice is particularly important for those for whom mobility is difficult, or who are over the age of 85.

The medical importance of fibre
The human animal evolved over millions of years to eat a diet rich in fibre; one in which large quantities of food could be eaten raw or, when cooked, in its entire state, including potato skins and husks of barley and wheat. In the last 20 years it has become very easy to get enough energy to survive without having to eat large amounts of unpeeled vegetables or whole grains of cereals, in part because of the development of sugar refining. In addition the food industry has significantly reduced the amount of fibre eaten in the last 100 hundred years as a result of the development of food technology. In this sense 'technology' includes everything from the humble potato peeler to the mechanized flour mills which remove the husks from grain and produce refined white, as opposed to fibre-rich wholemeal, flour.

A deficiency of fibre has a number of important results, and disorders like constipation, haemorrhoids (piles), obesity, diverticular disease (development of small pockets of tissue in the bowel which can become infected) and spastic colon with abdominal cramps are more common among people who are not eating enough fibre.

These disorders arise directly because of the lack of fibre in the bowel but other problems may be aggravated by fibre deficiency because the body's digestive process, and therefore its metabolism, is affected by the amount of fibre in the diet. Delicious and palatable ways to increase fibre in your diet are given in the chapter on 'Food and Cooking'. ▶

Eating more calcium

Osteoporosis is a disorder in which the bones become so thin that fractures occur more easily. ▶ It is caused by a number of different factors, not all of which are clearly understood. The bones of people with osteoporosis have less calcium than healthy bones but scientists are not agreed on the part that increasing the amount of calcium we eat can play in either preventing or treating osteoporosis. Some experts recommend a high calcium diet, others do not, but as a high calcium diet is not going to do you any harm it is sensible to ensure that you are taking enough calcium. ▶

Getting enough vitamins and other minerals

A lot of attention has been given to vitamin and mineral consumption in the last decade. Again experts are divided. Most experts believe that the average diet gives enough vitamins and minerals and that vitamin deficiency occurs usually in association with some other disease. Some believe, however, that all people would be better off with a higher vitamin intake. Similarly most people believe that the average diet contains enough minerals and does not need any supplementation by commercially-produced mineral preparations.

Increasing the amount of vitamins and minerals you consume will not do you any harm and if you feel run down and if no disease can be found by your doctor then a course of vitamin tablets containing the full range of vitamins may well make you feel better. These can be bought at any chemist shop.

YOUR ENVIRONMENT AND YOUR HEALTH

The environment you live in affects your health. In part your present state of health has been determined by places you have lived in the past; people who grew up in smoky, polluted industrial areas are more likely to have chronic bronchitis than those who grew up in the countryside. However, the past is past and it is now more important for you to think about the influence that the environment has on your health at present and will have on your future health.

Housing and health

The problems set out in the box are obviously severe, and many people try to avoid them by moving house, but many can be solved or at least reduced in the ways set out in the section on

SEE ALSO: ◀

FOOD AND COOKING:
High-fibre foods   p. 129

SEE ALSO: ◀

A–Z OF HEALTH
PROBLEMS:
Osteoporosis   p. 195

SEE ALSO: ◀

FOOD AND COOKING:
Food for strong bones
      p. 138

HOW HOUSING CAN AFFECT HEALTH

- By increasing the risk of accidents

- By being too cold for good health

- By causing you depression or anxiety, perhaps because of the cost of keeping up your house

- By making it impossible for you to look after yourself if you have a disabling disease

---

SEE ALSO: ▶

HOME FROM HOME:

Moving on   p. 63

housing, ◀ so that you may not need to move at all. There is, however, one good reason for moving house and that is to move nearer friends or family and the steps you can take to do this and the factors you have to take into account are described in the same section.

Health services

Your present state of health is determined in part by your lifestyle and the environment in which you have lived in times past. The way you live and where you live will continue to have an influence on your health, but health services also have a part to play in determining how healthy you are, particularly if you develop a disease or health problem.

Health services can help you stay healthy by offering preventive measures and can help you back to health again if you develop an illness. Most people know what services are available, but you may not always know how to make the most of those health services for your own benefit. There are several ways in which diseases and infections can be prevented or avoided, or caught in the early stages and treated before they become serious.

PREVENTING AND DETECTING DISEASE

Some diseases to which older people are particularly prone can either be prevented or detected at an early enough stage actually to cure or to prevent them developing into a serious condition. Changing your lifestyle as described above will help in some cases to prevent disease, and certainly may stop existing diseases from becoming worse; otherwise the health service can provide immunization and screening tests which can also prevent or detect.

Influenza immunization

The term 'influenza' is used to describe any generalized illness with respiratory symptoms such as a cough, combined with a headache and general feeling of tiredness and muscle pain. Influenza immunization will not protect against all of these diseases, but it will act against those which are caused by influenza viruses, called Influenza A and Influenza B. These viruses change from year to year so the resistance to infection given by vaccination lasts only two or three years. If you need influenza immunization, therefore, you should have it every autumn.

Influenza immunization is particularly important for people with chest or lung disease. If you think that you would benefit from influenza immunization you should ask your general practitioner and make a date in your diary now for next Autumn.

Health checks in retirement

You will often see health checks for executives advertised in newspapers and magazines but elderly people can also benefit from health checks.

Health checks have two main objectives: to find hidden disease in the body which is not causing symptoms because it is at such an early stage, by means of special tests, and to find problems known to the retired person but of which the doctor was previously unaware.

Tests for early disease

Tests that are available to detect disease at an early stage, before symptoms have brought it to the attention of the person suffering from the disease are called screening tests.

It was once thought that healthy people should regularly be given a series of tests to find disease at an early stage but, just as many people have found that regular car servicing does not always prevent problems and in fact can sometimes lead to complications, it has been discovered that many of the tests that were popular are now no longer thought

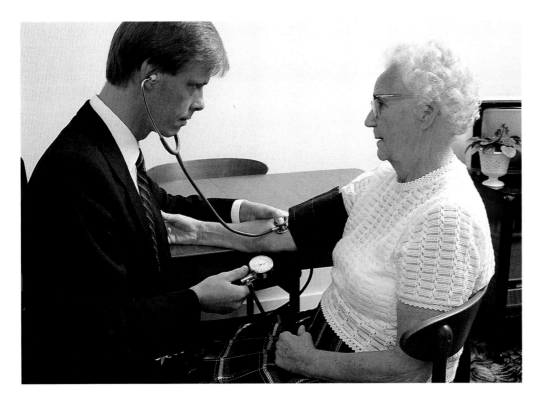

Having your blood pressure measured is painless and takes only a minute or two, but it is an important test for the early signs of possible disease, which can be treated.

to be effective in improving the cure rate.

There are only three screening tests which can be unreservedly recommended to people over retirement age.

1. Blood pressure measurement (men and women)
2. Cervical smear test to detect precancerous cells in the cervix (women)
3. Mammography for early breast cancer (women)

Blood pressure measurement

Just as water flows round a central heating system because it is under pressure, blood flows round your body because it is always under pressure. Every time your heart beats it acts as a pump and increases the pressure. If, however, the pressure rises too high there is an increased risk that a blood vessel in the brain will burst, causing a stroke. No one knows what causes high blood pressure but it is known that lowering the blood pressure by means of drugs, combined with other steps such as weight loss or a reduction in alcohol intake or increased exercise, can reduce the risk of a stroke.

Unfortunately raised levels of blood pressure hardly ever cause symptoms, even though it is widely thought that problems such as headache are caused by high blood pressure. The only way to detect whether blood pressure is too high is by measuring it, using an instrument called a sphygmomanometer. People should have their blood pressure measured regularly, at least once every five years up to the age of 75, although some people may need more frequent measurements if their doctor has reason to believe their blood pressure may be high, or is at risk of becoming so.

Over the age of 75 the measurement of blood pressure becomes less important because it has not been shown that treating raised levels of blood pressure

WHERE THE CERVIX LIES

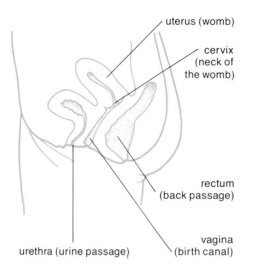

uterus (womb)

cervix (neck of the womb)

rectum (back passage)

vagina (birth canal)

urethra (urine passage)

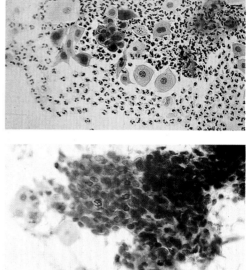

Right: The diagram shows the position of the cervix and surrounding area. Far right: Examined by a specialized technician, the smear can show whether the cells are normal (top), or are showing pre-cancerous changes (below), which at this stage can be treated completely and safely.

significantly lowers the risk of stroke. The reason why the link between blood pressure and stroke is different for those over this age is not known.

If you have not had your blood pressure measured recently you can simply ask your general practitioner to do it. Either the general practitioner or the practice nurse will measure it for you, and it only takes a few minutes.

Cervical smear test

The cervix is the part of the uterus where it is joined on to the vagina. Cells cover the cervix and form a continuous sheet with the cells covering the vagina and with the cells lining the uterus. Changes can arise in these cells which can proceed to cancer if they are not identified and treated. Unfortunately there are no symptoms of the precancerous stage so a woman does not know that she has these cellular changes that can turn into cervical cancer. Fortunately the cervical smear test allows those early changes to be detected.

In the cervical smear test cells are scraped from the surface of the cervix during the course of a vaginal examina-

tion using a soft wooden stick. These are examined under a microscope and the presence or absence of precancerous changes can be detected in most women who have them. The test can be uncomfortable but is not usually painful. However it is sometimes not possible to get enough cells from the surface of the cervix so the test may have to be repeated. This problem is more common among older women.

If the smear test is positive, showing some abnormality, then women are referred to a gynaecology clinic to receive a further examination, called colposcopy. This determines the type of abnormality and suitable treatment can be arranged, either as an outpatient or an inpatient.

If you have had one cervical smear test which was negative then you are at lower risk of cervical cancer than if you had not had any cervical smear tests, and if you have had two or more normal cervical smear tests then you are at low risk and do not need additional cervical smear tests after the age of 65.

If you need a cervical smear test make an appointment with your doctor to discuss the test. Not all women need the test and women who have never had a sexual partner are at such low risk that they do not need a cervical smear test. The test is free and is particularly recommended for women over the age of 65 who have never had a cervical smear test in the past.

Finding breast cancer early

Breast cancer is the most common type of cancer affecting women in the United Kingdom and becomes increasingly common the older the age group considered.

The cause of breast cancer is not known and it is therefore not possible to prevent it starting. The best way to improve the chance of cure is to detect it. There are two ways in which this can be done

- by screening, and
- by reporting changes in the breast early.

Screening for breast cancer

When breast cancers are very small they cannot be felt, but a proportion of them can be seen on an X-ray of breast tissue called a 'mammogram'.

By 1991 the whole of the United Kingdom will be covered by a breast screening service and women over 65 can have a free breast screening test every three years by asking their general practitioner if a test can be arranged. It may not be possible to arrange this test quickly because you will probably have to wait until a mobile screening van is in your area. If you have any of the symptoms of breast disease described below you will, of course, be referred quickly for mammography but for women who have no symptoms of breast disease it is recommended that breast screening be carried out every three years. The length of time you will have to wait will depend on just how the screening service is organized in your area.

REPORTING BREAST CHANGES EARLY

It is important that any changes in your breast which you notice while bathing or dressing are reported to your general practitioner. The changes to watch out for are:

- Changes in the appearance of the skin

- Changes in the way the breast feels or a part of the breast feels

- Changes in the shape of the breast

- Changes in the appearance of the nipple

- Any nipple discharge

What happens in mammography is that the breast tissue is compressed between two smooth surfaces. It is uncomfortable but should not be painful. The X-ray of the breast tissue is then examined by a doctor. About 90 per cent of women can be told immediately that no disease can be seen on their X-ray but the remainder, about 10 per cent, will be referred for further tests. Most of those referred for further tests, which include other painless examinations of the breast tissue, do not have breast cancer but this is obviously a worrying time for women so every attempt is made to arrange these follow-up tests as quickly as possible.

If you want further information about mammography either ask at your local health centre of surgery, or write to the Women's National Cancer Control Campaign or one of the other cancer charities listed later.▶

SEE ALSO: ◄

RESOURCES & BACK-UP:
Health   p. 204

FOOD AND COOKING

Most people know that good food usually means good health – the old saying, 'You are what you eat', has been so over-worked as to have become a bit of a cliché. Yet there is more to eating than just nutrition. It doesn't matter what age you are, looking narrowly at the concept of food being 'good for you' often destroys the natural enjoyment everyone should get from preparing and eating tasty meals which are incidentally nutritious. The approach of retirement and the long and active years ahead give you the time and flexibility to approach food and cooking in a new way, to spend as much or as little time as you want shopping and preparing meals, and perhaps sharing them with like-minded friends as the ideal focus for social occasions.

Both men and women may have spent many years following a rather set pattern of eating and mealtimes during their working lives – a pattern which is often continued even when a person is no longer working. You know the sort of thing – breakfast of toast and cereal, or less frequently nowadays, the full works of bacon and eggs, then lunch either of a packed lunch prepared at home, or a meal bought in the canteen or restaurant, and home to supper at 7 or thereabouts, with perhaps a snack later on before bed. This is a huge generalization of course – every household will be able to point out its own variations and daily exceptions. However, most people will admit that eating habits are just that and that they have been fitted into a daily routine established probably over a long period to make life easier.

Retirement may be a time to take another look at these daily routines – whether you are on your own or living as a couple. You may find, for example, that you are at home for most lunchtimes during the week, instead of just weekends, but that new interests or hobbies take you out during the evening at the time when you used to have your main meal. Or perhaps a more restful lifestyle means that you don't really feel hungry at 12.30 and you leave lunch till 2pm, and suddenly you find that suppertime has been pushed on to 9 o'clock in the evening, so you adjust its content to avoid going to bed on a heavy meal. The point is that you have the leisure to be as routine or as irregular as you like and at the same time to look a bit more closely at the quality of what you are eating. Even if cooking didn't really interest you before, you might find that a few simple experiments once in a while turn it into something of a hobby, and preparing a meal to share with family or friends can bring added enjoyment to your experience of food.

FOOD AND ADVANCING YEARS

Everyone needs food for warmth and energy, and for the everyday wear and tear on the body's tissues, skin, muscle and bone. Surprising as it may seem, our bodies are still working quite hard even when we are asleep – the heart must have enough energy to go on beating, the lungs breathing, and so on. Food also provides us with substances that help us build up a good resistance

INFLUENCES ON FOOD CHOICE BEFORE AND AFTER RETIREMENT

Time	While you may have bought quick convenience foods when running a home and maybe having a full-time job, you may have more time for cooking in retirement.
Money	Always an important factor in choosing foods and often spent to save time. Money may be tighter in retirement.
Availability	The wide range of foods in the large supermarkets may not be available to you if you don't have transport to get there.
Ability	The choice of foods is restricted if you are unable to open a tin or package easily, cannot cut up meat or peel vegetables, or are unable to read instructions because of failing eyesight.
Facility	A whole range of foods is denied to those who don't have a freezer or microwave.
Interest	There are many people who don't really enjoy food so have little interest in buying, preparing or cooking, often leading to a monotonous diet.
Acceptability	Choice is reduced if there are a lot of things you really don't like, can't eat or are even allergic to.
Tradition	Doing what you have always done often means not trying new things, leading to a repetitive diet.
Fashion	The opposite of tradition is creating an interest in new foods, although the media often portray what we should or shouldn't do which creates another whole influence on the choice of foods. Travel abroad and immigrant cultures have strongly influenced and widened the choice of food.
Advertising	Whether we admit to it or not this is a very strong influence on the choice of food, through TV, radio, magazines and newspapers.
The body's needs	Your health and well-being should be important influences on the food you choose and the way you prepare it, and you can consciously take account of this in daily life.

The change in personal circumstances provided by retirement is the time to think positively about changing your diet for your health's sake rather than cooking for speed or convenience.

to infection and keep the body's processes regular. Choosing what food we eat is important – getting the balance right is really what it's all about.

One of the characteristics of growing older is that for all sorts of reasons, people tend to eat less. Healthy, active older people have the same needs as everyone else, but if the quantity of food you eat does gradually decrease, it becomes more important to maintain balance, and not to allow essential substances to be left out of the diet altogether. If you have reached retirement age fit and healthy, you've probably been choosing a healthy diet already. You have certainly had a lot more experience of preparing and eating food than the rest of the population. After all, a person of 75 who has had three meals a day has eaten over 82,000 meals and could have shopped for, prepared and cooked over 60,000 of them – no mean accomplishment!

Last, but not least, you should really *enjoy* your food. As well as nourishing and protecting your body, food should give you pleasure, not just through its taste, but through the whole occasion of sitting down to a meal.

THE CHOICE OF FOOD
As has already been mentioned, we are what we eat, but in general what we eat nowadays is not very good, and it has been getting worse ever since the end of the Second World War. People were healthier then than they are today because the restrictions of rationing actually provided a really balanced diet. You may remember the *weekly* rations for one person:

4oz margarine
2oz butter
2oz cheese
4oz bacon
3 pints milk
2oz tea

8oz sugar
1 egg
3oz sweets/chocolate
Meat to the value of 1s 2d (6p)

In today's value, the last item would probably be just over £1, hardly the cost of a small, frozen chicken, which might be stretched to four meals for one, but would be pretty monotonous, even with the versatile chicken.

In the years of rationing people became very resourceful with ways of making the best of the shortages – one typical recipe was 'dried potatoes and a few drops of cod liver oil' masquerading as fish cakes! It is not really surprising then that at the end of rationing people decided they were going to enjoy themselves – even though that actually meant indulging themselves as far as food was concerned. The choice of foods has become almost limitless over the years and this wide choice has actually had a detrimental effect on eating habits.

FOOD AND ILL HEALTH
There is little doubt that eating an unbalanced diet does cause health problems, some of them quite serious. Most of these diet-related health risks have to do with too much or too little of a particular nutritional substance. It is quite widely known now, for instance, that too little fibre is related to some diseases of the intestines, and too much fat to heart disease. And above all, too much fat, sugar and highly refined foods cause obesity – in other words, they make you fat. Unfortunately it is often easy to become overweight as you get older, and overweight brings with it increased risk of diabetes, arthritis, gall bladder trouble, foot troubles, shortage of breath, heart disease and varicose veins. The self-esteem and self-image of overweight people is often low; being overweight can also make them accident-prone and clumsy, and it slows

ARE YOU A HEALTHY WEIGHT?

Take a straight line across from your height (without shoes) and a line up from your weight (without clothes). Put a mark where the two lines meet.

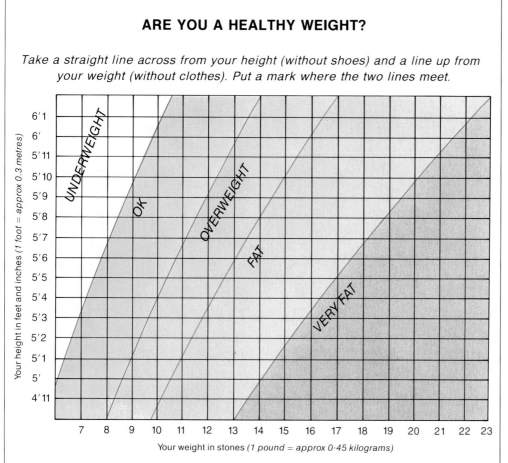

Your height in feet and inches (1 foot = approx 0.3 metres)

Your weight in stones (1 pound = approx 0·45 kilograms)

Underweight Maybe you need to eat a bit more. But go for well-balanced nutritious foods and don't just fill up on fatty and sugary foods. If you are *very* underweight, see your doctor about it.

OK You're eating the right *quantity* of food but you need to be sure that you're getting a healthy *balance* in your diet.

Overweight You should try to lose weight.

Fat You need to lose weight.

Very Fat You urgently need to lose weight. You would do well to see your doctor, who might refer you to a dietitian.

If you need to lose weight
Aim to lose 1 or 2 pounds a week until you get down to the 'OK' range. Go for fibre-rich foods and cut down on fat, sugar and alcohol. You'll need to take regular exercise too.

down recovery from surgery – all in all a rather awesome catalogue.

The problem for many older people is that they may be nothing like as active as they were during their working lives, while their eating habits remain the same. With less energy expended, the excess food gets converted into fat. It is important throughout life to keep an eye on your weight (both to avoid becoming too thin as well as too fat), but it is especially important as you get older to help prevent any of the problems like those above. The time to deal with excess weight is before it starts; have a look at the recommended weight to height ratio chart opposite and try to maintain a roughly even weight level. If this does mean reducing your weight to start with, the real encouragement will be when you find you can get around more easily, and clothes fit better. You will look and feel years younger, and people will tell you so too, which is really good for morale!

THE BASICS OF HEALTHY EATING

Everyone talks a lot about maintaining balance in protein, fat, carbohydrate, vitamins and minerals, but in point of fact there is no need to get locked into a sort of biology lesson, so that the kitchen becomes a scientific laboratory every time you prepare a meal. This is a sure way to drive you out of the kitchen and into the less-than-perfect world of pre-packed convenience foods. You really only need to keep in mind two basic facts about the food you eat – the importance of variety and balance, and the relationship of calorie intake to energy output.

Variety and balance

The meals you eat should come from as wide a variety of foods as possible to achieve the necessary balance for good health. The various bodies which have recently been studying the relationship between food and health for the population as a whole have all recommended the guidelines set out on the left.

Calories

All foods have an energy value which is measured in calories (k cal) with different foods having different calorific values. However, in terms of calories, what you take in as food should equal what you burn up in daily activities, and if you aren't very active your recommended daily intake may well be less

A HEALTHY OUTLOOK

▶ Cut down on fat, sugar and salt.

▶ Eat more fibre-rich foods.

▶ Eat plenty of fresh fruit and vegetables.

▶ Go easy on alcohol.

▶ Get plenty of variety in what you eat.

COMPARING THE MAKE-UP OF FOODS OF THE SAME CALORIFIC VALUE

Food	Portion Size	Calories	% Fat	% Carbohydrate
Wholemeal bread	6 slices	370	12%	72%
Jacket potatoes	1 lb/450g	370	1%	89%
Roast lean beef	8 oz/225g	370	26%	0%
Digestive biscuits	5	370	40%	52%
Whole milk	1 pint/560ml	370	55%	28%
Low fat spread	4 oz/110g	370	99.8%	0%
Butter	2½ pats (½ oz/12g)	370	99.8%	0%

BALANCING ENERGY OUTPUT WITH FOOD INTAKE

This chart compares the energy output (represented as Calories) required for different activities, with the energy input of different foods.

Activity	kcal/hour	Food	kcal
Walking Upstairs	1000	6 oz steak, 5 oz chips	1000 kcal
Ski-ing	875	4 oz butter	794 kcal
Swimming	575	1½ pints strong ale	600 kcal
Dancing	450	3 oz peanuts	450 kcal
Cycling	400	2½ pkts potato crisps	400 kcal
Scrubbing Floors	315	1 chocolate bar	328 kcal
Playing Bowls	260	2 oz cheddar cheese	220 kcal
Walking Slowly	185	3 slices white bread	172 kcal
Writing	115	3 oz ice cream	125 kcal
Standing	90	small tin baked beans	100 kcal
Sitting	85	½ pint lager	60 kcal
Sleeping	70	2 teas. sugar	60 kcal

(kilocalories) of energy used per hour

The energy expended by activity or provided by food is expressed by scientists in terms of kilocalories (k cal), more commonly referred to simply as Calories. The calorific values given here are only a guide, as all energy expenditure varies from person to person, so food intake will vary accordingly.

COMPARING ACTIVITY WITH FOOD EATEN

Look at the chart on this page and think about cutting out high calorie foods like biscuits, and increasing physical activity, like swimming or walking.

than the above. The diagram on page 125 shows the relationship between input and output. Dancing, swimming and even walking are very good at using up calories, and might be an enjoyable way of easing your conscience about the occasional pint of beer or chocolate bar. Conversely, these both put in an awful lot of calories for very little nutritional value. Weight for weight, some foods have more calories than others, so it is easy to pile on calories from eating very little of say, biscuits or butter. However, contrary to what many people used to think, there is actually less chance of over-indulging on carbohydrate foods since they are more bulky and fill you up more quickly, as well as often having the positive advantage of high-fibre content. The chart serves as a simple guide – it is instructive to think that a pound of potatoes baked in their jackets has exactly the same calorific value as the $2\frac{1}{2}$ pats of butter you might want to put on them!

FAT AND FIBRE

The received wisdom nowadays is to cut down on fat and eat more fibre, but it is important for you to be clear about what this means as you get older. Too much fat in the diet has been shown to be related to heart disease, but by the time you are over 70 it is probably too late to worry about this aspect of fat consumption. On the other hand, weight for weight, fatty foods are very high in calories, and if you continue to eat the same quantity as you always have done while becoming less active than previously, you may well find that you become overweight. This in turn can put a strain on joints which may discourage mobility, thus setting up a vicious circle of inactivity and obesity. In addition, elderly people who become overweight are more likely to become diabetic which requires strict management of the overall diet. If you are already a bit overweight, reducing your fat intake is a sensible way to slim.

Reducing fat intake

Some fat in the diet is of course needed for essential vitamins, but there are ways to reduce it sensibly. Bear in mind that low cholesterol fats are less important at this time of life – margarines and oils labelled 'low in cholesterol' still have the same calories as butter, and it is calories you are trying to reduce now. So look for low-fat spreads which have only half the calories of butter or margarine, and use light vegetable oils such as sunflower, corn or soya rather than lard to cook with. Another way to reduce fat in your diet is to change to skimmed or semi-skimmed milk. A pint of whole milk contains 11g of fat, whereas a pint of semi-skimmed contains less than half

this, and skimmed milk only contains 1g per pint. Skimmed milk is often less expensive and its taste is unnoticeable in sauces and cooked dishes.

The following chart gives some useful hints on how to reduce overall fat content without letting your meals become too boring.

- Choose low-fat spread or use butter and margarine sparingly.
- Choose sunflower, safflower, soya or corn oil instead of lard.
- Use skimmed or semi-skimmed milk.
- Use yogurt instead of cream.
- Choose low-fat and cottage cheese.
- Cook chicken without skin.
- Buy fish or chicken more often than red meat.
- Buy lean meat or cut off fat.
- Cut down on crisps, chocolate, cakes and biscuits.
- Grill, bake or steam rather than fry.
- Use a non-stick frying pan which doesn't need so much fat.
- Skim fat from stews, casseroles, curries and gravies.
- Choose or cut thick chips and thicker slices of bread to reduce fat absorption.

If you are housebound
Reducing the amount of fat may not however be advisable for very elderly, frail or housebound people with limited mobility and very small appetites. These people actually need the concentrated calories of fat, since they are unable to cope with large amounts of bulky carbohydrate-high foods.

HIGH-FIBRE FOODS
If you are reducing your fat intake, you will need the energy value of carbohydrate foods as a replacement. Choosing *high-fibre* carbohydrate foods can be of real benefit to older people. You may feel that constipation and old age are synonymous and that the daily laxative is unavoidable, but they can both be avoided by introducing more fibre into the diet. Lack of fibre is implicated in a number of so-called pressure disorders including diverticular disease, haemorrhoids (piles), hiatus hernia and varicose veins – diet not only affects their causes but their severity.▶ Constipation can be a problem but taking laxatives regularly can actually do more harm than good, while simply putting bran on to soups or cereals like a medicine doesn't really get to the root of the problem and makes those foods rather unpalatable when they could be prepared as delicious high-fibre dishes in their own right.

SEE ALSO: ◀

A–Z OF HEALTH
PROBLEMS:

Constipation	p. 190
Diverticulitis	p. 192
Faecal incontinence	p. 192
Haemorrhoids	p. 193

Below: *Some ideas for high fibre foods which could add variety as well as bulk to your daily food plan. Left to right: wholemeal bread; granary bread; whole wheat muesli; Swiss-style breakfast cereal; shelled almonds; Brazil nuts; brown rice; wholewheat pasta; sweetcorn; red kidney beans; carrots; Brussels sprouts; dried apricots; prunes; apples.*

However, eating more high-fibre foods may not be so easy to achieve if for years you have been led to believe that bread and potatoes were merely fattening! But if you look back at the calorie chart on page 126 you can see that if the bread is made from wholemeal flour and the potatoes don't have too much added butter they are not in themselves going to cause overweight.

Increasing fibre

On the whole, it is better to get fibre from a wide variety of foods than to resort to adding bran to foods or taking it as a sort of medicine. If you haven't had much fibre in your diet previously, don't overdo it to start with or you may suffer from indigestion or flatulence. Build it up gradually over the months, bearing in mind that there is fibre in a wide variety of foods. In fact you may have a high-fibre diet already without realizing it. In addition make sure you drink a lot of fluid as well – at least three pints a day.

Breakfast is an excellent time to increase fibre intake by trying one of the wide variety of high-fibre breakfast cereals and mueslis now available. This is one area where the food industry and the health experts have actually come together in common cause! However, the more traditional porridge, and whole or shredded wheat are also high in dietary fibre, and you can make up your own version of muesli. Shop-bought muesli often contains an unnecessarily high amount of sugar (look at the ingredients list on the packet) so you could make your own to your own taste. If you find it a little dry, it will probably be more palatable if you soak it in milk in the refrigerator over-night.

Wholemeal bread is often not very popular with older people because it can be indigestible. However there are many types of bread available now using bran-enriched white flour, or a percentage of wholemeal flour, which are much lighter. You might even feel able to try making your own bread if you have never done so before. There is definitely a cost saving here, especially if you have a freezer and can make several small loaves at a time.

You can also introduce wholemeal flour into your normal cooking – it is likely to be more acceptable if between a quarter and a half is added to white flour, enabling pastry and cakes to maintain their lightness. Wholemeal flour makes delicious crumble topping, dumplings and 'white' sauce.

Interesting salads are a good and appetizing way to introduce fibre and fresh vegetables to the diet, and they can provide light meals in their own right with the addition of boiled egg, cheese or ham pieces. Below left: Bean and rice salad, using leftover or drained, canned beans; centre: curried coleslaw, with a little curry powder mixed in to the mayonnaise to taste; and, right: pasta salad, using cold, cooked wholewheat pasta.

HIGH-FIBRE FOODS

(Recommended daily intake of fibre is 25–30g/about 1oz)

Bread (4 slices)		Vegetables and beans (continued)	
Wholemeal	11g	(1 serving)	
Brown	6g	Sprouts	2g
White	3g	Swede	2g
Breakfast cereals		**Fruit and snacks**	
(1 serving)		2 dried apricots	7g
2 Weetabix	5g	1 banana	3g
2 Shredded Wheats	5g	Raisins (30g)	2g
Puffed Wheat	4g	Unsalted peanuts (30g)	2g
Unsugared muesli	4g	1 apple	2g
Porridge	3g		
Cornflakes	3g	**Spaghetti** (1 serving)	
		Wholemeal	6g
Vegetables and beans		Ordinary	2g
(1 serving)			
Red kidney beans	10g	**Potatoes** (1 serving)	
Peas	7g	Baked in jacket	3g
Baked beans	6g	Boiled with skin on	3g
Spinach	5g	Boiled without skin	1g
Sweetcorn	5g		
Lentils	4g	**Rice** (1 serving)	
Carrots	3g	Brown	3g
Leeks	3g	White	2g

FRUIT AND VEGETABLES

Fruit and vegetables are high in fibre, as well as being nutritious in their own right in other ways. Fibre is mainly found in the skins of fruit and vegetables, so where possible leave these on. Boil or bake potatoes in their skins, don't peel apples and scrub rather than peel root vegetables like carrots or parsnips. Dried vegetables and pulses like beans, peas, lentils and rice (especially brown rice) are also rich in fibre and make a change from bread and potatoes. A homely tea of baked beans on wholemeal toast is actually a highly nutritious meal high in dietary fibre.

It is a good idea as often as possible to eat fruit and vegetables raw – make a simple fruit salad or a green salad enhanced with a few nuts. Nutritionists recommend a daily intake of 25–30g (1oz) of fibre which actually may not be as easy as it sounds; the chart opposite gives an indication of how many grams of fibre the highest fibre foods contain which should help you aim in the right direction.

Vitamins and minerals

Apart from their fibre content, fruit and vegetables contain vitamins and minerals essential for the maintenance of good health and well-being. Vitamin C is particularly important as the body does not store it, so foods containing Vitamin C should be eaten everyday. Vitamin C is only found in fruits, salads and vegetables. Citrus fruits (oranges, grapefruit, lemons, etc) are the best sources. Green vegetables, such as cabbage, lettuce and spinach, are quite a good source, but much is lost by overcooking. Soft fruits like blackcurrants, rhubarb

The greater range nowadays of fresh fruits all year round enables you to add fibre and essential vitamins to your diet in a varied and enjoyable way. This is one area where shopping in small quantities has positive advantages since storing fresh fruit and vegetables too long robs them of their vitamin content.

and gooseberries, bananas, raw tomatoes and new potatoes all contain significant quantities of Vitamin C. You can also supplement your Vitamin C by drinking pure orange or tomato juice, using pure bottled lemon juice on salads, fish and pancakes, and use instant potatoes that have Vitamin C added. Or you could eat 1 orange a day, which would supply 30 mg of Vitamin C, the recommended daily allowance.

Fresh versus frozen

Fresh fruit and vegetables are best but frozen ones are just as nutritious and contain the same minerals and almost the same amount of vitamins as the fresh. However, tinned fruit and vegetables lose a lot of their vitamins when they are processed.

Making the most of salads and vegetables

Vitamins are slowly lost from fruit and vegetables from the minute they are picked. Always buy them fresh in season and use them quickly. If you need to store them, find a cool dark but dry place and don't keep them any longer than necessary. Try to eat at least three different kinds of fruit, vegetables and salad every day, with a least some item raw.

When preparing vegetables for cooking peel thinly or leave the skins on where possible; most of the vitamins and minerals are under the skin and are lost in thick peelings. Cook vegetables quickly in a little boiling water; steaming or pressure cooking is an excellent way to avoid boiling away the goodness. Use the vegetable water to make gravy, soup or stews, and never add bicarbonate of soda since this destroys the vitamins altogether.

LOOKING AT SUGAR

Among us, we manage to get through about 33 kg (84lb) of refined sugar a

'HIDDEN' SUGAR IN FOOD

All measurements in spoonfuls mean a 'rounded' spoonful, i.e. the same shape above as below the level of the spoon.

PRODUCT	1 PORTION	SUGAR PER PORTION Amount in rounded teaspoons
Chocolate biscuits	2 biscuits	$1\frac{1}{2}$
Ginger nut biscuits	2 biscuits	$1\frac{1}{2}$
Ice cream	1 scoop	2
Fruit yogurt	1 small carton	$4\frac{1}{2}$
Baked beans (ordinary)	$\frac{1}{2}$ medium tin	$2\frac{1}{2}$
Mars bar	1 bar	9
Liquorice Allsorts	1 box (5oz)	22
Drinking chocolate	3 teaspoons	3
Lime cordial	1 diluted glass	$2\frac{1}{2}$
Lucozade	1 small glass	$4\frac{1}{2}$
Orange squash	1 diluted glass	3
Ribena	1 diluted glass	6
Tinned tomato soup	$\frac{1}{2}$ tin	1
Packet oxtail soup	$\frac{1}{4}$ packet	$1\frac{1}{2}$
Muesli	$1\frac{1}{2}$ tablespoons	$1\frac{1}{2}$
Bitter lemon	1 small bottle	$5\frac{1}{2}$

year per head of population – which is about 625g (25oz) a week – an awful lot compared to the 8oz a week that was the wartime ration per person. About half comes from actual sugar which people add to their own food, the rest from hidden sugar – in sweets, cakes, soft drinks and convenience foods. Sugar is pure energy – it goes straight into the blood stream and offers the body little or no other nutrients. And it doesn't make any difference what colour it is either.

This sort of sugar intake needs to be cut down by at least half by everyone, no matter what their age, and a good start can be achieved simply by cutting out sugar in tea and coffee. The taste for sweet things isn't innate but conditioned – right from childhood sweet things are usually given as rewards for good behaviour or as a way of showing affection, so they have a psychological association with pleasure as well as a pleasant taste and are therefore sometimes the hardest things to give up. Sweet things are usually low in fibre as well, so don't fill you up, so you eat even

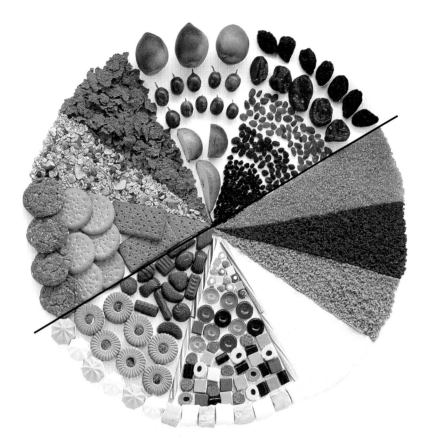

Use this 'sugar wheel' to help cut down on refined sugar. Foods from the top half of the wheel, above the line, are high in starches and dietary fibre, and either have no sugar or little added. Below the line are the sugars (including raw cane sugar), the sweets and sugar biscuits which should be avoided.

SEE ALSO: ▶

FOOD AND COOKING:
The Daily Food Plan p. 137

GOOD HEALTH:
Watching your alcohol
p. 115

more. A first step is to make sure that first you have all the food recommended in the Daily Food Plan before indulging your sweet tooth. ◀

Hidden sugar

It is wise to look at the labels on packaged foods for hidden sugar content – anything with '-ose' on the end (sucrose, dextrose, fructose, maltose) means 'sugar'. If you look at the chart on page 133 you may be surprised to learn how much sugar there is in everyday foods – even savoury ones. Taking a little more time with the preparation of food, buying fresh or frozen vegetables rather than tinned, or baking your own cakes and biscuits which require far less sugar are all ways of keeping control of the sugar in your diet while allowing for the undoubted pleasure that sweet things bring.

EATING LESS SALT

Although the general recommendation is to cut down on salt, the research associated with this is not yet proven. However the evidence so far shows we could do well not to use so much salt both in cooking and at the table, largely because, like sugar, there is so much already added to processed foods. Older people sometimes add even more salt to their food than they used to because their sense of taste appears to be lessening. If you feel this is the case with you it would be better to try improving the flavour of foods with herbs and spices rather than just adding salt.

DRINKING LESS ALCOHOL

You may well say 'Chance would be a fine thing' if you are trying to manage on a pension! Suffice it to say that a small drink may improve your appetite if it has become jaded, but if you drink to excess your appetite is ruined and the chances of malnutrition setting in are greatly increased. ◀

COUNTING THE COST OF GOOD EATING

Healthy food need not be expensive. Many of the recommended foods, like pulses, pasta, chicken and some fish, are less costly than traditional meat dishes, as are the old-fashioned favourites like tripe and onions, faggots and black pudding. What really puts up the cost of meals is when you buy a lot of prepacked and prepared foods, because you are having to pay for the labour involved as well as the ingredients. Now that you have more time to prepare meals yourself, and perhaps even grow fruit and vegetables in the garden, it is a good time to take a renewed interest in food.

Cookery classes at your local adult education institute or college may provide the right stimulus. Make shopping, preparing and cooking a combined venture with your partner or with a friend or group of friends, perhaps pooling resources for a really slap-up meal every now and again or taking it in turns to entertain if you like that sort of thing. Look too at ways of making cooking both less costly in terms of fuel cost and also in terms of the amount of work you have to do.

Money-saving ideas

If you have a freezer you probably already know the benefits of 'batch cooking' – cooking at least twice as much of any particular food so that extra meals can be frozen for eating at a later date. If you haven't got a freezer and, you have some savings to spare, think about investing in a small freezer – perhaps a fridge-freezer combined. Freezing your own meals helps add variety to your diet and gives the convenience of a well-stocked freezer without the expense of buying ready prepared frozen foods. Remember too even cold food helps to keep the body warm and is better than turning up the heating and going without food.

Soups, casseroles and stewed fruit are economically cooked in a slow cooker or pressure cooker. If you make more than you need, divide it into portions and store them in the freezer. Undoubtedly the best way to reheat from the freezer is in a microwave oven which not only reheats well in minutes but costs very little to do so. Nowadays a microwave oven can cost less than £100 and will soon pay you back your investment.

It often costs more to buy small quantities of food – economy packs are always the large ones. Small joints of meat seem to shrink away to nothing when cooked whereas larger joints have a much greater 'portion power' – the larger surface area helps to avoid shrinkage, and the meat juices provide delicious gravy. So when you can afford it buy a larger joint and freeze sliced portions in their own gravy to save time,

money and effort. It is important to undertake this freezing of meat and gravy quickly as soon as they have cooked as good hygiene practice. If you haven't chosen your retirement present yet put a slow cooker or pressure cooker and microwave oven high on your list. If that opportunity is past, treat yourself if you can and you won't regret it.

Time- and labour-saving equipment

Cooking shouldn't be a chore, and cooking methods are important in maintaining the nutritional value of foods and providing the variety which you need both for interest and healthy eating.

- A good non-stick frying pan is easier to use and avoids the need for so much fat when frying. It is also easier to clean than a regular frying pan.
- A vegetable steamer retains all the goodness and flavour in vegetables.
- A small electric mixer and blender make cakes easier to mix and allows you to prepare thick home-made soups without having to use a heavy white sauce.
- An electric can opener is safe and easy to use.
- Cling film on a wall-mounted dispenser is much easier to use and keeps leftover foods fresh.
- A pair of kitchen scissors is often easier to use than a knife when cutting rinds off bacon, cutting up herbs or shredding lettuce or cabbage.
- A bottle opener gripper is useful for obstinate jars.

There are many good ideas to make preparing food easier and safer. It may be worth discussing this with an occupational therapist at a Day Centre or

135

hospital department. For instance, a good way to scrub vegetables is to use an abrasive cleaning pad. Your local Gas or Electricity Board should also be able to adapt your cooker for easier use.

Cooking for one

You don't have to be old to realize that cooking for one is not much fun – single people young and old have the same problems in buying the right quantities so that food remains fresh and meals are not monotonous. Cooking appetizing and varied meals and presenting them attractively can all seem a bit of a waste of time when you are dining alone.

Make up your mind that you really will take an active interest in the food you prepare and eat for your health's sake. Try not to look on it as a necessary chore but as an interesting pastime. By far the best answer to the monotony of cooking for one is to share some of your meals with someone in the same position as yourself. It is much more rewarding for cook for an 'audience' and nice to go out on the return visit too. Some people organize small lunch clubs in their own homes – why not yours? It can make you bring out the best china and tablecloth which might otherwise never get used.

MENU PLANNING

It is a good idea actually to plan a week's menus in advance so that you don't

---

THE EMERGENCY FOOD CUPBOARD

Try to keep at least some from each section in your cupboard for emergencies, but check that you don't keep any single item for too long – use it and replace it from time to time.

Milk	Cartons of UHT (long life); tins of evaporated or condensed; carton of dried milk
Bread and cereals	Spare loaf in the freezer; packets of crackers or biscuits for cheese; packets of high-fibre cereal
Meat	Tins of minced meat, ham, stews or casseroles, corned beef, luncheon meat
Fish	Tinned mackerel, tuna, pilchards, salmon, sardines, cod's roe
Fruit and veg	Instant potato powder; tinned potatoes and carrots; dried and tinned peas and lentils; rice and tinned rice pudding; baked beans, tinned fruit in natural juice
Drinks	Fruit juices; fruit drinks containing Vitamin C; Marmite; Bovril; Ovaltine; Bournvita
For when you cannot eat	Milk shake mixes; malted milk powders; concentrated food substitutes (Complan)

DAILY FOOD PLAN

Bread, cereals and flour

Foods in this group include pasta, breakfast cereals, rice, biscuits and bread.

Eat two or three portions of food from this group each day, preferably the wholemeal varieties. Avoid the ones made with lots of added suigar and fat, like chocolate biscuits and rich gooey cakes as these are fattening.

Fruit, salads and vegetables

Eat two portions – fresh or frozen – every day, as well as potatoes. Choose as many different sorts as possible and eat some raw.

Milk and dairy products

$\frac{1}{2}$–1 pint each day. Most people manage this in drinks. Cheese, yogurt and dried and evaporated milk are the other dairy foods which could also be included.

Meat, fish and eggs

Most of us already eat enough enough of these foods because we have them twice a day.

Nuts, beans, other pulses and dairy products can be eaten instead.

Sugars, fats and oils

These have little food value and are expensive extras in a balanced diet and so not included in the food groups. Too many of these cause you to put on weight.

waste time and money shopping unnecessarily and you can plan to be more economical with your use of fuel. For example, plan to have an oven-cooked meal and bake a cake at the same time. It also means you'll be checking your store cupboard regularly so that you don't run out of essential ingredients if for any reason you are unable to get to the shops. Pin a photocopy of the Emergency Food Cupboard Chart to the kitchen notice board as a reminder.

THE DAILY FOOD PLAN

Once you're convinced that eating for health is important and interesting, the planning can be easy if you try to include food from the four different groups given in the chart on the previous page. This will take care of all the necessary protein, carbohydrates, fats, vitamins and minerals – after all we eat food, not nutrients, so it is food we should be thinking about first – not its chemical components.

AS YOU GET OLDER

Everyone has the potential to live to a much greater age than previous generations, so that the celebration of eightieth birthdays has become commonplace. But it may be that you are not so active or have some chronic illness or disability to cope with or may even be housebound. It is at this stage that there are a few special nutritional recommendations to ensure that you have no deficiencies in your diet.

Research has shown that there are four problem areas for the elderly – lack of fibre (as always), lack of Vitamin C and calcium and Vitamin D. The chart opposite shows the likely reasons why these particular deficiencies occur and what the consequences might be. In addition one might add 'under-nutrition', for a minority of elderly people simply eat very little indeed of any food. A guideline for everyone approaching these years could be to eat little and often – if you can't face the traditional three meals a day have four or five small, light meals instead. Eating more high fibre foods and fruit and vegetables has already been discussed – this is a recommendation for everyone, no matter what their age or state of health.

Food for strong bones

When you are unable to be as active as you would like, or get out into the sunshine, then you need to make sure you eat the right foods to keep your bones fit and strong. The vitamins and minerals needed here are Vitamin D and calcium. Calcium is needed to keep bones from becoming too brittle, and is found mainly in milk and other dairy products such as cheese and yogurt. Some breads contain added calcium too. However, the body cannot absorb calcium through the digestive system without the help of Vitamin D, which can be made by the body itself through the action of sunlight on the skin.

Sources of Vitamin D

Oily fish such as sardines, mackerel, tuna, pilchards, herring and cod's roe are the richest sources of Vitamin D, and it is added to margarine. Cheese, egg yolks, some of the bedtime milk drinks and evaporated milk also contain some of the vitamin. Butter does contain a little Vitamin D but only if the cow has been in the sunshine, so you may be better off using margarine if you want it as a source of Vitamin D, because it is added by the manufacturer.

Iron deficiency

Iron is needed to maintain the red cells in blood, which carry oxygen round the body so that food can be converted into energy. If there is not enough iron in the diet the body will not make enough red cells, and therefore less oxygen will be carried round the body. The resulting

PROBLEMS WITH FOOD AND COOKING AMONG THE OVER-80s

NUTRITIONAL DEFICIENCY	CAUSE	POSSIBLE EFFECT
Too little fibre	Eating refined foods Small appetites – less bulk No tradition of cereal breakfast Small quantities of over–prepared fruit and vegetables eaten	Constipation Piles Diverticulitis Bowel cancer
Low Vitamin C intake	Lack of fresh fruit, salads and vegetables. Poor storage, preparation and cooking of same	Less able to fend off infections Slow healing Poor soft tissue areas Affects iron absorption
Low iron intake	Insufficient red meat and dark green vegetables eaten Lack of cereal breakfast Poor variety in diet Lack of Vit. C to aid iron absorption	Anaemia Tiredness Listlessness Lack of energy Poor appetite Pale complexion
Low Vitamin D intake	Lack of sunshine on skin Dislike of oily fish Poor acceptance of margarine	Bones & joints weaker Poor healing in event of accidental injury More vulnerable to accidental damage Affects calcium absorption
General under-nutrition	Lack of appetite Lack of motivation or ability to prepare food Forgetful about eating	Lack of energy Apathy and depression Feels cold Vulnerable to illness & infections Specific deficiencies more likely.

condition is known as anaemia, and its symptoms are tiredness, listlessness, poor appetite and a pale complexion. Many elderly people suffer from anaemia because they are not getting enough iron in their diet.

There are four main sources of iron. The richest source is in offal such as liver, kidney and heart, and in foods derived from these meats, like faggots, black pudding or liver paté. Red meat, like beef and lamb, is also high in iron, while pork, chicken and rabbit have hardly any. Meat products derived from red meat like corned beef and meat paste or spreads, also contain iron. Eggs also contain iron, which is particularly useful for vegetarians or for people who simply can't face red meat. What is less well known is that wholemeal bread and breakfast cereals also contain iron (many cereals actually have iron added by the manufacturer) and so do dried fruits and all pulse vegetables, like peas, beans and lentils. So once again the humble baked bean takes its place as a nutritional blockbuster!

Under-nutrition

There is nothing sacrosanct about having 'three square meals a day' – if you are very inactive and have a small appetite you may well be better off with four or five small meals a day instead. It is important to make sure that these light meals or snacks are really nourishing and contain all the recommended nutrients in a more concentrated form. Try to stimulate the gastric juices by presenting the food in an attractive way.

Luncheon clubs and meals-on-wheels

Meal times spent in the company of friends and like-minded people are much more entertaining, but as you get older you may feel you are unable to entertain others in your own home. Many local authorities and voluntary organizations run luncheon clubs, even providing transport in some cases. Check with your local social services offices to find out about local facilities.

For housebound elderly people meals-on-wheels can make all the difference between being able to cope in your own home and not, as well as bringing a cheery, though usually very busy, visitor daily.

Increasingly local authorities are paying more attention to the nutritional value of the meals they serve to elderly people at luncheon clubs and meals-on-wheels, but it is important not to rely solely on this one meal a day to provide all you need for a healthy diet. Try to balance it out with breakfast, supper, snacks and drinks, checking the daily food plan regularly.

The time spent being classed as the 'older generation' could be as long as 30 or 40 years, almost as long as the normal working life. Just as your likes, dislikes, and circumstances changed during that time, so they will as you get older. Try to think in terms of 'stages of ageing', from the active 60s, through the slower 70s and on into the 80s and – why not – the 90s, and adapt your needs accordingly. Deciding what you eat is an important part of a healthy and enjoyable old age.

Changing attitudes to food

If you follow the advice of taking an active interest in the food you buy or eat during your early 'retirement' you will be better able to cope with more limited ability later. For example, having meals in the freezer for simple re-heating in the microwave will give a lot of independence to a housebound older person even if someone else cooked it in the first place. Family and friends may be able to provide frozen meals, and a greater variety of whole meals are appearing in supermarket freezer departments which are not over-processed,

---

SIMPLE IDEAS FOR HEALTHIER SNACK MEALS

☐ Buy cheese you can crumble if grating is difficult – Lancashire is good for this.

☐ Add grated/crumbled cheese to mashed potato, on top of canned spaghetti or to home-made soups.

☐ Add chopped, hard-boiled egg to mashed potato or to cheese or other bland sauces.

☐ Add an egg to pastry or scone mixtures.

☐ Make home-made pizza with tomato, bacon or ham pieces and cheese on a soft bread roll or pikelet.

☐ Squeeze lemon juice on canned fruit, vegetables and fish for extra Vitamin C.

☐ Add fresh fruit or Vitamin C enriched drinks to rice pudding.

☐ Keep salads and vegetables in closed bags in the fridge to maintain freshness and flavour.

☐ Make double or more quantities and store in airtight plastic boxes in the refrigerator or freezer to save time and avoid monotony. Sandwiches freeze well too.

☐ Use bran-enriched or partly wholemeal bread or rolls for sandwiches.

☐ Add sliced tomatoes, shredded lettuce or raw spinach to sandwiches filled with cheese, ham, hard-boiled egg, corned or cold beef, chicken, or mashed tuna or sardine.

---

though undoubtedly convenient. They are a bit more expensive, but will add variety to your weekly meals so may be worth investing in. Many local authorities are providing frozen meals too for re-heating by clients, as an alternative to traditional meals-on-wheels.

Even if a home help, family member, friend or neighbour does your shopping for you, make your own lists to be certain that he or she is buying what you want. The daily food plan and the emergency store cupboard list, given on pages 136 and 137 of this chapter, will be helpful here. Following their advice will mean that you can keep control of what you are eating, even if you are unable to get to the shops to buy your own weekly groceries.

Problems with teeth and dentures

If you have difficulty in chewing food because of loose teeth or ill fitting dentures, there is no need to suffer it – go to the dentist and have them fixed. ▶ In some areas the community dentist can visit you at home. However, you can't really expect dentures to do the job of biting and chewing as well as your own teeth did, and there will always be some things, like apples, which need to be peeled or cut up rather than bitten into straight away.

Calcium and Vitamin D will help keep your own teeth strong, and Vitamin C helps to avoid gum soreness, although if this is caused by dentures, consult your dentist.

SEE ALSO: ◀

GOOD HEALTH:

Changes in the gums and teeth   p. 106

MOVEMENT AND EXERCISE

Of all the Seven Ages of Man, the last stage of life seems to be the most varied and holds the most interest for others. It could literally be 'sans everything', but it does not have to be. Instead it can be a time of self-realization and personal growth, and one of the keys to this is movement.

You may think this is an odd sort of idea, but the reason why this is so is contained in one word – oxygen. The body is composed of millions of different kinds of cells, which all have one necessity in common: they need oxygen to function. Just as any motor car cannot work without petrol, so any cell in your body will die if it has no oxygen. Four seconds without oxygen in your brain cells and you have brain damage, four minutes and you are dead.

Oxygen is breathed into the lungs from the outside air and is carried round the body in the blood. This movement of oxygen-rich blood is dependent on the action of the heart pushing the blood into the arteries, and on the movements of joints plus the action of muscles sending the blood back to the heart. On each heart-beat, the heart pushes out the exact amount of blood it has already received, so it would appear that a good return ensures a good output.

If we want to remain healthy and able to enjoy living, therefore, we really have no choice but to continue good breathing habits and exercising the muscles and joints all our lives. There are many ways of achieving these aims through movement and exercise and you can choose which you find most attractive to your personality and suitable to your way of life from the suggestions that follow.

THINKING ABOUT MOVEMENT
Movement is natural. The more natural it is, the more useful it is to the individual. A set of exercises labelled 'Good for you' is often useless, not only because they may be unnatural but also because the label is off-putting and people just do not attempt them. We may well feel resentful at being told what to do by someone else, and as we grow older, we may also be disinclined to change our habits to fit in with what others think we should do.

Continuing with sport
People who are naturally fond of sport will almost certainly carry on at their chosen activity for as long as they feel comfortable, or perhaps change to a more suitable form. When you reach your sixties, you may prefer indoor or outdoor bowls to cricket, curling to rugby, or dancing to hurdling. The important thing is not to give up some form of activity completely, or you may find yourself facing the dread prospect of loss of muscle power and increase in fat, with its miserable picture of diminishing returns of energy and enjoyment.

Food and fitness
There seems to be a connection in the lower brain with adequate movement and an appropriate appetite for food. Unfortunately this also seems to enable some people to exchange the desire for

exercise for the desire for food – with predictable results! Balance, as in all body control, is the answer. With a sufficiently enjoyable and healthy diet ▶ including three to five pints of fluid daily and an amount of movement suitable for your age and personal history, health and satisfaction in living can be maintained for years.

Taking exercise

You might like to join a class or attend a well-equipped gymnasium, with instructors to give advice. In either case, be sure you look for well-trained teachers with adequate experience, especially in the needs of the older person, and check with your doctor before you begin, as you should before any programme of exercise. General daily activity is the aim, not just a violent outburst once a week which could do more harm than good.

If you don't like joining groups and are not naturally competitive, then try a little re-arrangement of your daily habits. Look at the suggestions in the table below. There are numerous alternatives to choose from to suit all abilities, preferences and circumstances . . . as the saying goes:

'The world is so full of a number
                              of things
I'm sure we should all be as
                    happy as kings.'

WHEN EXERCISE IS DIFFICULT

Even if you have never enjoyed exercise, or have health problems such as arthritis, or have had to endure surgery or serious illness but are on the way to recovery, it is still essential to include movement in your daily programme if you are not to sink into the 'sans everything' category. It may be a struggle but it will be worthwhile. You will feel happier and have greater emotional satisfaction in living, as well as a much more active brain, even if your body is

not as perfect as it might be.

Remember that there is no such thing as a perfect person: everyone is disabled in some way. Whether the defect is physical, such as legs that do not function easily, or emotional, so that the person suffers from greed, jealousy, selfishness or another unfortunate personality trait, there is no need to differentiate between them, or for the physically handicapped to feel – or be treated as – inferior.

Remember, too, that health and general well-being depend on more than just exercise and diet – they are achieved by examining and improving a person's whole lifestyle. We are such complicated creatures of body, mind and spirit that any up-grading of any part of us renders service to the whole being. Even people with gross physical disability, recurring pain, and those suffering from long dependency on drugs, can be greatly relieved by following some of the suggestions that follow. Every disabled person is capable of improvement. Begin with the parts easiest to adjust. Give yourself a plan to follow that you will enjoy, with rewards along the way.

ESSENTIALS OF EXERCISE

If you want to try exercising by yourself, there are essentials suggested for each part of the body. Specific movements are described and illustrated in detail in the second section of this chapter, from pages 149 to 161, followed by the Mitchell Method of Relaxation, pages 162 to 165. Blind or partially sighted people, or those with hearing problems, may find the following general outline of exercises sufficient for their needs or they could attend classes.

Probably everyone knows from the publicity already given to the subject that one should begin any exercise regime gently and increase gradually. It

SEE ALSO: ◀

FOOD AND COOKING:
Basics of healthy eating
                      p. 126

DAY-TO-DAY ACTIVITY

• Use stairs instead of lifts
• Fetch your own daily paper instead of having it delivered
• Walk to appointments instead of taking the car or a bus
• Never sit for longer than half an hour at a time, except of course when entertaining or being entertained.
• Develop a hobby with activity in it and an end result, for example, joinery of all kinds, bread making, gardening, house decorating, photography
• Develop a new interest or activity, like the retired naval officer who took on an early morning paper delivery, or the retired accountant who took up fishing, making his own flies and learning to row a boat

- If you have had difficulty going out, find out what local facilities for cheap transport are available (see page 219).
- Join a group for physical movement. Choose the kind you like. Margaret Morris Movement is particularly useful and pleasurable (address on page 203).
- Join a group for mental stimulation, debating, political discussion, creative writing, acting.
- Join a group giving service to others. You can often do jobs for them at home, (see Resources and Back-up, page 220).
- Join a group for spiritual and creative interest, such as your local church, synagogue or temple, or a pottery, photography, dressmaking or cookery group (see Resources and Back-up, page 211).

is also important, if in any doubt, to consult a doctor as to the suitability of increasing activity. It is not a good idea, however, to try to govern your activity by taking your own pulse. This is often described as a safe rule to follow, but in actual practice it is very difficult to feel one's pulse quickly, and almost impossible to count it correctly. If pulse counting is deemed necessary, then you should do your exercising in a training centre where the coach would be proficient in taking an accurate measurement, both of your pulse and of your general fitness for exercise. The coach would then guide your progress.

Always begin and end any session with gentle activity. This is called 'warming up' and 'warming down'. Always rest between exercises, and do not exercise at all if you feel ill or have a raised temperature. Progress slowly and enjoy what you are doing.

Trying to improve your state of health by exercise, movement and training dexterity of hand and eye is like any other effort. The result depends on your attitude of mind. As Frederick Langbridge wrote:
'Two men look out the same bars, One sees the mud and one the stars.'

'Warming up' and 'warming down'

These are the terms used by dancers and athletes for the preparation of the body for prolonged or strong activity, and also for its care after the action has been completed. If such exercise is initiated without this preparation, there may be danger of damage to muscles and other soft parts. Joints also can be strained. Without warm-up exercises, breathing may be inappropriate for the amount of carbon dioxide given off during strong muscle work and the supply of oxygen inadequate.

Warming up may therefore consist of easy swinging of arms and legs plus some gentle definite performance such as alternate knee bending and stretching; arms gently lifting in all directions and easy body action of the spinal joints in all directions. Add some deep breathing using all parts of the chest.

This regime is repeated at the end of the main session, and is then called warming down, as it helps the body to get rid of its extra heat gently, and to re-establish normal physiology of all the soft parts and joints, which may have been used strenuously.

The time involved will obviously depend on the strength of the main exercise. A very short time would probably suffice for you – perhaps no more than a minute or two – but you must learn to recognize your body's needs.

DEEP BREATHING

Let us begin with thorough breathing, because if you did nothing else but improve that, you would be giving your whole body a treat. Noses are for breathing through, both in and out. There are tiny hairs and a sticky fluid on the lining of the nose which trap dirt and bacteria from the air as it passes along, and prevents them reaching the lungs. Immediately under the lining of the nose there are numerous blood vessels to warm the air. By this arrangement, clean, warm, damp air is ready to give up its oxygen in the lungs and receive the waste carbon dioxide which the blood has collected from the working cells all over the body. By breathing out through the nose, the air rushing along the passages tends to dislodge the dust and other particles, clinging there, and this can then be safely collected into a handkerchief by blowing the nose.

If you spread out all the little passages forming the lungs, surrounded as they are by blood vessels as thin as a hair, they would cover a tennis court. So this vast area should be used for the exchange of carbon dioxide for oxygen as thoroughly as possible. All you have to do to achieve this is to widen your chest as far as possible in all directions, and air will pour into the lungs to fill the available space. Interchange then takes place without any effort. If you then stop pushing out your chest, the ribs fall back against your lungs on all sides, the diaphragm rises to press against them from below and the breath is pushed out. There is no muscle work in breathing out, merely a relaxation of the muscles that caused the enlargement of the chest to breathe in. (See page 149.)

EXERCISING THE HANDS AND ARMS

The tendency for hands is to bend inwards, and some people even encourage this by perpetually squeezing a tissue, thinking that this is a way of exercising their hand muscles. In fact, they are encouraging deformity and weakness of the muscles that open out the hand, and it is these which need to be worked. (See pages 152–3.)

EXERCISING THE SHOULDERS

It is of the utmost importance to keep your shoulder joints free all your life, as this is their natural state. (Never lift a child up by the arm, as the shoulder joint will easily pull out one and a half inches. See pages 154–7.)

Muscles of hands, arms and shoulders needing strengthening

1 Extensors of fingers and small muscles of hands that open and close fingers and thumbs
2 Flexors of fingers with purpose, and against resistance (holding a substantial object)
3 Rotators of forearms; flexors and extensors of elbows
4 Muscles that take arms to the sides and above the head
5 Muscles that take arms forwards and backwards at the shoulders
6 Associated movements of the head

7 Outward and inward rotators of shoulder joints
8 Muscles that lift your collar bones and shoulder blades upwards and those that pull them downwards. Notice that the latter only work when you actually pull the bones downwards strongly – not just drop them
9 Muscles that pull your shoulder blades together and downwards at your back.

EXERCISING THE LEGS AND FEET

The job of the legs is to move our weight about, so they need very strong muscles for support. It may not have occurred to you, but we spend a great deal of time with our weight just on one leg – as in walking or running, for example – so balance has to be considered in exercising the legs. (See pages 158–160.)

Balance

When you have mastered the simple exercises given here for improving balance, there is no reason why you should not progress to making up your own exercises.

As in all easy muscle training for health and pleasure you must find for yourself what your own body can safely and happily achieve. Every body is different; so start gently, balancing for perhaps a quarter of a minute, then progress at your own rate of safe control.

Always have some support near you that you can hold on to if necessary. You are supposed to be enjoying yourself and becoming body conscious, not training for an Olympic medal!

Muscles of legs and feet needing strengthening

1 Those that bend the leg towards the body (flexors)
2 Those that extend the leg backwards (buttocks)
3 Those that take the leg out to the side (especially those which help our bal-

Add extra resistance to leg exercises by fixing a weight, such as bags or cans of food, to your feet with a crêpe bandage.

ance. The muscles which bring the legs together do not usually need special work.)

4 Those that straighten the knees (necessary to get up from sitting)

5 Those that bend the knees (surprisingly, we use these to fix our knees when standing)

6 Those which bend up our feet at the ankles, some of which help to support the arches of the feet

7 Those which bend down our feet at the ankles, some of which help to support the arches of the feet

8 The smaller muscles in the feet supporting the arches and giving spring to our step.

Some people may like to make up their own exercises from this list, or check what they already enjoy doing, to see if they want to add any further movement.

You may want to add extra resistance to the work by wearing heavier shoes or boots and later, adding a weight tied on to the boot. Be sure you tie it on. It must not dangle down below, but must become part of the foot. A tin or packet of food, whose weight you know, is useful for this; you can then increase the weight by using a larger container. Try bandaging it on to your foot with a crepe bandage or scarf.

Walking, jogging, running, jumping, skating, cycling or skiing are all good exercises for legs and balance. Intersperse one with another as you find suitable. All games are good for gregarious people, as is dancing. There are so many forms available: try any one of them, and if you don't like it, change it.

If you try teaching any of the exercises to someone else, you will find it will clarify them in your own mind and you will have greater understanding of the uses and difficulties of each exercise. Remember, your brain only orders *movement*, so you must dictate an action, not the muscle work. This will automatically take place if you give the correct order. Telling yourself, 'Straighten your knees,' will be much more effective than saying, 'Use your quadriceps,' for example. If the knees are still somewhat bent, say, 'Straighten more and more and more.' You will find they will try to do so. Give yourself these instructions, and you will feel the results in the position of your joints.

BODY MOVEMENT
The body moves at the joints of the spinal column with the hip joints sometimes involved. The diagram shows the areas of the vertebral column with the movements possible in each region. All

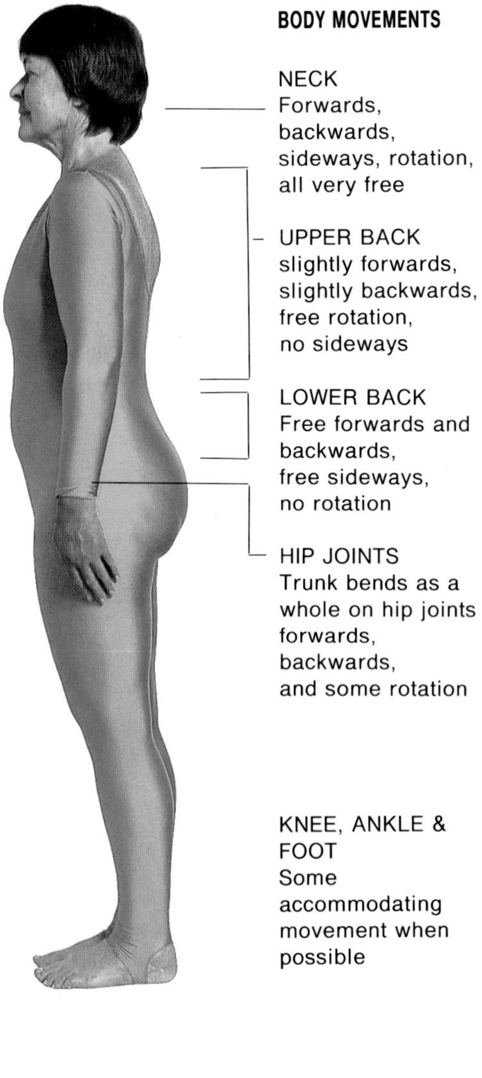

BODY MOVEMENTS

NECK
Forwards, backwards, sideways, rotation, all very free

UPPER BACK
slightly forwards, slightly backwards, free rotation, no sideways

LOWER BACK
Free forwards and backwards, free sideways, no rotation

HIP JOINTS
Trunk bends as a whole on hip joints forwards, backwards, and some rotation

KNEE, ANKLE & FOOT
Some accommodating movement when possible

movements in the spine are accomplished by an accumulation of tiny movements between the joints. It is quite common for some joints to be stiffer than others, while those above and below may therefore be a little looser. Consequently, you should never force any movement of the spine or you may cause damage to the already looser joints. You might also damage the fine discs of cartilage lying between every spinal joint.

The diagram opposite indicates where each type of movement is possible to show which areas to concentrate on for voluntary movement, thereby avoiding those which put strain on the joints and connecting ligaments and can cause pain. For instance, if you wish to bend sideways, concentrate on bending at the waist (low back) area, not the chest. If you want to encourage rotation, then concentrate on turning the chest (upper back) around, not the low back, where it is impossible due to the formation of the bones.

You can create your own body movements to suit you, to be performed sitting or standing; remember it is normal to associate arm or leg movements with spinal ones.

As you twist, turn and rotate your trunk, clap your hands at the same time. You may think this sounds silly, but people of all ages enjoy clapping their hands: just try it with any group and immediately everyone starts smiling. Smiling is the best beauty exercise for the muscles of the face, so don't despise it. In any case, activity should be pleasurable, not a chore to be got through, and it should never, never cause any pain. If anything hurts, stop at once, and later try repeating the movement more gently.

Low back pain

This common condition can be caused by stress, bad posture, accident, or spinal irregularities of bones and ligaments. It is therefore essential to have medical advice, and to carry out the treatment ordered. This will probably be advised by a physiotherapist, including relaxation and movement.

Remember the normal movement of the spinal column I have indicated; always move gently, do not force any movement more than is comfortable, and never cause pain.

POSTURE

One way to help avoid back pain is to be aware of the importance of good posture. Good posture means every part of

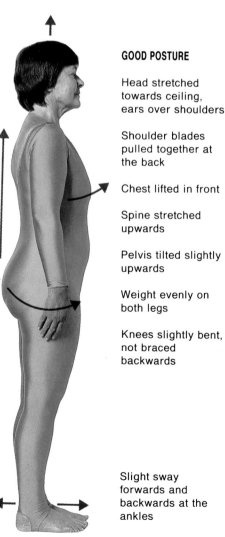

GOOD POSTURE

Head stretched towards ceiling, ears over shoulders

Shoulder blades pulled together at the back

Chest lifted in front

Spine stretched upwards

Pelvis tilted slightly upwards

Weight evenly on both legs

Knees slightly bent, not braced backwards

Slight sway forwards and backwards at the ankles

EXAMPLE OF MOVEMENT FOR RELIEF OF BACK PAIN

- Lie on your side with knees bent up and a pillow under your head
- Gently roll your pelvis forwards and backwards, at the same time flexing your lower spine comfortably. DO NOT FORCE.
- Graduate the length of time as your body dictates.
- Roll on to your other side if you wish, and repeat. This manoeuvre often gives relief when getting into bed at night and may reduce muscle spasm.

147

the body is in the best position for it to function well, whether standing or sitting. Making good posture a habit as early as possible prevents trouble and even deformity developing later on. Try to cultivate the habit of correcting the way you stand and sit frequently. Tiny adjustments are best. The diagram shows exactly how each part of the body should be positioned and indicates how each is dependent on the other.

REST AND RELAXATION

Rest from activity is a normal part of the cycle of life for all living things, from trees to human beings. Did you realize that if you lived for 100 years, your heart would have stopped working for over 50 of those years? The heart beats about 72 times every minute, varying of course with age and what you may be doing. In every heart-beat, there is approximately 0.3 of a second work, and 0.5 of a second rest – we may therefore agree that rest is a natural activity!

There are many schools of thought on how to relax the whole body fully. On page 162 you will find a description of my own method – the Mitchell Method

of Physiological Relaxation, so called because it is based entirely on the physiological rules which govern the working and relaxing of the muscles. This method has been in use since 1957. I was asked by the World Confederation for Physical Therapy to demonstrate it at their International Congress in Copenhagen in 1963; it is now used all over the world, and is described briefly here. (For a full explanation, see *Simple Relaxation* by Laura Mitchell, published by John Murray, second edition 1987.)

From stress to ease
During stress the body adopts a certain posture: hands clenched, arms across the body, head and body bent forward, breathing either held, or high, short breaths. If sitting, the legs are crossed and the top foot bends upwards; if standing, the person tends to walk about. This position tends to emphasize the dangerous cycle of increased heart-beat and blood pressure. Less blood circulates in the abdomen, causing loss of activity in the food canal, kidneys, liver and other organs, the skin becomes blanched and sweating increases.

To change this stressed condition to one of ease, you have to give yourself positive orders to make small movements. The way to appreciate your new condition is to feel the positions of your joints and the pressures on your skin. Only these are registered in the brain, not muscle tension.

The orders in the Mitchell Method are selected to obtain relaxation in the opposite group of muscles from the ones which are tensed. All groups of muscles work reciprocally – that is, if one group works, the opposite group must relax. However, the muscles do not understand the word 'relax', so do not use it: say 'stop' instead. This will lead to reciprocal relaxation in the muscles holding the stressed position.

Right: The typical posture indicating stress involves tensed muscles, hunched shoulders which encourage shallow, rapid breathing, fingers gripping tight and teeth clenched.

MOVEMENTS FOR IMPROVED WELL-BEING

These beautiful pictures demonstrate exactly the movements I would like you to perform. We have put the models in very simple outfits so that the movements can be easily seen. I hope you will follow them at any time, at any place, dressed as you happen to be. And of course, they are all equally suitable for both men and women. I hope you enjoy feeling your bodies become more mobile and active. You may like to sing a tune to help reinforce the rhythm of your movements.

Improving your breathing

When doing this exercise, only take two deep breaths at any time. As you are resting, you will not be making carbon dioxide in your muscle cells; as the need for breathing depends on the amount of carbon dioxide in your blood, you may upset the breathing centres in your brain if you carry on breathing deeply when it is not required and it could make you feel dizzy. If you do feel faint, *stop at once* and do some quick arm movements. If you find you tend to hold your breath, immediately breathe out. You will always breathe in again, and thus restore the normal cycle.

Once you have learned it, you may do deep breathing every hour, in any position you like, while walking about or doing other exercises. (See also page 144.)

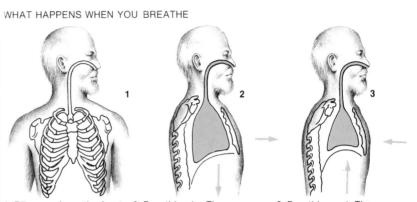

WHAT HAPPENS WHEN YOU BREATHE

1 Rib cage from the front

2 Breathing in. The diaphragm descends, the ribs swing out to the sides and the breast bone is pushed forward.

3 Breathing out. The diaphragm ascends, the ribs and the breast bone fall inwards and the air is pushed out of the lungs.

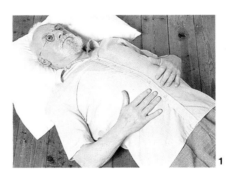

1 Lie on the floor or bed with a pillow under your head, or sit with your back and head well supported. Place your hands loosely on the upper part of your abdomen so that the fingertips meet each other.

2 Breathe in gently through your nose and let the upper part of your abdomen expand forward under your hands. Go on breathing in and encourage your ribs to move outwards and upwards on either side towards

your armpits. Continue breathing in and feel the air behind your nose. Stay like this for a moment, and then gently start breathing out through your nose and feel your ribs fall down again and your tummy get smaller. When all the air has come out, wait a moment and then repeat the process.

Exercising the face

The muscles in your face and neck should be exercised daily if you want to help delay those wrinkles we all abhor. Wrinkles form in the skin at 90 degrees to the pull of the underlying muscles, so we find they are horizontal in the brow and around the eyes (commonly called 'crow's feet'), and vertical on both lips. If we use the muscles attached to the the skin just under these wrinkles, we stretch out the wrinkles and, by thus strengthening the muscles that support the skin, we discourage the wrinkles from forming.

As you work through the face movements that follow, you may like to use a hand-mirror to watch and enjoy your own performance. One other face movement not shown here is the best of all – smiling. And it cheers the spirits too.

1 Brace the neck muscles, pushing the chin forward at the same time. Repeat twice.

2 Lift the right side of your mouth towards your right ear, then slacken it. Repeat twice.

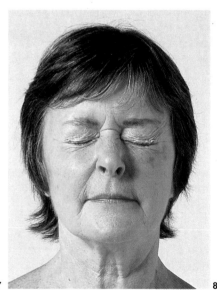

6 Raise the right side of your nose towards your right eye, then slacken it. Repeat twice.

7 Raise the left side of your nose towards your left eye, then slacken it. Repeat twice.

8 Squeeze the eyes tightly shut. Repeat twice.

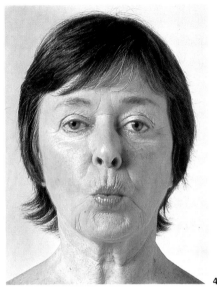

3 Lift the left side of your mouth towards your left ear, then slacken it. Repeat twice.

4 Purse your lips and push them as far forwards as possible. Repeat twice.

5 Draw your lips backwards as far as possible, keeping the lips touching. Repeat twice.

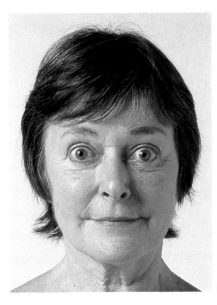

9 Open your eyes as widely as possible. Repeat twice.

10 Draw your eyebrows together. Repeat twice.

11 Relax your eyebrows and smooth your brow. Repeat the movement twice.

Exercising your hands

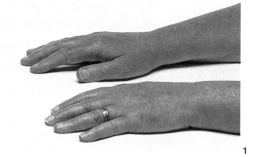

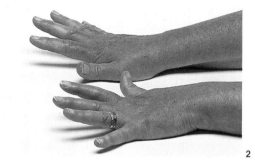

1 Place your hands in front of you, palms down, on your thighs or on a table.

2 Lift your fingers and thumbs upwards, opening them as widely as possible as you do so, and keeping your forearms flat. Drop your fingers and thumbs back on to the support.

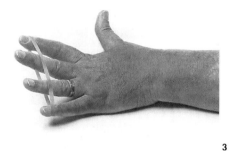

3 To give resistance to the muscles which open out the hand, you can do the same exercise with an elastic band around your fingers and thumbs.

4 A good exercise to strengthen all hand muscles is to throw a small, coarse towel on to the table, and gather it up by grasping it into a ball.

Washing small articles in warm water and then pegging them out to dry above your head is excellent work for the hands, and is also a satisfying job to do.

5 Spread the towel out again. Repeat as often as you wish.

Exercising your arms

1 Tuck your elbows into your sides (1a). Twist your wrists in all directions (1b & c).

2 Then turn your palms upwards (2a) and downwards (2b) very fast. (This movement takes place in the forearm. To keep the muscles there very strong, try wringing out your face flannel in alternate directions.)

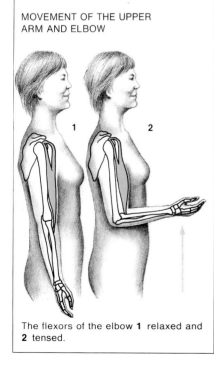

MOVEMENT OF THE UPPER ARM AND ELBOW

The flexors of the elbow **1** relaxed and **2** tensed.

3 Now bend your elbows so that your hands touch your shoulders (3a), then straighten them out again fully (3b). To give extra resistance, hold a heavy object in each hand.

Exercising your arms and shoulders

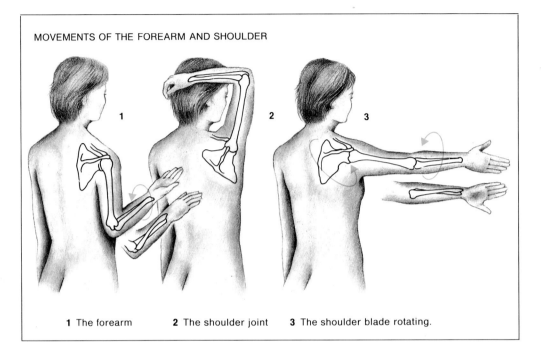

MOVEMENTS OF THE FOREARM AND SHOULDER

1 The forearm   **2** The shoulder joint   **3** The shoulder blade rotating.

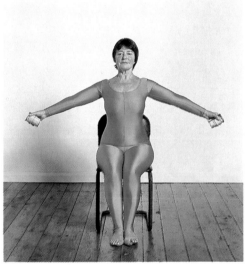

1 Sit on a chair and lift your arms up sideways till the sides of your arms touch your ears. In order to keep all the muscles strong, you could hold something heavy in each hand.

2 Slowly lower your arms sideways.

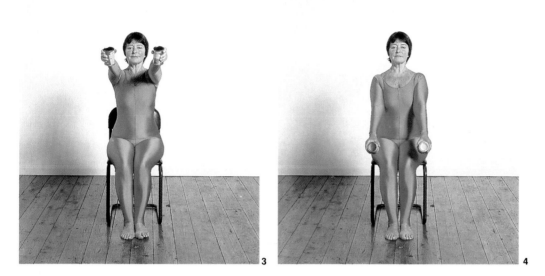

3 Now lift your arms up forwards till they touch your ears.

4 Lower them back slowly to your sides.

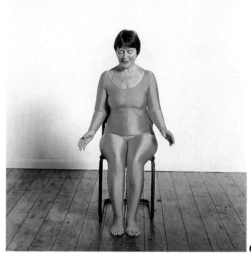

5 If you have been using weights, put them away. Repeat the sideways raise, clapping your hands above your head twice.

6 Lower your hands and slap your thighs twice. Sing as you raise and lower your hands, and make your head follow the direction of your hands.

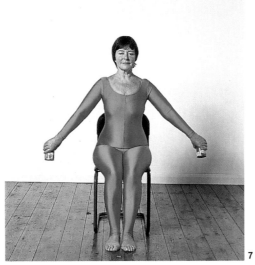

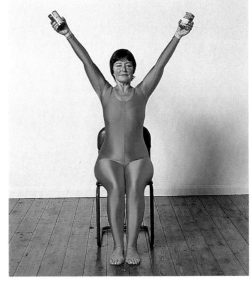

7 Take up your weights again (if using), and slowly raise your arms sideways as in the first exercise, twisting your arms inwards and outwards as you do so.

8 Slowly lower your arms in the same way, twisting them as you lower them. This rotation of the shoulder joints is essential for full use of the hands and arms. They are often allowed to become stiff, so that tasks like putting arms into a coat become difficult.

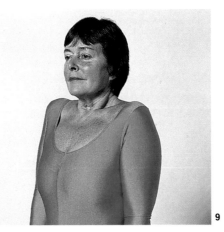

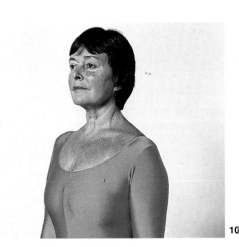

9 Finally, stand with your arms drooping by your sides (put aside your weights if using them). Raise your shoulders (i.e. shoulder girdles, collar bone and shoulder blades) up as high as you can.

10 Push them downwards strongly.

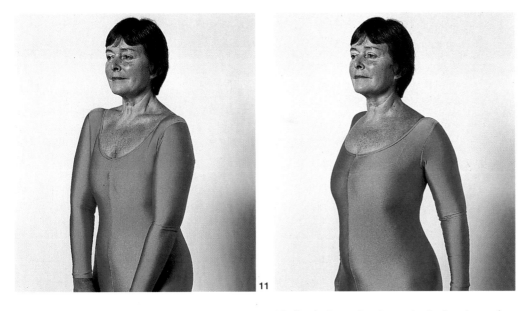

11 Bring the shoulders forwards.

12 Push them backwards, trying to make your shoulder blades come closely together at the back. Repeat.

13 You may like to finish by whirling your arms loosely in circles in any direction you wish, singing as you do so. If this makes you breathless, all the better. Sit and recover with a long breath. (Experts tell us we should do an activity that makes us breathless – but not so breathless we can't speak – at least once a day.)

Exercising your legs

1 Stand on one foot, with your arms at your sides to begin with. Then increase the work you have to do by raising your arms to shoulder level, as above.

2 Increase the work still further by raising your arms above your head.

3 Finally, stand on tiptoe with your arms above your head. Count or sing as you go through the exercise. Repeat with the other leg.

Heel raising and knee bending

1 Hold on to a strong support when you first do this exercise. You can try it freestanding when you feel stronger.

2 Keeping your body and head upright, raise yourself up on to your toes, then bend your knees to lower yourself as far as you feel safe. You must not fall over, so don't bend any further than you can comfortably manage.

3 Still standing on your toes, stretch your knees to straighten your legs, then lower your heels to the floor. Increase the exercise by counting the number of times you bend your knees and the depth of bending. Vary it by having your knees facing forwards or turned outwards while bending.

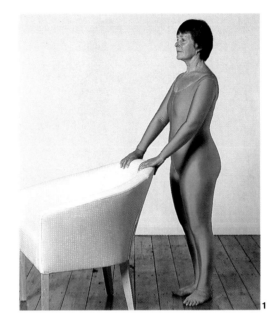

Leg swinging

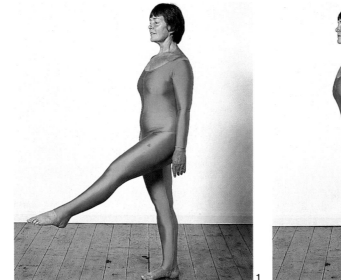

1 Stand on one leg and swing your other leg backwards and forwards. Be sure you keep your body and head absolutely upright. Do as you wish with your arms.

2 Hold the swinging leg motionless in front and then behind for as long as you find possible. Count and then resume swinging. Change to standing on your other leg and repeat.

3 Repeat the exercise while swinging your arms.

4 Repeat again holding your arms motionless as before, in any position you wish.

Body movements

1 Fling your arms wide, and standing with legs comfortably apart.

2 Raise one knee. Bend towards it with your head and arms, as far down as is comfortable. Return to starting position. Raise other knee and aim towards it with head and arms.

You can add arching your spine and throwing your head and arms backwards in between each forward bending. This sequence is very pleasant if you breathe in on the backward movement, and breathe out on the forward one. Repeat as you wish.

3 Another body movement which does not involve balancing on one leg is to clap your hands above your head as you turn your body to face the opposite wall.

4 Turn to face forwards and bring your arms down to clap the sides of your thighs. Repeat 3 and 4 as often as wished alternating the direction you turn when clapping above your head.

The Mitchell Method of Relaxation

The easiest position in which to enjoy this method is lying flat in bed or on the floor, with one pillow under your head, but the orders will work in any position you care to adopt – sitting, leaning backwards or forwards, etc. You should not try to change the 'self orders' in any way. You may change the sequence when you have learned the method, but never the words, which have been carefully selected to obtain the desired result. (See also page 148.)

List of self orders

ARMS
1. Shoulders
Order: Pull your shoulders towards your feet. STOP.
Result: Feel your shoulders are further away from your ears. Your neck may feel longer.

2. Elbows
Order: Keep your elbows on the support and push them outwards. Open your elbows. STOP.
Result: Feel how your upper arms are away from your body and feel the wide angle at your elbows. The weight of both arms should be resting on the floor, chair arms or pillow.

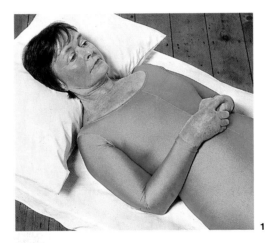

1

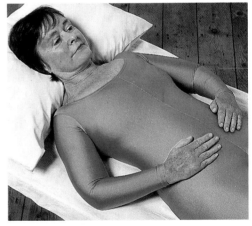

2

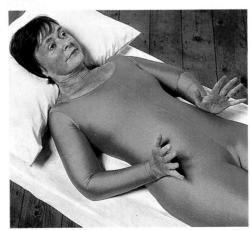

3

3. Hands
Order: Fingers and thumbs long and stretched out from your wrists. STOP. Your fingers fall back on to the support.
Result: Feel your fingers and thumbs stretched out, separated, and touching the support, with the nails on top. In particular, feel how heavy your thumbs are.

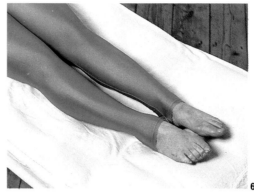

LEGS

4. Hips
Order: Turn your hips outwards. STOP.
Result: Feel your thighs rolled outwards, with the kneecaps facing outwards.

5. Knees
Order: Move slightly until comfortable if you wish. STOP.
Result: Feel the resulting comfort in your knees.

6. Feet
Order: Push your feet away from your face, bending at the ankle. STOP.
Result: Feel your dangling, heavy feet.

7. BODY
Order: Push your body into the support. STOP.
Result: Feel the contact of your body on the support.

8. HEAD
Order: Push your head into the support. STOP.

Result: Feel the pressure of your head on the pillow.

9. BREATHING
Breathe gently in, moving your tummy forwards and your ribs sideways. Breathe out gently and they will fall back. Repeat only once.
(See also page 149.)

Relaxation method continued

FACE

10. Jaw
Order: Drag your jaw downwards. STOP.
Result: Feel your separated teeth, heavy jaw, and soft lips gently touching each other.

11. Tongue
Order: Press your tongue downwards in your mouth. STOP.
Result: Feel your loose tongue touching your lower teeth.

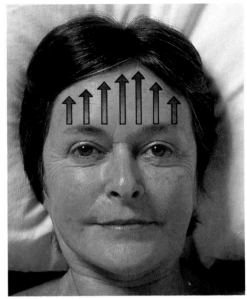

13

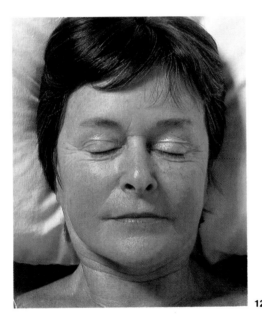

12

12. Eyes
Order: Close your eyes. STOP.
Result: Feel your upper lids resting gently over your eyes, without any screwing up around the eyes. Enjoy the darkness.

13. Forehead
Order: Begin above eyebrows and think of smoothing gently up into your hair, over the top of your head and down the back of your neck. STOP.
Result: Feel your hair move up in the same direction.

14. MIND
Order: Repeat the above sequence around the body, possibly more quickly
or
Choose some subject which you will enjoy thinking about and which has a sequence (such as a song, prayer, poem, or multiplication table)
or
Relive some past personal happy occasion. Let the mind play over these thoughts effortlessly, just to keep it occupied.

Return to full activity

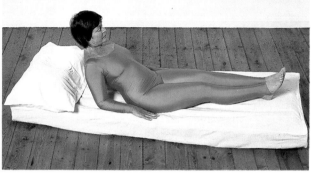

1 Stretch limbs and body in all directions and yawn. Do not hurry.

2 Raise yourself up slowly, leaning on your lower arms.

3 Sit up with knees gently flexed.

4 Tuck your legs beneath you.

5 Lean forward into a kneeling position, resting your weight evenly on your hands and knees.

6 Extend one leg, and wait for a minute or two before standing up.

THE CARERS' GUIDE

It is an unfortunate fact that advancing years can bring with them increased frailty and a variety of uncomfortable conditions. Disablement poses problems at any age, although most people face life stoically and with amazing good humour. However, it is not surprising that an older person who has been fit and healthy for most of his or her life may find the restrictions of age cause worry, frustration and guilt. Most people want to be independent – to look after themselves as long as possible and not to be a 'burden' on their family and friends. Yet many find themselves obliged to a greater or lesser extent to accept the help of someone else in carrying out the normal tasks of everyday life. It is the person who helps who has become known in recent years as a carer.

The word 'carer' is a fairly new one in our language. It has been in use for less than 10 years, and then mainly by certain sections of the community, such as social workers, health workers and social researchers. The media too have recently caught on to the word and many television and radio programmes and magazine articles now feature items about carers. However, the word is still not readily understood by the world at large, and most significantly carers themselves often do not recognize the word, or apply it to themselves. The woman who is looking after a disabled child or the man caring for his housebound wife does not think 'Oh, I'm a carer' – they merely think, 'I'm a mother', or 'I'm a husband'.

WHAT IS A CARER?
So what is a carer? A carer is someone whose life is restricted to an extent by the need to look after someone else whose physical or mental condition means he or she is unable to manage alone. This usually, but not necessarily, means living with the cared-for person. For instance, a daughter who is not actually living in the same house as her mother but who is nonetheless spending a great deal of time ensuring that she is all right is just as much a carer as one who is actually living in the same house. Caring does not necessarily stop when the cared-for person enters residential care, either, and many carers also try to hold down a full or part-time job at the same time.

THE CHANGING ROLE OF CARERS
The word 'carer' may be a fairly new one in our vocabulary but the activity is certainly not new. Caring has been going on since the dawn of time, but two things have undoubtedly brought it into more prominence in recent years. The first of these is the rapidly increasing number of older people in society. While many elderly people do live full and active lives and, indeed, many of them are carers themselves, inevitably some of them need looking after and cannot cope on their own without a great deal of support.

Care in the community
The second important factor in bringing carers more into prominence in recent years is the commitment of

All sorts of people find themselves in the role of carer, and many of these are actually in the same age group as the elderly people in need of their care.

successive governments since the 1960s to so-called 'care in the community' policies. The idea that it is better to be cared for in your own home than in any kind of institution is deeply rooted in our national consciousness and owes a great deal no doubt to the fear of the workhouse which was so common in the nineteenth century. A series of reports, published in the 1960s and 1970s, which detailed the atrocious conditions in which some elderly, mentally ill and mentally handicapped people were living fuelled the anti-institution feeling, coupled perhaps with an underlying feeling that community care was somehow cheaper as well as better than institutional care. When professionals first began to talk about 'care in the community' it was never about the community at all, it was only about closing hospital beds. Moreover it was a long time before anyone came to realize that care in the community usually meant care *by* the community and that the community often meant the family, and usually the responsibility falls on one particular member of the family.

No one knows how many carers there are. The official figure is 1.3 million but recent research indicates that there are more likely to be 3 million. Because carers do not readily identify themselves as such and because the very role isolates people, it is difficult to arrive at an accurate figure. It is certain though that more women are looking after an elderly relative at home than are engaged in caring for children, and that women between the ages of 30 and 45 stand a one in three chance of becoming a carer. It is interesting to think how much money is being saved for us all by the work of these carers. According to figures published by the Family Policy Studies Centre in 1985, if we take the estimate of 1.3 million carers, reckon that they are caring for between 25 and 36 hours weekly (a very low estimate, since many carers are on duty 24 hours a day) and cost out their time as if you were paying them like a home help, the cost to the national Exchequer would be between £5.1 and £7.3 billion per year!

BECOMING A CARER

Caring always takes place within the context of a relationship – that is one of the few facts that we state with certainty. The relationship may be of various kinds – a relative, a friend, a marriage partner, a neighbour – but it is clear that some relationships carry with them an expectation of caring. Much caring arises out of love: a wife or husband naturally wants to make an ailing spouse's life more comfortable; a son or daughter hates the idea of a beloved parent having to go into a home so takes over caring to maintain a degree of independence. However, it is also true that society as a whole expects certain relationships to involve caring where necessary. First, spouses are expected to care for each other when they become ill or disabled. This seems to apply even in great old age – it is not unknown for a 91-year-old woman to care for her husband of 101, and for a man of 98 to be the sole carer for his 87-year-old wife. Second, daughters are expected to care for parents, whereas sons are usually, though not always, expected to see that care is provided rather than to provide it themselves; hence many daughters-in-law find themselves carers for a parent-in-law.

These 'rules' are not some code of practice which could be found written down anywhere, but they are the expectations which people have very deeply entrenched in their minds and which are always mentioned when carers talk about why they took on the task of caring: 'It's my duty isn't it? I married him for better or for worse.' 'You can't let your mother go into a home can you?' 'There is only me to do it and I'll carry on as long as there's breath in my body.'

The moral obligation which people feel to look after their disabled and elderly relatives is very strong indeed. People care out of love, or out of a sense of moral duty or because they know they would feel guilty if they didn't. They may also be influenced by pressures which are brought to bear on them by, say, a hospital consultant, as this caring daughter describes:

'There was no question of anyone asking me if I wanted to be a carer, they just called me in when I was visiting her on the ward after her stroke and the doctor said that she was ready for discharge and what arrangements would I be making to fetch her. It was all so sudden I didn't have time to think and anyway I wouldn't have let her go to a home.'

It is perhaps more common than it once was to hear carers say that they have been asked if they would take on the task, but the experience of this daughter is still all too frequent.

People may also become carers because of the lack of any reasonable alternative. As already mentioned, policies of caring in the community have meant that less residential care is available except for those who can afford to pay for it. Very often too there is no particular moment when the decision to become a carer is taken – it doesn't happen suddenly as in the case of a spouse having a stroke, but creeps up on the carer by the very gradual decline in the cared-for person. So the carer's life becomes gradually more restricted, the tasks which she performs become more heavy and before she knows it she is unable to change the situation.

Not that carers usually want to give up caring. On the whole they continue because they love the person for whom they are caring or because they feel a duty to do so and don't want to stop. What they *do* want is help to care most effectively, to do so with less strain and to be able to take advantage of support which may be available. This short carers' guide is about pointing carers in the direction of that help and to alert them to the problems they may face. As a society we don't plan for caring, although most of us will find ourselves caring for someone at some time in our lives. Perhaps this is just because we don't want to bring ourselves to face a prospect we find scaring or distressing but prefer to bury our heads in the sand and hope it won't happen.

This attitude is equally true for the cared-for person. Anybody who has lived independently finds it difficult to admit to the small inconveniences and slip-ups which indicate that life is becoming more difficult to manage without help. Bottling up worries about failing health and the amount someone else is having to do on your behalf can be very stressful. It is therefore only too easy to drift into a rather unsatisfactory situation which can sour a relationship, whereas if at all possible it is better to think about caring as a partnership and to try to talk about the problems in the relationship before they become overpowering. Both parties can feel very isolated when in fact there is help both for the cared-for and the carer; the sections on practical help given later ▶ indicate some of the options.

PROBLEMS THAT CARERS FACE

Caring can be a rewarding experience; there can be joy in it and even fun. It is important to say this because inevitably in a guide of this kind we have to focus a good deal on problems and how to solve them. In addition, it is not only carers who face problems. The needs of the carer and those of the cared-for person are inextricably entwined and it is impossible to consider one without the other. For cared-for people, there are inevitably conflicts in setting the need for independence against growing physical disability, the desire to be cared for at home with the guilt possibly felt at being a burden, even when the carer, in fact, is quite happy to be of help. As one cared-for person wrote:

'I've been a carer myself, but now I am an unfortunate "caree". I hear so much about the difficulties which carers face that it makes me feel really guilty. I try so hard to be understanding and considerate. I know I am a burden but I hope I don't make my daughter unhappy.'

If carer and cared-for can acknowledge and discuss their situation and its problems, they will have taken an important step towards solving them.

The problems which carers undoubtedly have to face generally fall into at least one of three categories – financial, practical or emotional.

Financial problems

Caring costs money, there is no doubt about it, even though the cared-for person will be contributing from his or her own income. If you are looking after an elderly person, you have to pay for extra heating costs, perhaps for special food or incontinence aids such as pads and sheets. You may need to have special adaptations to an existing home or you may have to move house altogether. Carers may have to give up paid employment in order to become carers, they may have to give up the option

THE MILK ROUNDSMAN'S CARE CODE

▶ Check if milk is left on the doorstep for more than one day. Someone may need help.

▶ Contact the neighbours if in doubt. Early concern could save a life.

▶ Call for help – and do what you can meantime.

SEE ALSO: ◀

THE CARERS' GUIDE:
Practical help   p. 173

The local milk roundsman can be very reassuring to older carers, in terms of both personal contact and also to keeping an eye for signs of trouble.

perhaps of part-time work when they have retired. They may well have to pay for a substitute carer to take over occasionally while they take a break, or for residential care for the cared-for person while they have a holiday. They may find themselves keeping on a larger house than they had anticipated in order to make room for an extra person and they often find it necessary to keep running a car after they would ordinarily have given up doing so in order to take the person for whom they are caring to hospital appointments or for the occasional outing. No independent income is available to older carers to meet these costs, though carers under retirement age receive a small allowance. In the next section we shall look at what benefits are available to carers even though many carers resist asking about benefits or making any requests for help. If you became a carer, try to take advantage of these benefits; ideas about 'taking charity' or 'looking after your own' die hard, but you may

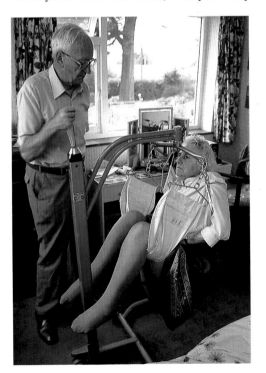

Caring for a severely disabled person who has perhaps been immobilized by a stroke can be a great physical burden to any carer, particularly if he or she is an older person as well. Mechanical aids to lifting such as this one can help in certain situations and your local social services department can help you obtain any available equipment.

be making your task unnecessarily difficult if you do not claim what is legally yours.

Practical problems

If you have absolutely no training or experience, how would you go about feeding, dressing, changing, bathing an immobile, heavy, helpless person with whom you can barely communicate? Most of us would find it difficult if not impossible and yet this is what many carers are expected to do. Training for carers is at best minimal and more usually non-existent. There seems to be an assumption, particularly where female carers are concerned, that if you love someone and have lived with them for a long time then somehow or another, you know how to cope with their incontinence, to get them in and out of the bath and even how to administer their drugs. The reality is of course that carers do not know instinctively how to do these things but that most manage to learn by trial and error.

Apart from the actual physical care of the person they are looking after, one of the other problems which carers face is how to leave the cared-for person for any time, how to get a break. Most people in paid employment expect to have weekends off and a holiday at least once a year. Carers cannot automatically expect this. But that does not mean that they need breaks less. On the contrary, for many carers a little time off now and then is what makes it possible for them to continue. But taking any time off may be difficult. For a start, a break for the carer depends on the cared-for person being willing to accept an alternative form of care or a different person caring for them. At first they may not be happy about doing this, even for a very short time, but do not assume this. If you have not actually asked the person you are looking after whether he or she would mind being looked after

Moving a bedridden person safely

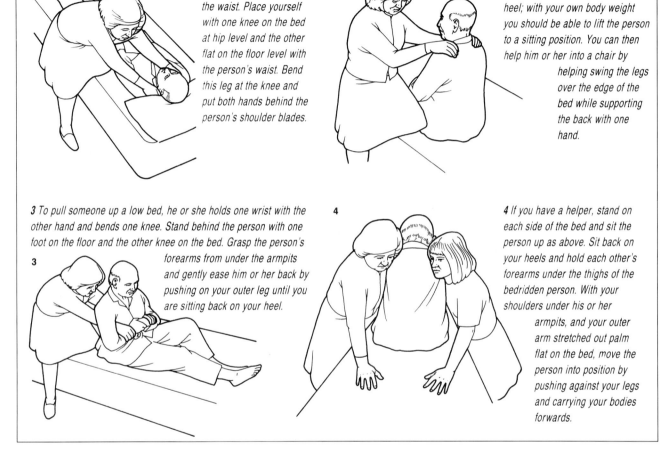

1 *To help someone sit up in bed, his or her arms should be folded across the waist. Place yourself with one knee on the bed at hip level and the other flat on the floor level with the person's waist. Bend this leg at the knee and put both hands behind the person's shoulder blades.*

2 *Keeping your arms in position behind the shoulder blades, lean back so that you are sitting on your heel; with your own body weight you should be able to lift the person to a sitting position. You can then help him or her into a chair by helping swing the legs over the edge of the bed while supporting the back with one hand.*

3 *To pull someone up a low bed, he or she holds one wrist with the other hand and bends one knee. Stand behind the person with one foot on the floor and the other knee on the bed. Grasp the person's forearms from under the armpits and gently ease him or her back by pushing on your outer leg until you are sitting back on your heel.*

4 *If you have a helper, stand on each side of the bed and sit the person up as above. Sit back on your heels and hold each other's forearms under the thighs of the bedridden person. With your shoulders under his or her armpits, and your outer arm stretched out palm flat on the bed, move the person into position by pushing against your legs and carrying your bodies forwards.*

for a while by someone else you cannot know for sure whether there will be any objection. For an elderly person who feels tremendous guilt about the position of his or her carer, the idea of allowing a break – or 'respite care' as it is known – may well be a tremendous relief. It is all too easy in such a potentially isolating situation for a carer to feel she is indispensable. It is important to accept a break if it is offered; many carers find this difficult because they have guilt feelings about even thinking of asking for anything for themselves,

even when they are physically ill.

Of course, the break must be available to the carer at the time it is needed. If at all possible plan ahead through the agencies for help listed later, ▶ rather than finding that you are being offered a hospital place at the end of the month after next, when you are at the end of your tether today. And the respite care must be appropriate for the needs of the cared-for person; again this should, if possible, be discussed with the person concerned so his or her views are taken into account.

SEE ALSO: ◀

THE CARERS' GUIDE:
Health services   p. 174

**LOOKING AFTER
YOURSELF AS A CARER**

If you are a carer, your
own well-being is just as
important as that of the
person in your care —
you cannot do the job
properly if you are run
down or depressed. Don't
be shy about talking to
professionals like the
family doctor, health
visitor or social worker
about your own health or
feelings, even if they do
not ask about you
directly. They will not
think you are
complaining.

Emotional problems

Many carers feel that the emotional stress which they suffer is by far the worst aspect of their situation:

'I've learned to lift him and I've learned to change him and I've even learned a little bit how to fight the system to get the help I need, but what I've not learned is how to cope with the emotions, how to cope with the isolation and most of all how to cope with the guilt I feel for having those feelings in the first place.'

Guilt is perhaps the most common feeling which carers have to cope with and perhaps the most difficult. Somehow, whatever they do, they don't feel it is enough. But there are other difficult emotions.

Isolation Friends call less frequently and outings are often out of the question. Carers cannot get to the pub or the cinema or the church and they probably find that even family members come round less often. People who do not understand what the burden of caring can be like find it hard to be tolerant of someone whose life has become much less interesting and who finds it difficult to talk about anything outside the home.

Anger Carers can direct this at the situation which confines them, at the person they are looking after or at the services which do not help them. They may feel so angry towards the dependent person that they want to harm them physically. This type of anger is likely to be followed by even more guilty feelings that they could possibly have been angry with someone who can't help being helpless.

Embarrassment The behaviour of some elderly dependent people is antisocial and unconventional, which may embarrass the carer. Incontinence too can be a problem, and one that is difficult for other members of the family to accept. A teenager, for example, is likely to be acutely embarrassed if his elderly grandparent is incontinent or shows bizarre behaviour.

Sense of loss One of the most difficult problems for a carer to come to terms with is the sense of loss they feel for the relationship they once had for the cared-for person. This may especially be the case where the infirmity causes a personality change, such as that which comes over someone with Parkinson's Disease or with Alzheimer's Disease. The carer may mourn the loss of the person they once knew and for the relationship they once enjoyed.

All these problems can be alleviated to some degree as the next section shows. The most important thing is for carers to recognize that they are common problems and not confined to their particular situation.

Emotional support

No one can take away the pain and suffering which caring sometimes brings but there are some things which can help:

'When a new doctor came to the house, instead of just ignoring me like the other one had done for years, he turned to me as soon as he was through the door, before we even went in to see my husband, and said 'Now how about you? You are the most important one here, you know.' I felt ten feet tall and somehow I can cope better knowing that at least someone understands how I'm feeling'.

Support from professionals is very important but carers often feel diffident about mentioning their own needs, fearing that the professionals are too busy or will think they are complaining. For their part the professional may not think to ask the carer how she is feeling, not for any malicious reason but simply that all their training has been focused on the ill person, the client or the sufferer. They may not have been

---

HELP FOR CARERS: 1

If you identify yourself as a carer, think carefully about the practical help you need; it really is important not to think of it as 'charity', 'hand-outs' or 'do-gooding'. On the contrary, as a carer you deserve all the help available.

FINANCIAL HELP

There are three main state benefits which help carers. ▶ Carers have a *right* to benefits and there is no need for them to feel guilty or apologetic about asking for them.

Attendance allowance Anyone who is severely disabled either physically or mentally and has needed the attention of another person by day or night or both for at least six months can claim this. Attendance allowance can be paid to anyone regardless of age or income. It is not means-tested and not taxed. There are two rates:

- Higher Rate – for someone who needs attention or supervision by day *and* night.
- Lower Rate – if attention or supervision is needed by day *or* night.

Mobility allowance This can be claimed by anyone between 5 and 66 who is unable or 'virtually unable' to walk. It is not means-tested but stops at age 75.

Invalid care allowance Since June 1986 this has been payable to men or women (single, married or co-habiting) who have given up work to care for a person who is receiving attendance allowance.

PRACTICAL HELP

It is important to remember that most services are provided on a local basis and will vary from area to area, so the following can only be a guide – there may be more services available in your area, there may be fewer. But don't forget the Disabled Persons Act of 1986. According to this act, if a disabled person or his or her carer asks a local authority (or council) to assess his or her needs, that local authority has a duty to do so. The assessment must include the person's need for help in the home, recreational facilities both in and outside the home, assistance with transport to such facilities, aids and adaptations, holidays, meals and telephones. When the local authority makes this assessment, the ability of the carer to continue to provide care on a regular basis must be taken into account.

SEE ALSO: ◀

MANAGING YOUR MONEY: Help from the state p. 32

---

trained to see the needs of the carer but once they are aware of them it may be that they can help more, or at least offer the most important thing, a sympathetic understanding ear.

Professionals often need to be reassured too. They may be afraid to ask the carer how she or he is feeling for fear that the carer will say she is unable to cope any more. At a time of very scarce resources and cuts in public expenditure, the professionals may fear raising hopes and expectations that they will be unable to meet. They often need to be reassured that what the carer may need above all is the knowledge that someone recognizes the value of what they are doing.

HELP FOR CARERS: 2

Because the need for caring is almost always associated with health problems, there are several sources of medical help for the carer as well as the cared-for person both within the community and hospital-based.

HEALTH SERVICES

AT HOME:

Family doctor (GP) – The doctor is often a link to many other services as well as the person you first contact when you are caring. It is important that you feel you can ask your doctor for help, tell him or her how you are feeling and talk about any difficulties you may be having.

District nurse – The family doctor usually arranges for the nurse to visit. The district nurses will attend to dressings, injections, bathing and so on and can give advice on all nursing problems. They can also provide aids such as commodes, urinals and incontinence pads.

Health visitor – They can advise on any health problems you may be having.

Community psychiatric nurse (CPN) – These nurses will provide care for mentally ill patients at home and also support their families.

Chiropodist: – These specialize in foot problems and can sometimes call at your home. Your family doctor can arrange for an appointment. ◀

IN HOSPITAL:

Consultant geriatrician – The geriatrician specializes in care of the elderly and if your dependents go into hospital they will be supervised by the geriatrician to whom they have been referred by the family doctor. If they have any mental problems such as dementia, a psycho-geriatrician will be involved.

Occupational therapist (OT) – The OT's job is to help an elderly or disabled person to cope with disabilities and help him or her manage daily tasks such as dressing or cooking.

Physiotherapist (Physio) – The physiotherapist helps patients to become more mobile through exercise and may also be able to advise carers about lifting etc.

Hospital social worker – These people can advise you about any practical or emotional problems connected with admission or discharge from hospital and can also put you in touch with community services.

Respite care – Some Health Authorities can arrange short-term admission to hospital for the cared-for to give carers a break.

Problems with Health Services – If you have any difficulties with any aspect of the Health Service, contact your local Community Health Council (CHC) whose address is in the phone book.

SEE ALSO: ▷

GOOD HEALTH:

Foot care   p. 108

Someone to talk to

Some carers *may* need considerably more emotional support than a simple recognition of their contribution. *Counselling* can help by providing an understanding person to talk things over with. It can help the carer see things a bit more clearly, to understand her own feelings, to come to terms with how she is feeling and be better able to cope. Carers can usually find a counsellor in their area although they will almost always have to pay for the service.

For most carers, their most important support comes from members of their families, but many find that their families are unable to help in this situation, either because they withdraw and do not wish to be involved or because the carer feels unable to discuss her true feelings with them. *Carers' groups* can be a very helpful form of support. Many carers find they share the same sort of problems, worries and fears and that it is a great help to be able to talk things over and to be open about their difficulties with a group of people who are in similar situations:

'Of course it doesn't solve your problems, but just to know there are others who are having problems is such a comfort. And it isn't all gloom you know, we swap "ideas" and have a bit of a laugh. I really look forward to it'.

Some carers' groups are organized by social services departments, others are attached to health centres or organized by voluntary groups such as the Carers' National Association or Age Concern. The groups vary greatly in what they do. Some simply provide a place for carers to share problems; others organize social events or training for carers in skills such as lifting or dealing with incontinence. Still others link activities for the cared-for people or perhaps a sitting service so that the carer can attend the group without worrying. Some carers' groups have a strong cam-

paigning motivation and see themselves as being in the business of changing things for carers. Some do this by mounting local publicity campaigns and by lobbying local councillors and Members of Parliament, whereas others try to become involved in policy-making and planning. For example, carers groups are represented on community health councils, or on joint care planning teams which are planning future services.

It has to be stressed that services and support for carers are patchy and irregular. Information about them is often

Calling on the services of a home hairdresser is a relatively inexpensive way to help raise the self-esteem of a housebound person, and may allow a carer a welcome break.

HELP FOR CARERS: 3

Social service departments (SSDs) are organized on a country-wide or district basis and will be listed under the name of your local authority in the phone book. They are often divided into areas.

SOCIAL SERVICES

Social worker – If you ask for help from a social services department you may be visited by or meet a social worker, who can arrange services and also help with any emotional difficulties you may be having. Some of the services which a social worker may be able to arrange are:

Home help – Because there is a shortage of home helps they tend to be sent to old people who live alone but it is worth asking for a visit from the Home Help Organizer. Home helps do housework and shopping and also often befriend elderly people. Many authorities now provide home care services which substitute for carers.

Meals on Wheels – Hot meals can be provided for those who have difficulty in preparing food.

Day centres – These are places where elderly people who are fairly fit can get lunch, enjoy the company of others and perhaps take part in activities.

Day care centre – Day care centres are for those who need a little more help. The elderly person will be picked up in the morning from home and returned about mid-afternoon.

Short stay care – Residential homes can sometimes offer a place for a couple of weeks so that the carer can go on holiday; arrangements should usually be arranged well in advance.

Residential homes – These are for elderly people who do not need hospital care but can no longer remain at home.

Aids and adaptations – A wide variety of aids to help disabled people is available. Fitments to help turn on taps, hoists and bathing aids can be very useful. Social services departments can also arrange for changes to be made to your house to help you with caring. For example, you might need a ramp or a hand rail installed or a doorway widened to take a wheel chair.

Holidays – Many social services departments can arrange holidays for infirm or disabled people.

Problems with social services – If you have any difficulties with your local SSD, write first to the Director of Social Services or contact your local councillor who will take up the matter.

difficult to come by but can usually be ferreted out if you are persistent. If no services are available at all, carers must start shouting! The Griffiths Review of Community Care published in the Spring of 1988 makes it clear that if community care is to work satisfactorily, then carers must be supported. The Carers' National Association talks about the needs of carers as being for the three Rs: they need Recognition, they need Respite and they need Reward. Once carers become aware of their needs and more importantly, become convinced that those needs are legitimate, they can frequently get some of those needs met, particularly if they know where to go for help. ◄

SEE ALSO: ▶

RESOURCES & BACK-UP:
Carers   p. 201

HELP FOR CARERS: 4

Caring is itself a voluntary act, so it is not surprising that many people volunteer their services to help carers and the cared-for.

VOLUNTARY SERVICES

In each local area there will be a network of voluntary services which can help and support carers and their dependents. Each network will be different and the amount of support available will vary from place to place. There may be a volunteer organizer at the hospital or at the social services department who can direct you to local services. You will certainly be able to contact either a Council of Voluntary Service (CVS) or in more rural areas a Rural Community Council (RCC), who will be in touch with all the local voluntary organizations.

The Citizens Advice Bureau (CAB) or another advice agency will be able to point you in the right direction also and many of the national organizations listed on p. 201 will have local branches. The public library will have a list too and there may be a Volunteer Bureau which put people wanting to do voluntary work in touch with those needing volunteers.

ENDINGS

Caring eventually ends, however long it has gone on for. It may end in the death of the cared-for person or it may end with the carer being unable to continue and deciding that residential care of some kind must now be considered. The decision to seek residential care and to bring to an end the period of being cared for at home can be a difficult one for the carer and cared-for alike. Carers often find it difficult to come to terms with the decision and the guilt they have felt if their situation becomes even more widespread. For the dependent person too, the idea of going into residential care and never coming out again is not easy.

Ideally these situations should be discussed in the home, perhaps with the help of a skilled professional or other person who is not emotionally involved. If residential care for respite periods has been part of the routine for some time, periods in the home can be gradually extended, which makes the transition easier. For many carers though, the change to residential care comes unplanned, brought on by a crisis, either in the health of the carer or by a sudden deterioration in the condition of the cared-for person. The needs of carers do not end when the cared-for person goes into residential care and carers should remember that adjustment takes time.

It takes time also to adjust to the death of the person for whom you have been caring. If you have been looking after someone pretty well full-time for several years, or even just a year, when that person dies, you are in a very real sense bereft. As well as losing a loved one you may also have lost all your friends, all your social contacts and indeed any sense of the way of life you had before you were a carer. Very often too if people do not understand, you will be denied time for mourning since many of the people you meet will say that they expect your bereavement is a 'happy release'. Eventually carers will be able to take up their lives again but it won't happen instantly and will take time and effort on the part of those with whom they are in contact.

AFTER A BEREAVEMENT

One of the most distressing chores after a person dies is sorting out his or her personal belongings.

▶ Don't embark on this task until you really feel up to it, and certainly not until several weeks after the funeral.

▶ Try to avoid doing this job by yourself; enlist the help of a sympathetic friend or relative.

PROBLEMS WITH HEALTH

Problems with health can occur at any age, but it is an unfortunate fact that the older you are, the longer you have had to be exposed to the factors which produce disease. As has already been pointed out in Chapter 6, ageing itself does not affect your state of health directly until you are very elderly. Even so there are many conditions which require medical help and are particularly prevalent among older people or may affect them in a different or more disabling way. In the second part of this chapter, health problems are set out in alphabetical order for convenient reference; firstly, however, it is important to know how to get the best out of the health services on offer.

WORKING WITH YOUR GENERAL PRACTITIONER

Everyone in the United Kingdom is entitled to be registered with a general practitioner but because there are thousands of them their quality obviously varies. Not everyone can be a champion GP. Furthermore, not all doctors practise in the same way. Because of this wide range of types of doctor and expectations of patients it is not surprising that doctors and patients do not always get along with one another in perfect harmony.

You may well have been registered with a GP for a number of years and are probably happy with the service he or she gives. However, many people move at the time of retirement, or for some reason find they are no longer happy with the service they are getting, and may be faced with the task of finding a new doctor. Choosing a new doctor because you have moved is one thing; changing your doctor because you are somehow dissatisfied is quite another and needs careful thought. Working with your doctor means building up trust between you, and having confidence in his or her competence.

Finding a new doctor
It is very hard for the public to judge doctors. The more letters a doctor has after his name does not necessarily indicate that he or she will be a better doctor and the best way to find a trustworthy doctor is to ask around, talking to your friends or neighbours.

Once you have found a new doctor and been accepted and registered as a patient your notes will be transferred. If you are changing doctors because you have moved, the new practice will usually write to your previous doctor and arrange for your notes to be sent on. If you are changing doctors within the same area, yourself you may have to ask for the notes to be sent on.

Building a better partnership
You can trust your doctor but still not feel that you are getting along with him all that well and there are different reasons for this. If you feel that your doctor is not listening or that you have not told the doctor all you wanted to tell him, work out exactly what you are going to say before you go to see the doctor. A vague or imprecise answer to your doctor's first enquiry gives a doc-

tor who is not all that good at communicating the chance to jump in and take over the consultation.

Make sure you say the most important thing you want to say within the first minute or two of the consultation. If you say something clear such as 'I've had this pain in my neck and left shoulder when I climb stairs and as it's just come on in the last three weeks I thought I would come and see you about it', there is no doubt about the reason for your consultation and you will feel more in control of the situation.

Similarly, if there are questions you want to ask write them down and let the doctor see the list. Don't worry that the doctor will think you are a hypochondriac; most doctors will now think that you are simply jotting down things you want to remember in the way they use their diaries or note pads.

The doctor's manner

Some doctors are consistently pleasant and courteous, no matter how tired or harassed they may be, but doctors are human and, like all humans, they don't always behave consistently. Some doctors are offhand; others downright rude. If it is an isolated incident and you trust your doctor you probably just have to accept this, but if the doctor's manner always upsets you then you may have to look for another doctor.

Seeing a woman doctor

If your doctor is part of a team then it may be that one of the other doctors on the team has a style and approach which suits you better. If you particularly want to be seen by a woman doctor you may be able to find one in the health centre. If, however, you want to see a woman doctor regularly then you may have to change to a partnership in which there is a woman principal or assistant, which is the name given to a part-time doctor working in the practice.

Getting a second opinion

If you really aren't sure about your doctor's diagnosis or treatment of your condition, you could try getting a second opinion. You could suggest tactfully that perhaps referral to a hospital consultant might help to clarify the situation, or you could see a specialist privately for which you will have to pay a pre-arranged fee.

Making complaints

If you have a complaint about your doctor's service then you can discuss it with your doctor himself, but if you are nervous at doing this or if you have tried to do this and been rebuffed, you can either write to your Family Practitioner Committee or to the Community Health Council who can help you decide whether or not to complain, or how to solve your problem in some other way.

ADAPTING TO THE CHALLENGE OF ILLNESS

Illness increases with age because older people have been exposed for longer to the factors which cause illness. However, illness in old age is not something which has to be accepted with resignation: it is a problem which has to be tackled and overcome.

Doctors, nurses and other health service workers can help you with this task but self-care is the most important form of care, and below are outlined several ideas which you can use when you are facing up to illness.

Tackling illness

There are two different types of illness – curable and incurable. If you have a curable illness your objective is to try to get over it as quickly as possible. If you have an incurable illness then your objective is to adapt to the illness so that it has the least possible impact on your enjoyment of life.

To achieve both these objectives you have to work in partnership with health workers of one kind or another; usually partnership is uneven and if you want to have an equal partnership in which you and the doctor are working together you may have to press for the information that you need. Often people leave the doctor's surgery without really knowing what is wrong with them. Some people trust their doctor completely and are not bothered by this but some people would like to know more about their disease.

Useful questions to ask

1 'Can you tell me the name of the problem again, doctor? I didn't quite catch it when you first said it.' Then, when the doctor has said the name of the disease or repeated it, ask:

2 'Could you tell me a little bit more about it, what causes it and what exactly does it do to the body?' Then when you have the diagnosis clearly established you can ask about the future or, as the doctors call it, the prognosis:

3 'What is likely to happen – is it a curable condition or something I've got to learn to live with?' Once you have established whether it is a curable or incurable disease, you can ask:

4 'What can I do to help myself get better more quickly?' or, if it is an incurable disease, 'What can I do to help myself cope with this disease as well as possible?' You may have to ask the doctor specifically if there are things that you should and should not do because the doctor may only give you one or other in response to this question.

Finally, it is often useful to make contact with one of the societies for people suffering from particular diseases, such as the Parkinson's Disease Society or the Chest, Heart and Stroke Association, so you can ask your doctor:

5 'I don't want to take up any more of your time, Doctor. Is there anywhere I can write for more information about my illness?

A list of some of the common societies is given at the end of the book ◄ but new societies are being set up all the time so you need to check to find out if there is a society particular to your needs or if one of the major national societies has a local branch.

COPING WITH DRUGS AND MEDICINES

For many diseases your doctor will prescribe a medicine, and although drugs and medicines bring many benefits to older people they can also cause problems. If taken in sufficient quantities, almost any type of drug will have side effects, that is effects other than the treatment of the disease. There are some drugs, however, in which the concentration in the blood which causes side effects is only very slightly higher than the concentration required to treat the underlying disease, so you are almost bound to experience side effects. Furthermore, the biological effects of ageing reduce the body's ability to dispose of some drugs and the older you are the more likely are you to have side effects from drugs as well as beneficial effects. In summary, therefore, drug treatment of disease in old age brings many benefits but you have to use drugs sensibly. The questions and answers in the table (opposite) provide a useful check-list to go through with your doctor when he or she prescribes a course of drug treatment.

All medicines are potentially dangerous if taken in the incorrect dosage or without prescription. This is particularly the case with children, so keep

SEE ALSO: ▷

RESOURCES & BACK-UP:
Health   p. 205

drugs locked away, out of reach if children visit you at home.

Questions about drugs

What is the medicine for? You may not want to know what the medicine does or it may be obvious why you are being prescribed it, but many people want to know more about the drug that has been prescribed for them. Ask your doctor what problem the drug has been prescribed for and about the way it will work. For example, it is helpful to know that diuretics act on the kidneys to help you get rid of surplus water, which causes breathlessness and swollen ankles, but that this results in increased frequency in urinating.

How does it affect the patient? People often wonder whether they will actually feel the drug making them better or not and sometimes stop taking the medicine if they do not feel positively better. However, drugs can be divided into two types: drugs whose effects can be felt; and drugs which change the way your body works in some way to reduce your risk of disease but which do not have any effect that you can feel. These drugs are often given to prevent some disease developing; for example, drugs for high blood pressure lower the blood pressure and reduce the risk of strokes but you will not feel the effect of this beneficial lowering of the blood pressure. It is therefore important always to take the complete course of drugs exactly as prescribed (see below).

How should the drugs be taken? The prescription you receive will usually tell you how many times a day to take the medicine but there are other questions about taking medicine that need to be answered. Should they, for example, be taken before or after food? Will they interact with alcohol? Will they interact with other drugs you may be taking for an unrelated condition?

The pharmacist is an excellent source of this type of advice if you do not get it from the doctor who prescribed the medication.

Are there any side effects? It is helpful to know if there are going to be any side effects of treatment, for example if your blood pressure is lowered too fast you may feel dizzy and unsteady when standing up after lying down for some time. It is also helpful to know about the common side effects of drugs because it is sometimes difficult to decide whether you are feeling unwell because of drug side effects or because of some other health problem which may have developed, such as influenza. If you feel funny in any way after starting medication then you can phone the doctor who prescribed it or seek the advice of the pharmacist who dispensed it. Pharmacists know a great deal about drugs, their effects and their side effects, and if you ask to see the pharmacist in a chemist's shop he or she will be able to answer your questions about drugs and medication.

What happens when the course of drugs is completed? The doctor should tell you what steps to take when you have finished the medication, whether for example you should come back again if the problem recurs or whether you should make another appointment at about the time when the medicine will be finished. If he or she does not make this clear, then remember to ask about it at the consultation.

BEING REFERRED TO HOSPITAL

Hospital referrals are common because general practitioners often find it helpful to have a second opinion even when they are confident that they have got the right diagnosis and are giving you the best treatment. More often, it is because the hospital has better facilities for tests, such as X-rays or ultrasound scans, or because the doctor suspects you may require an operation. When referred to hospital there are some things that are helpful to know; the questions below are the sort of subjects you could ask your doctor if he or she suggests hospital referral.

Questions to ask about hospital referral

What tests might be done? You may not be bothered at all by the idea of going to a strange place and having tests done to you, and simply want to wait until you arrive at the hospital to see what happens. But many people prefer to know what is in store for them. Your general practitioner should be able to tell you about the tests which are commonly used; however, your doctor cannot be absolutely certain about all the tests and investigations that may be carried out because the hospital doctor may decide to investigate some other aspect of your health problem when he has had a chance to talk to you.

When will the appointment be made? In most parts of the country general practitioners are informed about the waiting time for clinics by the hospital, so your doctor should be able to tell you when the appointment will be. He or she *won't*, however, be able to tell you how long you will have to wait when you actually arrive at the outpatient clinic, because that depends upon local problems occurring within the hospital service.

Are there any advantages in having a private consultation? In general the National Health Service sees people quickly who have urgent medical problems, but this does not take into account the fact that you may be very anxious about your health problem (even though the probability that it is medically serious is low). If you are anxious, then it may be worthwhile going privately if you can afford it, or if you are

covered by a health insurance scheme. Your general practitioner will be able to make arrangements for a private consultation if you wish one.

What should be done before going to the outpatient clinic? Sometimes there are specific instructions about going to the outpatient clinic but this question will be answered when you receive your letter of appointment from the hospital. This letter will explain any necessary preparations, for example whether or not you may eat before you go to the clinic, or whether to bring a sample of urine.

INFORMATION AT HOSPITAL

Most hospital outpatient departments and wards are extremely busy places. Often they are not as well organized as they should be, and a visit to outpatients can be a bewildering experience. Your first approach could be to ask the questions given above but if you have tried to do this without success and still feel puzzled or concerned after the hospital doctor has left you, you can ask one of the nurses at outpatients if you can have a word with her. Nurses in outpatients often work in the same outpatient clinic for a long period of time and get to know about the problems that people have when they come there and can answer the questions that people commonly ask.

If you think that your health problem will have some serious effect on your family or if you have housing or financial problems, ask the nurse or the receptionist at the outpatient clinic if you can make an appointment to see the medical social worker.

If you are prescribed drugs at the outpatient clinic and have been unable to ask the doctor at the clinic all the questions you want to ask about them, you can ask the hospital pharmacist if you are sent to the hospital pharmacy to pick up your prescription. Alternatively if you leave the hospital with drugs or medicines, but do not know everything that you wish to know about them, you can call at the nearest chemist, and ask the pharmacist about the drugs that have been prescribed for you.

If, after leaving outpatients, you still want information your general practitioner will do his or her best to explain the results of the tests and investigations you have had – but remember, a doctor is dependent on the information contained in the letter he or she receives from the hospital, and hospital letters are not always as clear as they could be.

When you are a hospital inpatient you may also have problems in finding the information you want from the doctors and again you can ask to speak to the ward sister or the medical social worker to get more information.

USING ALTERNATIVE THERAPIES

The type of medical care delivered by doctors working in the National Health Service is only one of the many types of health care available. There are a number of other types, including osteopathy, chiropractic, homoeopathy and acupuncture. There are also therapies given by healers working with various ethnic groups. This list is not intended to be complete and in addition there are other types of activities such as the Alexander Technique, particularly good for people with back and neck problems, and yoga, of which the promotion of good health is one of the main objectives although they are more often used for the prevention of health problems rather than their treatment.

Alternative or complementary?

At one time the medical profession was hostile to these different types of therapy and called them 'Alternative', meaning that they were something completely different from the type of medical care offered by the National Health Service. Attitudes have changed in the medical profession and most doctors now see these as complementing the services provided by themselves within the National Health Service.

When to use complementary therapies

The medical care offered by the National Health Service is effective for a large number of different diseases so it is important to seek NHS care as a first step. However, once you have had investigations carried out in the National Health Service and they tell you either that they cannot cure or even treat your problem, or if you have had the best treatment the National Health Service has to offer and are still left with pain or discomfort or some other distressing symptoms, then you may wish to use complementary medicine, as the name suggests, to complement the treatment that you have received from your National Health Service doctors.

Homoeopathy

The principle of homoeopathy is that disorders should be treated with very, very small amounts of natural chemicals. Homoeopathy helps many people with problems that cannot be helped by conventional medical treatment and concentrates on considering the needs of each individual patient, so that his or her own particular physical and chemical make-up can be taken into account when preparing the treatment.

Homoeopathic medicine is available on the National Health Service to a limited extent, and there are in fact some homoeopathic hospitals ▶ to which admission can be arranged by the general practitioner if it is thought appropriate.

The Yellow Pages of the telephone directory contain a list of homoeopaths. Some are shown to be medically quali-

SEE ALSO: ◀

RESOURCES & BACK-UP:

Alternative therapies

p. 205

fied by having letters such as MRCP or MB, BSc, after their name, but the majority are not. You can approach these homoeopaths directly but will not receive National Health Service treatment from them, so you will have to pay a fee. Most homoeopaths are very alert to the problems they cannot treat and quickly refer people back to their own doctors, but an alternative approach is for you to discuss the problem with your own doctor first of all and then ask him or her to recommend a homoeopath.

Chiropractic and osteopathy
These two types of practice are similar. Both involve manipulation of the joints of the spine and occasionally other joints, and both are very effective in dealing with back and neck pain and sometimes with other chronic pain disorders which have their roots in the alignment of bones in the spine.

In the past general practitioners and orthopaedic surgeons were very reluctant to use the skills of osteopaths and chiropractors but this has changed now and the simplest way to find a dependable osteopath or chiropractor is to ask your general practitioner whom he or she would recommend. The training of osteopaths varies from one course to another and anyone can call themselves an osteopath, so it is important to get some advice before choosing an osteopath to treat you. ◀ Neither osteopathy nor chiropractic are available on the National Health Service, so you will have to pay a fee.

Herbalists
Herbalists believe that only natural herbs and medicines derived from plants should be used in promoting health and treating illness. Herbal medicine helps many people and one of its strengths is that is has few side effects.

As with homoeopathy the important first step to take is to ensure that you are not suffering from a disease which can be effectively treated by the National Health Service before seeking the help of a herbalist.

Herbalism is not available on the National Health Service and you will pay for all the treatments prescribed. It is not possible to select herbalists on the basis of their degrees or qualifications and you will simply have to act on the recommendations of your friends.

Acupuncture
Acupuncture is a type of treatment originating in China. The basis of acupuncture is that it is believed that every part of the body has connections with a certain area of skin, so by stimulating the skin in a certain way it is possible to influence some internal part of the body.

A large number of acupuncture practitioners are listed in the Yellow Pages telephone directory. Some are listed as members of the 'Traditional Acupuncture Society' or as 'Member of the British Acupuncture Association' but it is usually best to rely on the recommendation of your general practitioner or friends.

Acupuncture is beneficial for a very wide range of problems and is said to be effective in relieving pain which could not be relieved by conventional treatment. It is not available on the National Health Service, so you will have to pay for the services of an acupuncturist.

CHANGING PEOPLE'S ATTITUDES
No-one exists in isolation. What you want to do for your health is influenced by what other people think and how they behave towards you and one of the problems that people face as they grow older is that the attitudes of other people towards them change. Other people tend to become over-protective with

SEE ALSO: ▷
RESOURCES & BACK-UP:
Alternative therapies
p. 205

older people, trying to shield them from what they see as the risks or harsher sides of life. It can be difficult, for example, for an older person to have a good political argument with a younger person because of these attitudes.

It may also prevent an older person who suffers from a disabling disease such as arthritis from being as independent as he or she could be. Both these types of over-protectiveness are misguided, since older people's opinions are as valid as anyone else's and use of the intellect helps to keep older minds active, just as allowing an arthritic older person to do as much for himself as possible helps to maintain mobility and to minimize the effects of the disease. Older people need, as tactfully as possible, to display their strengths as well as their weaknesses so that outsiders can give help where it is needed, without being overpowering.

ILL HEALTH AND THE LAW

For those facing retirement and old age the prospect of ill health and its attendant worries and the possibility of diminishing mental resources are particularly worrying. It is important that you should consider what should happen should you become too ill or frail to cope.

Consent to treatment

If you do not want hospital or medical treatment you cannot normally be forced to have it although it is not usual for your formal consent to be required unless you are to undergo surgery. If you do not consent to treatment you can, however, be treated against your will if you fall within the terms of the Mental Health Act 1983 and are suffering from a serious mental disorder.

If you are ill or housebound

There are several ways of making things a bit easier for you if you are hospital-ized or housebound.

Agency This is a relatively simple way in which you can nominate someone as your agent to collect your pension or other benefits. There is a specific form of wording required by the Department of Social Security (the DSS). The wording is available from the Post Office or from the DSS.

Appointeeship If someone is old or infirm, but not necessarily mentally incapable, the Secretary of State can appoint someone to exercise on behalf of that person any of his rights under the Social Security Act. The person who is appointed is called an appointee and he or she will be interviewed before being accepted by the Department of Social Security.

Power of attorney A power of attorney is an arrangement whereby one person gives authority to another to act on his or her behalf and this can include signing documents, cheques, etc. The person empowered with the power of attorney should act on the wishes of the person giving him the authority. A power of attorney can be limited to particular acts, such as signing the transfer of a house, or it can be more general. A person cannot execute a power of attorney if she or he is unable to understand what she or he is doing. Until recently a power of attorney was automatically terminated if the person granting it declined mentally. However, as a result of the Enduring Powers of Attorney Act 1988 certain powers of attorney can continue if the person granting it has become mentally incapable. It is important that such a power of attorney should be executed in accordance with the Act. The power should be in a particular form and solicitor's advice should be sought if you are contemplating executing one.

The court of protection This Court exists to protect and direct the management of the estates (ie income and

WHEN TO CALL 999

For the types of problems listed below, you should call an ambulance by dialling 999:

► chest pain
► breathlessness
► blackout or collapse
► vomiting blood
► weakness of one part of the body

Until the ambulance arrives, reassure the patient, and make him as comfortable as possible. If the person has lost the power of one side – a sign of a stroke – call the doctor immediately.

capital) of those who cannot manage their affairs because they suffer from mental disorder. Application is usually made to the Court by a nearest relative or by a local authority officer. Medical certificates will be necessary to prove the condition of the ill person. The Court then appoints a receiver to manage the ill person's affairs.

Compulsory detention in hospital
This can only happen to the seriously mentally ill who need treatment and refuse it. You can only be compulsorily detained in hospital if your mental condition falls within the terms of the Mental Health Act 1983.

PREPARING FOR EMERGENCIES
Emergencies are very common, but fortunately they only happen to individuals occasionally, and this is part of the difficulty because it is hard to prepare for them. As you get older the risk of acute medical problems increases, but if you have a partner or a close friend you may be called upon to help them.

Rather than try to go through all the medical emergencies that can occur, the author's best recommendation is for you to enrol in a First Aid Course such as that run by St. John Ambulance Brigade or the British Red Cross Society. By learning about first aid you will prepare yourself for all emergencies, and people who have been on a first aid course not only know what to do, but find emergencies less stressful because knowing that you are taking the right step is a comforting thing to do when you are faced with a frightening problem. Furthermore, it is also very comforting afterwards to know that you did the right thing. There are few things worse than blaming or reproaching yourself after the event for things that you might have done differently.

First Aid Courses are set at different

levels. Even if you have done a course before, if it was some years ago, it would be worth enrolling in one again, because ideas have changed.

Reporting symptoms to the doctor
Some people are diffident about reporting apparently trivial symptoms to their doctor, and yet they may be signals that something more serious is amiss. Some indeed may have a simple cause, but you should report them all the same so that the doctor can act appropriately. Some of them may be noticed more by other people – if you notice a personality change in someone close to you, a quiet word with the doctor is a good idea.

The symptoms in the box opposite, should be treated as emergencies and if they happen to you or to someone who is with you, you should call an ambulance by dialling 999 or take the person immediately to a hospital accident and emergency department.

WHEN SOMEONE DIES
If you think someone has died, you should not try resuscitation unless you have training in this. If the death was expected, you should call the doctor; if unexpected, call the ambulance service.

Anyone whose spouse has just died is obviously in a great state of shock, and it is difficult to give general advice about how to help such a person. Some appreciate practical help, others may prefer just to have some company. The only way to find out what you can do is to ask.

Registering the death
If your spouse or a close relative dies at home it is the duty of the nearest relative to register the death. This is done by giving the death certificate to the local Register of Births, Deaths and Marriages. The death certificate must be signed by one doctor who attended the deceased if the body is to be buried, and by two doctors, one who attended the

deceased and one quite independent doctor, if the body is to be cremated. The Register is usually located in the Town or County Hall and a telephone call there will tell you where to go. In order to obtain the death certificate to be signed by the doctor you must contact your doctor as soon as you discover the death and he will provide you with the signed certificate. The Registrar will then give you a certificate of registration of death which you give to the funeral director.

Post mortem

A post mortem examination is only carried out if the doctor attending the deceased during the illness does not know of the cause of death, or if a coroner orders that a post mortem examination take place to try to establish cause of death. Provided that there is a death certificate and the cause of death is known there will be no need for a post mortem examination.

If someone dies abroad

In the unfortunate circumstance of a death overseas a number of things can happen. If the person was insured while travelling abroad then the insurance company will arrange through the International Funeral Directors to bring the body back to Britain. A special form must be obtained from the Home Office and completed by the nearest relative and a death certificate (preferably in English) must be obtained. Upon receipt of these documents the Home Office issues a licence enabling the body to be brought back into the country and buried. Before burial, the death must be registered with the Registrar of Births and Deaths by sending all the papers plus the licence issued by the Home Office. It is very important that you take out travel insurance especially when you travel abroad. If you are faced with dealing with the tragic circumstance of

an unexpected death and the deceased person is not insured you should go to the nearest British Consul's office to seek help.

SYMPTOMS TO TAKE SERIOUSLY

Visit your GP without delay if you notice any of the following:

Black stools
Blood in stools or urine
Confusion especially at night
Coughing blood
Difficulty or frequency in urinating
Difficulty in swallowing
Dizziness
Excessive thirst
Falls
Feeling despondent, hopeless or
  persecuted
Flashes of light before the eyes
Hearing aid losing effectiveness
Haloes appearing round objects
Joint swelling or stiffness
Loss of vision (sudden)
Loss of weight without dieting
Lumps anywhere on the body,
  especially in the breast
Noticeable memory loss
Numbness or persistent pins and
  needles
Pain in the chest, arm or throat
Pain in the eye
Pain or discoloration of toes
Persistent constipation or diarrhoea
Persistent fatigue
Persistent hoarseness
Persistent indigestion
Prolonged loss of appetite
Shaking or trembling
Seeing double
Spots or sore places which fail to
  heal
Sudden skin dryness or irritation
Vaginal bleeding

INVOLVEMENT OF THE CORONER

► If it is a death in which the deceased person was not seen by a doctor

► If the Registrar has been unable to obtain a duly completed certificate of cause of death

► If the cause of death appears unknown

► If the Registrar has reason to believe that death has been unnatural or has been caused by violence or neglect or there are suspicious circumstances

CHAPTER 10

A-Z OF HEALTH PROBLEMS IN OLDER AGE

ALZHEIMER'S DISEASE

This is a disease of unknown origin (although it has recently been suggested that aluminium is in some way implicated), previously known as senile dementia (see also *Dementia*, page 191). Its distressing consequences for the sufferer and those who care for him or her have been given wider recognition in recent times. Its symptoms are progressive, severe loss of memory combined with other evidence of intellectual decline. It is important to realize that minor memory slips such as momentarily forgetting a name or telephone number, or inability to remember what you went into a room for, are not symptoms of early Alzheimer's Disease. In addition, there are many other reasons for forgetfulness (see page 193) or confusion (see page 190), many of which can be treated. Alzheimer's Disease develops slowly and gradually over a number of years.

It is important to maintain the mental and physical activity of people with Alzheimer's Disease for as long as possible. People close to a person with this disease need a great deal of support, although unfortunately hard-pressed health services may have few resources for this purpose. The Alzheimer's Disease Society organizes local support groups; their headquarters (address on page 214) will be able to put you in touch with one in your area.

ANGINA

Angina is a symptom of coronary artery disease (see page 194), namely narrowing of the arteries that supply the heart muscles. When these arteries narrow, the heart muscle receives insufficient oxygen when it is asked to work hard and the result is pain – usually a crushing pain in the chest which may go up into the neck and down into the arm.

The pain comes on during exercise and goes away when the exercise stops. In severe cases the pain comes on when a person is at rest.

Pain in the chest or neck or arm coming on during exercise is a reason for consulting a general practitioner. Treatment can be very successful: it consists of reduction of weight and blood pressure, giving up smoking, taking gentle exercise (under medical supervision) and sometimes adjustment of the diet to reduce fat intake, although over retirement age the deposits of fat in the arteries that cause coronary artery disease are already in place and probably can't be reduced. However, reducing fat in the diet is, in any case, an important element in weight loss (see page 195). There may also be drug treatment – and for severe cases, surgery (see page 194).

ANXIETY

Everyone is anxious from time to time and when people say they have 'anxiety' they mean that they feel anxious to such an extent that their everyday life is upset. If this happens to you, you may be able to help yourself by discussing your anxiety with someone you trust, or tackling the cause of your anxiety if you can identify it. If it is difficult to pin down a single cause, think of three things that make you anxious and tackle them. It helps to take up some other activity such as swimming or walking to help you feel better physically. You can also consult your general practitioner, especially if anxiety is so severe as to interfere with sleep, work or leisure pursuits, or if anxious thoughts keep you awake or keep coming into your mind when you are trying to do something else or speak to someone.

Medical help may include advice on ways to control your anxiety, or the prescription of tranquillizing drugs.

Nowadays doctors are more circumspect about these drugs because of the dangers of dependence on them. If it is felt necessary to prescribe these, be extremely careful never to exceed the prescribed dose.

ARTHRITIS

Arthritis means disease of the joints. The cause of arthritis is not clearly understood; only a very few cases are caused by infection. There are four common types of the disease. *Rheumatoid arthritis* is an inflammatory disease, affecting a number of joints and other parts of the body. It is much more common in women than in men, but attacks both sexes in middle life, mainly in the mid-forties. *Osteoarthritis* is of two types: it can either affect one joint, such as the knee or hip, or can be generalized, affecting many joints. It is purely degenerative and, although it is believed that some people are genetically prone to it, it can also be caused by wear and tear on the joints earlier in life due to occupation, obesity or injury. Unfortunately osteoarthritis is usually already present by the age of sixty, and although it cannot be prevented it is important to try and prevent it from progressing. The fourth type of arthritis affects the back and neck (see back pain, below).

Pain in the joints and stiffness are the two common symptoms of arthritis. The joints may become swollen as well. Increasing stiffness normally occurs with ageing but can be prevented by suppleness exercises. However, when pain develops there is often arthritis present rather than just normal ageing. Actions to help people with arthritis include:

- exercise, particularly the exercises which keep the muscles strong and promote suppleness (see *Movement and Exercise* page 149); consult your doctor or physiotherapist about the type of exercise that will be most helpful.

● physiotherapy to maintain mobility. You may be referred to the physiotherapy department in the hospital, or the physiotherapist may be able to visit you at home.

● rest during an acute flare-up of arthritis.

● anti-inflammatory drug treatment.

● operations can be helpful if arthritis affects one joint, such as hip or knee – the joint may be completely replaced by an artificial one.

● osteopathy and chiropractic can help with arthritis of the back and neck.

● help with weight loss and prevention of obesity if necessary.

● maintenance of a good diet, particularly to avoid anaemia, and high in calcium (see *Food and Cooking*, page 140).

BACK PAIN

Persistent or chronic pain in the back and neck is usually due to arthritis (see above) of the joints between the vertebrae. The vertebrae in the spinal column are separated by discs of firm but flexible material which sometimes narrow or even tear in old age and this can lead to acute back pain. There are other causes of back pain as well, for instance, osteoporosis. The causes are not always clearly understood but probably derive from a lifetime of strain on the back, particularly unnatural strains caused by poor posture or lifting in the wrong position. The strain on the back is obviously increased by obesity.

You can help alleviate back pain by sleeping on a firm bed; put boards under your mattress if the bed is too soft. Watch how you sit; whenever possible avoid slumping and sit with your back in its natural arch. Be careful when you lift. The correct way to lift without putting strain on your back is to bend the knees, keeping the back as straight as possible. When you are free of pain, take up exercises which strengthen the back and increase suppleness, for example, swimming or yoga (see also page 143).

Your general practitioner can prescribe painkillers and muscle relaxants, because some of the pain in backache is due to muscle spasm. He or she may

refer you to an orthopaedic surgeon; operations to relieve back pain are relatively low risk and have a good chance of long term success. Before this, however, you may wish to try osteopathy or chiropractic (see page 183).

BED

Bed is a dangerous place except for those eight or so hours which you spend sleeping. The older the person is the more quickly the effects of being in bed – namely muscle wasting, bone thinning and the risks of thrombosis of the veins – increase. That is why all medical treatment and rehabilitation is aimed at getting people back on their feet again as quickly as possible.

BLACKOUTS

Blackouts are caused by momentary loss of blood supply to the brain. There are many causes of this, but anyone who loses consciousness suddenly should consult the doctor as soon as possible (see also page 192).

BLINDNESS

Some degree of visual loss is inevitable due to ageing, but this only leads to severe visual impairment if disease develops. The three common causes of blindness developing in older age are:

● cataract (see page 190)

● glaucoma (see page 193)

● macular degeneration (see page 195)

Uncontrolled diabetes (page 191) can affect sight, as can high blood pressure (page 119). Detached retina (page 191) is another, less common type of visual impairment.

If visual impairment cannot be cured, there is usually plenty of help through the National Health Service and voluntary agencies to help the person who has lost vision. Every social services department and hospital eye department has a social worker with a special interest in blind people, who will be able to inform you about the services and benefits available.

BREAST CANCER

This is the most common form of cancer in women over 50, so regular screening (see page 121) and self-examination of the breasts is essential for early diagno-

sis. If a lump is found, initially it will be investigated with a biopsy, which means that a small piece of tissue will be removed for examination to see whether it really is malignant (non-malignant or benign lumps or growths are quite common and are simply removed surgically). If cancer is found early enough, nowadays it is not usually necessary to remove the whole breast (*mastectomy*), but only the lump itself and as little as possible of the surrounding tissue will be removed. Lymph glands leading up to the armpit may also be removed, even if it is found not actually to be affected, in order to avoid further spread of the disease. Follow-up treatment with radiotherapy, chemotherapy (drugs) or both is standard, and this is usually very successful. If you have to have a mastectomy or a significant amount of tissue removed, you will be fitted with a *prosthesis* – an artificial breast made of soft material which you can wear under a normal bra. The prosthesis is not noticeable under clothes – even thin blouses and summer dresses.

BRONCHITIS

Bronchitis is one of the commonest diseases among older people in the United Kingdom, caused by a combination of air pollution, exposure to dust in the workplace, and cigarette smoking. Chronic bronchitis is different from acute bronchitis in that its symptoms are permanent, even when no infection is present. Upper respiratory infections aggravate the condition rather than causing it. Once chronic bronchitis is established, it is obviously too late to prevent it, but it is possible to alleviate the symptoms and avoid secondary complications.

In bronchitis the tubes that lead from the throat to the lungs become inflamed and produce mucus. The result is a chronic cough with sputum, together with a reduction in the amount of oxygen passing through the lungs. This causes breathlessness, particularly on exertion. Chronic bronchitis is sometimes combined with emphysema (see page 192).

One of the first things to do if you are diagnosed as having chronic bronchitis is to stop smoking (see page 114); it is never too late. Take as much exercise as possible, depending on the advice of your general practitioner or hospital doctor, and avoid becoming overweight, which puts a strain on the lungs and heart (see *Obesity* page 195). Have an annual influenza jab (see page 118) to avoid problems with secondary infection.

Professional treatment may include anti-spasmodic drugs to treat the asthma which sometimes develops, prompt treatment with antibiotics to combat infection and physiotherapy to help loosen and expel sputum to keep the airways as clear as possible.

CALCIUM DEFICIENCY
Calcium is a chemical in bones, and deficiency in calcium can contribute to excessive thinning of the bones – a condition known as *osteoporosis* (see page 195), which increases the risk of fracture. High levels of calcium intake probably slow down the rate at which bones thin (see *Food and Cooking*, page 138, and *Good Health*, page 117).

CANCER
Cancer can affect people of any age, but it is more common among older people simply because they have had longer to be exposed to the factors (many of which are not known) which cause the disease. Cancer occurs when cells in the body, which normally only divide regularly and steadily to replace dead or lost cells, start to divide frequently and irregularly. This happens much faster when normal cells are lost so that the cancer cells invade the areas of normal tissue around them. The collection of cancer cells which spread is known as a *metastasis*. In addition in some cancers the abnormal or malignant cells break off from the original source and spread to other parts of the body, particularly through the lymphatic system.

Although the actual cause of cancer is still not known, various factors are known to be associated with different forms. Exposure to radiation, excessive exposure to sunlight, industrial dyes and other chemicals, cigarette smoking and heavy drinking are all implicated.

Many cancers can now be treated successfully if caught early enough. In women, cancer of the breast and of the cervix can both be prevented or successfully treated if detected through screening (see page 120 and 121). Other symptoms which should be reported immediately to your doctor are:
- blood in urine or faeces
- abnormal bleeding from the vagina
- change in frequency of passing urine or bowel movements
- change in the voice
- unexplained and sudden weight loss
- chest pains
- coughing blood
- breathlessness
- persistent cough

These may be symptoms of other diseases too, but in all cases cancer would have to be ruled out.

The public generally has too gloomy a view of the diagnosis of cancer, which does not always result in severe illness or death. In fact the rate of growth of cancer cells is very variable, and tends to be slower in older people, so that even though an older person may have been diagnosed as having cancer, he or she may not die of it.

CATARACT
The eye contains a lens, working on exactly the same principles as a camera. In almost everybody, some minor degree of clouding of the lens occurs by the time they are 80 – this is one of the normal processes of ageing. This clouding or opacity is known as *cataract*. In some people the clouding occurs more quickly than in others, which without treatment may lead to loss of sight. Diabetes (see page 191) is also associated with the formation of cataracts if the disease is not controlled.

The gradual loss of vision associated with cataracts is painless and sometimes quite lengthy, and it may be confused with glaucoma, but cataracts can be removed and sight restored by a very successful and safe operation, so it is important to report any vision impairment to your doctor as soon as it becomes apparent to you. The affected lens is removed. It is sometimes replaced with an artificial lens, otherwise vision is restored with the help of glasses or contact lenses.

CONFUSION
Confusion is a deterioration of intellectual function usually revealed as either problems with memory or difficulties in knowing where one is or in carrying on a rational conversation. Acute confusion coming on over a period of days or weeks often results from some treatable condition, usually an infection anywhere in the body, such as chest infection. The onset of confusion over a longer period of time – months or years – is usually caused by Alzheimer's Disease but may also be caused by some curable medical condition such as vitamin B12 deficiency or diabetes (page 191).

If you notice someone becoming confused then it is appropriate to encourage them to see their general practitioner to try to identify a treatable cause.

CONSTIPATION
Because the frequency of bowel habits varies very much from one person to another the best definition of constipation is that it is a change in frequency of bowel habit. If the change comes on very slowly and is not accompanied by passage of blood or mucus or pain, or by alternating periods of diarrhoea, it is simple constipation. If any of these other signs occur then a doctor should be consulted quickly because this may indicate some more serious bowel disease (see page 192).

Simple constipation is best treated not by laxatives but by dietary change, namely by increasing the amount of fibre in the diet (see page 128). Cereal fibre is in general better than vegetable fibre for preventing or overcoming constipation.

Be careful about taking high bran products – that is, either bran alone or cereal containing extra bran – because suddenly increasing the amount of bran in the diet can cause severe diarrhoea.

CORNS
Corns are thickening of the skin of the foot usually caused by tight-fitting shoes. Make sure that your shoes do not pinch your feet – fashions nowadays don't call for pointed shoes or high heels, which force the feet down into the toes of shoes.

If a corn develops, use corn plasters to spread the pressure over a wider area. Great care should be taken with the self-treatment of corns, and people with diabetes (see page 191) or peripheral vascular disease (see page 196) should not attempt to cure their own corns because of the danger of infection.

Talk to your doctor, health visitor or chiropodist at the local health centre, or make an appointment with a reputable private chiropodist who may well be able to make a home visit.

DEAFNESS

Some loss of hearing occurs as a part of normal ageing, but this does not usually affect the ability to talk to people or use the telephone. Difficulty with conversation or with the telephone is a problem which should be discussed with your general practitioner. The simplest cause is wax in the ear which can be cleared painlessly in your doctor's surgery, but this is only the explanation in a proportion of cases. Further investigation is often necessary to find out the exact cause and type of hearing loss.

If you know someone who is deaf, you can help by speaking more slowly rather than by shouting and by positioning your face in the light so that it can be clearly seen. However, don't try to emphasize lip or mouth movements. Few older people learn lip reading and the easiest way to help them is with slow clear speech. On the other hand this does not mean using baby language either – it is insulting to talk to a deaf person as though they can't understand English properly.

Hearing aids are effective and it is sometimes necessary to consider a type that is not available on the National Health Service. It is unwise to approach firms selling hearing aids direct without first seeking a medical opinion. The local Ear, Nose and Throat department of your hospital is the best source of advice and your general practitioner will probably refer you there for a specialist consultation.

DEMENTIA

Dementia is a general term used to describe the brain failure resulting from disease of brain tissue. The commonest type is Alzheimer's Disease (see page 188) which was formerly called senile dementia. The second most common cause is dementia due to narrowing of the arteries sometimes accompanied by lots of tiny strokes (see page 197) which do not paralyse the individual but affect intellectual ability.

There are other rarer causes which are treatable so that people who are developing confusion should always be referred to a doctor (see page 190).

DEPRESSION

Everybody gets depressed from time to time. However, severe depression, which interferes with sleep or makes life a misery or leads to thoughts of suicide, or even makes it difficult to have a conversation with family or friends without turning the conversation to the cause or feelings of depression, is not a normal part of ageing.

There are many causes of depression in older age, notably the loss of a spouse or close friend. Bereavement can take a long while to work through – much longer than outsiders sometimes realize; there are sympathetic support groups who can help bereaved people work through their own grief in their own time (see *Resources and Back-up*, page 200). Physical illness can also result in depression. However, it can sometimes be difficult to detect a single cause.

Tackling depression yourself is similar to tackling anxiety (see page 188). If you can identify a single cause, try coming to terms with it – but if everything seems depressing, tackle the two most depressing aspects of life first. It is important to share your problems with a friend or someone you trust.

Someone who experiences severe depression at short notice should see his or her own doctor, as should anyone whose ability to enjoy life and get on with other people is interfered with by depression and sadness. Medical help may include advice on overcoming the feelings of depression combined with the prescription of anti-depressant drugs.

If someone you know seems very depressed, particularly if there is talk of suicide, but the individual won't consult the doctor, it is worth having a word with the person's doctor or health visitor yourself. Never belittle the seriousness of depression – a person suffering from depression can no more 'pull himself together' than someone with a broken arm can mend it himself.

DETACHED RETINA

In detached retina, the light-sensitive retina of the eye develops holes or tears

through which the fluid from inside the eye (the *vitreous humour*) can escape into the two layers of the retina. The initial symptoms are flashes or streaks of light, or clouding of the vision. Detachment can be due to injury, but usually this just makes worse an existing situation, which may have many causes, including long-term inflammation, high blood pressure or short-sightedness (*myopia*). Fortunately, this is a relatively unusual condition, but if you do experience any problems with your eyesight, you should of course consult your doctor. It is important not to ignore any unusual problem with vision. If caught early enough, detached retina can be repaired – modern techniques of eye surgery involving lasers have proved very successful, but if the detachment has extended too far it is irreparable and the sight of the eye will eventually be lost.

DIABETES MELLITUS

Diabetes is a metabolic disorder caused by shortage or lack of the hormone insulin which is needed to process carbohydrates, fats and proteins. It causes a build-up of sugar in the blood stream as it blocks the utilization of sugar and, if unchecked, causes the classic symptoms of *hyperglycaemia* – loss of consciousness, leading ultimately to coma.

The onset of diabetes can be suspected if you have been experiencing excessive thirst, increased frequency of urination, and extreme hunger, while probably losing weight at the same time. Diabetics may feel tired and lethargic and are susceptible to skin complaints like boils or fungal infections.

Diabetes is a common condition in older age, and the risks of becoming diabetic later in life is higher in people who are very overweight (see *Obesity* page 195). This type of diabetes is known as 'mature-onset diabetes', and unlike the diabetes of childhood, which requires daily injections of insulin, mature-onset diabetes can usually be controlled by a reduction in weight brought about by dietary change and increased exercise, and, in some cases, tablets to control blood sugar levels. People with diabetes in older age are usually able to lead a completely normal life with the exception of their need to eat a sensible diet with low levels of fat and refined carbohydrate, and high levels of fibre (see *Food and Cooking*, page 128). However, it is important to take the advice of your doctor and dietician seriously, since if uncontrolled, diabetes can involve not only its own dangerous complications, but it can also trigger other diseases, such as coronary heart disease (page 194), stroke (page 197), kidney disease (page 195), peripheral vascular disease (page 196) and blindness (page 189).

DISABILITY

Disability is, as its name suggests, a loss of ability usually due to disease. The same type of disability, for instance in walking, can result from a number of different illnesses. The first approach to tackling disability is to try to reduce the effects of the disease causing it by ensuring that it is accurately diagnosed and is being well treated. The second step is to teach the person with the disability to overcome it with the help of professionals.

The occupational therapists and physiotherapists who work with disabled people try to help them maintain independence, sometimes introducing special aids such as a stick which can pick up objects from the ground, or even by adapting the dwelling such as installing a downstairs toilet for people unable to climb stairs.

Only when these efforts have proved ineffective should tasks be taken over by someone like a home help. People with disabilities benefit from doing things for themselves if they possibly can and not from others taking over from them.

DIVERTICULITIS

Diverticulitis is inflammation of small pouches (*diverticula*) that bulge out of the walls of the colon. This often occurs from middle age onwards and is basically the result of years of a diet low in fibre and high in refined, processed foods. Diverticulitis usually manifests itself as recurrent bouts of pain in the lower, left side of the abdomen accompanied by constipation or diarrhoea.

The danger with diverticulitis is if one of the inflamed diverticula bursts, which can lead to *peritonitis* – generalized infection of the abdomen – which is a medical emergency. It can also lead to *haemorrhage* (severe bleeding) and in-

flammation of other organs. However, the condition can be treated by laxatives and dietary change to increase fibre content. Surgery, which may involve permanent or temporary *colostomy* (in which faecal matter is passed out into a bag avoiding the rectum and anus), is used in chronic cases or where there has been severe bleeding.

DIZZINESS

Dizziness is common in older age and some people experience it when they stand up after lying or sitting. This is due to a momentary drop in blood pressure as you change position, and usually passes quickly. Try not to get up too quickly if dizziness tends to occur, and sit quietly until the dizzy spell passes.

Dizziness can sometimes be a sign of disease such as ear problems, anaemia or diabetes, so it is therefore wise to seek the advice of your general practitioner if it develops. However, it is only rarely that dizziness is found to be a symptom of severe disabling disease.

DROP ATTACKS

Older people are sometimes subject to a particular type of fall known as a drop attack. The individual's legs seem to fold up, without him or her losing consciousness and it seems impossible to get them moving again. There are many different causes of drop attacks, some of which can be treated successfully, so attacks of this kind should always be reported to the doctor.

The danger from drop attacks lies in falls when the individual is alone, or if the bones are brittle, leading to fracture. However, if you get to your feet as soon as possible and then rest for a while you will probably be all right. To get to your feet, try shuffling along on your backside until you can push your feet against a wall, or get in to a kneeling position so you can push your feet one at a time against the floor. It is probably not necessary or even advisable to go to bed after a drop attack. Always consult the doctor after a drop attack, and try to remember what you were doing at the time it happened which can help correct diagnosis.

DYSURIA

Dysuria is the name given to a sensation of burning or stinging when passing

water. In men this sensation is almost always due to a bacterial infection which can be treated. In women it may be due to a bacterial infection, but it can occur for no obvious detectable infective cause. Some people have frequent attacks of dysuria.

Apart from consulting your doctor, perhaps the most important thing to do is to keep drinking large amounts of fluid during an attack. The doctor can treat dysuria if he can find a bacterial cause. If not, and you are a woman, it may be useful to speak to the district nurse, particularly if you have a male doctor, as the nurse is often able to give sympathy, advice and support.

EMPHYSEMA

When the lungs have been subjected to long-term damage through chronic bronchitis (see page 189), persistent heavy coughing and/or smoking, the tiny air sacs (the *alveoli*) through which oxygen is transferred to the bloodstream become distended. This condition, known properly as *pulmonary emphysema* but more usually just as *emphysema*, severely reduces the surface area available for oxygen transfer and insufficient oxygen reaches the blood, starving the body of oxygen during exercise. The slightest effort leads to breathlessness or coughing, and the individual's life has to slow down to walking pace.

If a person who smokes is diagnosed as having emphysema, it is very important that he or she gives up smoking immediately. Even though the lungs are damaged, giving up smoking can help by preventing the condition from becoming worse and allowing the maximum possible oxygen to be absorbed. Under medical advice, it is also important to take exercise, since this improves the circulation of the blood. Exercise also helps your muscles make the best possible use of the oxygen that is absorbed through the lungs. If your doctor thinks it is appropriate, it may also be sensible to have an annual influenza immunization (see page 118). In fact much of the treatment effort is directed towards the prevention of complications, such as infection.

FAECAL INCONTINENCE

It is not normal to have staining of the

underpants or sheets. The most common cause of faecal incontinence is severe constipation, sometimes aggravated by over-use of laxatives. In severe constipation, hard faeces build up in the lower bowel, causing the muscles to distend and lose efficacy, so that liquid matter is allowed to escape. It is paradoxical that this embarrassing condition should be caused essentially by constipation, but once the constipation is treated incontinence usually disappears with it.

Changes in bowel habit including faecal incontinence should always be reported to the general practitioner, not only because they may be a sign of a more serious disease than constipation, but also because if the cause is only constipation the problem can usually be solved (see page 190).

FALLS

As the body ages, the walking pattern can change and some people do not lift their feet as high as they did when they were younger, making them liable to trip. Liability to tripping is also increased by visual problems and difficulties with co-ordination such as occur after a minor stroke.

In addition the ability to recover from loss of balance becomes progressively impaired the older we grow. For these reasons falls become more common with increasing age.

A fall is a problem that may also be a symptom of another problem, an underlying disease or perhaps problems caused by medication that the person is taking. It should also always be regarded as a reason for going to see the doctor because many falls have causes which can be identified, treated and cured.

Falls give particular cause for concern among elderly people because increasing brittleness of the bones (see page 195) can lead to fractures with very little stress. It is therefore important to make your home as safe as possible, well lit and with well-fitting carpets especially on the stairs (see also *Drop Attacks*, page 192).

FORGETFULNESS

Normal ageing is accompanied by changes in memory. The long-established memories, for example of childhood, are retained and can be recalled easily but recently acquired memories, for example, the names of individuals met the previous day, are more easily lost in old age. The onset of this type of memory loss is not an early symptom of Alzheimer's Disease (see page 188), but if someone is worried about memory loss, he or she should see the doctor for reassurance.

Because memory is lost in old age it is helpful to think of ways in which you can compensate for it. Many people find the use of lists, diaries or a loose-leaf notebook can provide the jog to memory that is needed from time to time.

GLAUCOMA

Glaucoma is the name given to visual impairment due to increased pressure inside the eye. It occurs when the mechanism controlling the build-up of fluid inside the eyeball is defective. The commonest form, which affects a significant minority of people after middle age, is a slow and gradual deterioration of the field of vision, which narrows almost imperceptibly. One of the earliest signs is that lights appear to have a halo around them. However, visual impairment may not be noticed by the individual until an ophthalmologist (doctor specializing in diseases of the eye) examines it. If uncorrected, it can lead to total blindness, but it can be controlled by the use of drugs which slow up the rate of fluid formation.

Acute glaucoma is accompanied by pain, and comes on suddenly. It is caused by a physical block in the eye and can be corrected surgically.

Because chronic glaucoma is so prevalent among the older population, it is very important to have your eyes tested annually to make sure it is picked up at the earliest possible stage to avoid serious deterioration of sight.

GOUT

Gout is an inflammation of the joints (a form of arthritis) caused by deposits of uric acid. The accumulation of uric acid in the bloodstream is due to a chemical defect. Gout usually manifests itself first in an extremely painful attack in one joint, perhaps the big toe.

The old idea of the florid old gentlemen getting gout from drinking too much port developed from the fact that alcohol consumption can precipitate an attack – however, you do not have to be a heavy drinker to contract gout. Chronic cases of gout can also cause the build-up of solid uric acid deposits in the kidneys, as kidney stones. Sometimes these are the first symptoms of the disease – any pain in the side, or difficulty with passing urine should always be reported to your doctor (see also page 197).

The tendency to gout is probably hereditary, but it is thought that a very high protein diet can make the situation worse, so if gout is diagnosed you will probably be given dietary advice. The condition is much more common in men from middle age on – it is rarer in women, and only usually appears after the menopause. Acute attacks can be treated with anti-inflammatory drugs, and the condition can be treated in the long term with drugs to control the production of uric acid. It is also very important to maintain a good diet and to take exercise even though the symptoms may have subsided, because there is always the danger that uric acid deposits may reform.

HAEMORRHOIDS

Haemorrhoids (sometimes known as piles) are small varicose veins which swell up like small grapes under the surface of the skin around the anus. The skin over the small swellings becomes inflamed and this leads to itching. Haemorrhoids come to your attention either because of the itching or because they bleed. If the blood on the haemorrhoid clots it may become very sore and painful. The cause of haemorrhoids is most usually years of straining to have a bowel motion, although there seems also to be an hereditary tendency to have them.

Haemorrhoids are very common and if you are sure of the diagnosis you need not go to the doctor right away. It is important to avoid straining for a bowel movement, so avoid constipation by adjusting your diet to include plenty of fibre, and also drink plenty of fluids. If however you do strain and pass blood you should consult your doctor. If you have itching the doctor will prescribe medication which will relieve it.

Haemorrhoids can retreat or shrink spontaneously, but if they are particularly troublesome, you could have an operation to remove them, and you will be referred to hospital for this.

HEART DISEASE

The commonest cause of heart disease is a disorder called *atherosclerosis*. This is similar to furring of domestic water pipes. The arteries become lined with a yellow fatty substance which narrows them and as a result the heart muscle becomes starved of oxygen-rich arterial blood. This oxygen deprivation first becomes evident during exercise as a crushing chest pain called *angina* (see page 188). If the oxygen deficiency is sudden and severe, such as may be caused if a clot builds up in a narrowed artery and cuts off the blood flow completely, the heart muscle may die – a disorder called *myocardial infarction*, but commonly known as a heart attack. The symptoms of this are extreme chest pain, pallor, cold sweat, breathlessness, wheezing or coughing. This is a medical emergency and an ambulance should be called immediately. However, even severe heart attacks may be treated either by drugs or by an operation – a coronary artery bypass. This is done by taking parts of a vein from the leg to be used to bypass arterial narrowing.

Atherosclerosis can also affect the rhythm of the heart, causing it to beat irregularly, or to miss beats. This can cause drop attacks, breathlessness or even heart failure. The rhythm of the heart can be controlled by drugs or a pacemaker. Many people have pacemakers now – they are safe, effective, and one of the miracles of modern medicine.

Unfortunately there is little someone over 60 can do to reverse atherosclerosis which arises partly as a result of decades of an unhealthy, high-fat diet combined with lack of exercise and smoking. However, it is possible to stop it getting worse – changing the diet to low-fat and high-fibre, and cutting out smoking can slow down the degenerative effects of atherosclerosis.

There are other causes of heart disease, notably high blood pressure, childhood rheumatic fever which can narrow the valves of the heart, rhythm disorders, and even lung disease. Breathlessness and swelling of the ankles can be symptoms of heart disease.

Treatment involves the use of drugs which either act on the heart directly, or reduce the work it has to do, or a combination of drugs may be used.

HERNIAS

A *hernia* is a weakness in one of the muscular sheets of the body which allows an organ or part of an organ from another part of the body to protrude through. When used by itself the term means a weakness of the lower abdominal wall above the groin which can allow abdominal contents to protrude and be seen as an obvious bulge above the groin. However, there are many other hernias (see *Hiatus Hernia* below). Hernias are a nuisance, can be painful and they are occasionally dangerous if a part of the bowel becomes trapped inside the hernia.

Hernias do not have any single cause, but they are more common in older age due to muscle weakness, and the risk of a hernia is increased by obesity, by having a heavy job which requires lifting and straining, and probably also by constipation because of the straining which is associated with it.

When you have a hernia probably the most important thing is to lose weight, but it is very difficult for a hernia to be repaired once a muscular weakness has appeared. Your general practitioner can prescribe a truss to support the hernia but it is not always a satisfactory form of treatment and it may be more appropriate to operate. The operation is simple and has a high success rate, and it can be carried out under local anaesthetic.

HIATUS HERNIA

The *diaphragm* is a sheet of muscle separating the abdominal cavity from the thoracic cavity, or chest. The *oesophagus*, or gullet, passes down through the thoracic cavity and joins on to the stomach below the diaphragm. If the muscles are weak at the point at which the oesophagus passes into the stomach, the stomach can bulge through into the chest and allow acid to go from the stomach up the oesophagus which it does not usually do, because the diaphragm pinches the lower end of the oesophagus tightly. This can cause heartburn and waterbrash. The causes of hiatus hernia are similar to the causes

of abdominal hernias (see above).

To avoid some of the unpleasant symptoms of hiatus hernia you can:

- avoid wearing tight belts, corsets or clothes
- prop up the head of the bed by putting each of the legs at that end on a brick
- use pillows to keep your head and chest elevated during sleep
- try to lose weight
- avoid stooping over; bend your knees if you want to lift anything

Medical treatment is of two sorts. The first is drug treatment designed primarily to treat the symptoms and reduce the discomfort. The second type is operative, but it is a major operation and is only considered in the most severe cases.

HYPOTHERMIA

Hypothermia is a condition in which the body temperature drops below its normal level. It occurs because the thermostat in the brain, which controls body temperature, becomes less efficient as we grow older. In some people it becomes so inefficient that when they are exposed to a low environmental temperature, for example, a chilly bedroom with a temperature only a little above freezing, their body temperature drops to danger level.

It is important to keep your house temperature above 16 C° (about 65 F°) in living room and bedroom, and your home will also feel warmer longer if you can keep the hall and stairway at this temperature too. If you have one part of the house warm and the other parts cold the air will rush from the cold area into the warm, creating draughts. Keeping your house warm reduces the risk of respiratory disease, accidents and strokes. If you have difficulty in keeping your house warm for financial reasons, get in touch with your local social services department or the Citizens Advice Bureau. Hypothermia is a dangerous condition which can lead to death, so you need not feel you are being a nuisance (see also *Resources and Back-up*, page 206).

IMPOTENCE

In impotence, the man has an inability to have an erection and this makes sexual intercourse impossible. The cause is usually psychological rather than physical and it can become a vicious cycle. The more anxious the man becomes about his problem the less well does he perform. The most obvious advice is to try not to worry about it and to talk about it to your partner rather than bottling it up. Positive steps may be to have a holiday together in a new place or try making love in a different room or at a different time of day. Professional help usually consists of counselling and is given either by the general practitioner or by a specially trained counsellor from an organization such as Relate (formerly the Marriage Guidance Council), or at a local psychiatric clinic. (See also *Sexual Difficulties*, p. 196.)

KIDNEY DISEASE
Kidney disease occurs more commonly amongst older people. In men a common cause is enlargement of the prostate which results in an increase of pressure in the bladder which, in turn, produces back pressure on the kidneys. When a man notices that his stream of urine is slow to start, or that there is dribbling when he tries to stop, he should consult his general practitioner.

Among women frequent infections of the urine can lead to repeated kidney infections – *pyelonephritis*. Pain on passing urine is therefore a sign of illness that should not be ignored. In both men and women both diabetes and high blood pressure can cause kidney disease.

LEG ULCERS
Leg ulcers are usually caused by problems with the circulation in the lower limbs, especially varicose veins (see page 197) which may become blocked, leading to a build-up of pressure in the small veins under the skin. Leg ulcers usually appear on the ankle, often on the inner surface and may actually be started by a knock on the ankle.

Leg ulcers can be cured either by firm bandaging or by keeping the leg elevated by going to bed and thus reducing the pressure on the veins in the leg, or both these methods. If a leg ulcer develops you should consult the district nurse right away, usually by going to see your general practitioner first, but you can contact the district nurse directly.

You should not put any ointments on the ulcer yourself because the skin is very sensitive and can develop allergic reactions to the wrong treatment. If the ulcer is very large, small skin grafts can be applied to speed up healing. When it has healed you can prevent it from recurring by keeping your weight down, continuing to wear the elastic bandage, being careful to avoid standing for long periods and taking exercise, especially walking, to keep the circulation pumping in your legs.

MACULAR DEGENERATION
This is a visual impairment which seems to be associated with ageing. It is characterized by slow degeneration of the retina, although the direct cause is not known. It is an irreversible condition, which is difficult to treat, but rarely leads to complete blindness. People suffering from this condition lose the ability to see well enough to do work such as sewing, but can continue to get around on their own.

MENOPAUSE
The menopause is a normal biological event occurring at the end of the period during which women are fertile and produce eggs. Changes in the ovary result in changes in the hormone balance, which in some women produce physical and psychological symptoms. These may not be linked by the doctor with the menopause so that some women with problems which could be treated with hormone replacement therapy (HRT) are erroneously treated with drugs for depression or anxiety. If you consult the doctor for these latter problems and you are of menopausal age (45–55), make sure your doctor considers the possibility of HRT before prescribing tranquillizers.

Hormone replacement therapy has some risks but also benefits most people for whom it is prescribed. HRT can reduce the level of psychological and physical symptoms and also reduces the rate of bone thinning (see below right). It is usually only prescribed for symptom relief but women who are at particular risk of osteoporosis, for example heavy smokers whose bones are very light because they are very small, can benefit from HRT even though they have no distressing symptoms. General practitioners can prescribe HRT but referral to a menopause or gynaecology clinic at the hospital is sometimes necessary.

OBESITY
Obesity has a very simple cause – the amount of energy taken in is greater than the amount of energy used. However, obesity is also very complex and no one really understands why some people put on weight much more easily than others. Obesity is a health problem because it is implicated in or exacerbates so many other conditions and diseases – such as heart disease, diabetes, varicose veins, high blood pressure, back pain and so on.

There are two basic steps you can take to reduce weight. The first is to cut down your energy intake. Very low calorie diets are all the fashion but only really useful for removing a few pounds, for example, before going on holiday when you want to look your best. Of greater importance is a long term dietary change with a reduction in the amount of foods you eat which are rich in carbohydrate or fat and an increase in the amount of foods you eat which contain fibre. (Look at *Food and Cooking*, page 128, for advice on this.) It is important to eat fewer energy-rich foods but to try to avoid the mistake of eating less of everything because this often creates hunger and leads to a desire to nibble. Fibre-rich foods are filling without being fattening providing, of course, that you don't accompany wholemeal bread with lashings of butter and jam or put large lumps of butter on your baked potato.

The second step is to take more exercise. Small amounts of exercise taken regularly can have a major impact on body weight, for example, an extra quarter of an hour's walk a day is equal to about seven pounds of weight if it is done over a whole year.

You can get expert advice on diet either from your doctor or health visitor. It is not common for the doctor to refer obesity to a hospital clinic or to a dietician.

OSTEOPOROSIS
It is normal for everyone's bones to become increasingly thinner from the age of about 30 onwards, a process known as osteoporosis. In women, this

process accelerates after the menopause. Some people's bones thin more than others, causing them to become very brittle indeed; sometimes a very mild movement or knock is enough to cause a fracture. Bones at particular risk as a result of osteoporosis are the hip bone, the radius (the bone in the forearm) and bones in the spine.

Osteoporosis is sometimes without symptoms, except that people usually lose height, until a bone is fractured, but the bones of the spine (vertebrae) are particularly vulnerable and may collapse spontaneously causing back pain and gradual curvature of the spine. This can be made worse if the postural muscles are weak already.

Bone loss can be slowed down by:
- stopping smoking.
- increasing calcium and Vitamin D intake (Vitamin D is needed for calcium absorption – see page 117).
- taking exercise – bones benefit from use.
- hormone replacement therapy for women. Oestrogen is also needed for the absorption of calcium. HRT can have side effects (see *Menopause*, page 195) but it is known also to benefit those most at risk from osteoporosis.

PARKINSON'S DISEASE
This is a disease of the brain which affects the body's ability to move. The early symptoms of Parkinson's Disease include tremor and shakiness, particularly of the hands, which may lead to drinks being spilled, and slowness of movement. It leads on to a characteristic bowed posture and expressionless face, and extreme stiffness of other muscles. In severe cases the ability to speak clearly can also be affected.

As well as drug treatment, physiotherapy is important to maintain mobility. Fortunately there are effective treatments for Parkinson's Disease although these work to a greater degree for some people than for others. If these symptoms develop the general practitioner should be consulted.

PERIPHERAL VASCULAR DISEASE
In peripheral vascular disease, the arteries of the lower limbs become narrowed. The main cause of this is

cigarette smoking. Because the arteries to the lower limb are narrowed, the leg muscles, particularly the calf and thigh, do not receive enough oxygen when they are working, and pain can develop when the person is walking, coming on more quickly when going uphill. The pain is usually so severe that the person affected has to stop and then the pain disappears.

It really is impossible to treat peripheral vascular disease properly unless you stop smoking (see page 114 for advice on this). You should also continue taking exercise; this increases the ability of the muscle cells to extract oxygen from the blood which reaches it, because even if the flow of blood is not improved, the oxygen supply to the muscles is increased and the person has fewer symptoms.

Some people require an operation to replace the blocked arteries but wherever possible doctors try to help individuals with peripheral vascular disease take action for themselves to prevent the need for operation and decrease pain.

PROLAPSE
There are two common types of prolapse – prolapse of the rectum and prolapse of the uterus. In prolapse of the rectum, parts of the tissue surrounding the back passage bulge out. In its early stages this disorder may be confused with haemorrhoids by the person affected. Many people find they can push back the prolapse themselves but they should seek advice from their general practitioner who may be able to give them advice about ways in which the prolapse can be prevented from recurring. Straining while at the toilet due to constipation both causes and aggravates rectal prolapse and constipation is therefore to be avoided, preferably by an increase in fibre in the diet (see page 128). Referral to hospital may be necessary in severe cases.

Prolapse of the uterus is caused by a weakness of the muscle of the pelvis which allows the uterus to drop down into the vagina and sometimes protrude outside. It is often associated with stress incontinence and may result in infections of the vagina.

The cause is usually severe weakening of the pelvic floor muscles due to damage at childbirth many years pre-

viously. This is often aggravated by general muscle weakness and obesity. It is possible to learn to contract the muscles in the pelvic floor and strengthen them at any age, but the strengthening of these muscles is best done immediately after childbirth and it is difficult for some older people to regain sufficient strength completely to control prolapse or stress incontinence.

People suffering from either of these complaints should try to increase muscle strength and learn what it feels like to contract the muscles of the pelvic floor. The general practitioner, health visitor or district nurse may be able to explain how to do this. In some parts of the country physiotherapists are attached to gynaecology departments and run special clinics for women with weak pelvic floors. Constipation is also a problem best avoided. Prolapse of the uterus can be treated by a ring which supports the uterus but this does not always work, particularly in severe cases. An operation may be necessary, either to tighten the tissues around the uterus or to remove the uterus completely.

SLEEPING PROBLEMS
Sleeping problems are sometimes a symptom of underlying anxiety or depression but some people with sleeping problems are simply not taking enough exercise, or napping too much during the day, or drinking too much strong tea or coffee late at night, or perhaps watching too many lively TV programmes before going to bed.

The first approach to sleeping problems is to try to establish a regular evening ritual, for example no TV after 10, a warm drink at 10.30, a bath and bed by 11 with light reading, and the light out by 11.15. This type of regular pattern of going to bed can help prevent and solve sleeping problems.

If sleeping problems become pronounced then the general practitioner may prescribe hypnotics – drugs which improve sleeping – but they are very reluctant to do this because this type of drug can become habit-forming.

SEXUAL DIFFICULTIES
Sexual difficulties may be caused by problems of either the man or the woman, or both. Similarly they may be

either psychological or physical problems, or both. So great is the range of causes of sexual problems that it is difficult to give general advice except to say that normal biological ageing does not usually result in sexual difficulty and there is almost always some specific cause to be found.

Common causes of sexual difficulties include physical diseases, such as arthritis or vaginal infection, or psychological problems such as anxiety or depression. Anxiety about sexual difficulties can of course aggravate something which may have started off as a simple physical problem.

The best plan is to seek help when sexual difficulties start, either by consulting the general practitioner or, if he or she is not particularly sympathetic or easy to approach, by making contact with Relate (the Marriage Guidance Council) to see if there is any source of specialist advice which can be approached directly.

STROKE

A stroke is the interruption of the normal blood supply to a part of the brain. If the stroke persists the brain will be permanently damaged. The precise effects of a stroke depend upon which part of the brain is affected. The most common cause is high blood pressure but other factors sometimes play a part, notably heavy alcohol intake.

The body has great powers of recovery and much of the recovery achieved by stroke victims is through their own efforts rather than because of professional medical treatment. Hospital admission is not necessary for a full recovery from the effects of stroke but the advice of a physiotherapist or occupational therapist is often helpful.

To prevent a recurrence of the stroke it does seem that a small dose of aspirin taken daily is effective and people who have had strokes should discuss this possibility with their general practitioner.

Even though people recover from strokes largely on their own, professional medical assessment is needed to rule out any of the rare causes of stroke which require special medical or surgical treatment, and to prevent complications of stroke such as skin problems or fixed deformities of the limbs. Profes-

sionals can also pass on hints and ideas, and give encouragement to stroke victims.

URINARY INCONTINENCE IN MEN

At the base of the bladder lies the prostate gland. This gland surrounds the tube leading from the bladder to the penis to the outside, the tube called the *urethra*, through which urine passes out of the body. It is normal for the prostate to swell a little bit as men grow older and in some people this swelling pushes into the urethra and blocks the flow of urine.

The early symptoms of this include difficulty in starting the stream and dribbling at the end of urination but the first symptom of trouble may be pain in the lower abdomen. A man with this symptom should consult his general practitioner as soon as it develops because back pressure on the bladder can lead to damage to the kidney.

A prostate operation is relatively safe and usually effective, although some people do have difficulty in controlling their water in the early stages afterwards.

URINARY INCONTINENCE IN WOMEN

Many women who have had children suffer from what is called 'stress incontinence', namely passage of small amounts of urine when the woman coughs, laughs or runs for the bus or takes some other form of exercise. This is very common even among younger women.

The main cause is a stretching of the muscles in the floor of the pelvis as a result of childbirth and the condition is more common in women who have had a number of deliveries. People who are very overweight are also at greater risk of stress incontinence.

The power of the muscles which control the flow of urine can be improved and the woman who is affected can ask the district nurse, who works with her general practitioner, for advice on exercises she should do to improve her muscular strength and control (see also page 196). For some women an operation is necessary to tighten up the pelvic muscles and allow the woman to regain control but the general practitioner has to refer her to a gynaecologist for an opinion on the benefits of an operation; gynaecologists sometimes

prefer to try a ring pessary to strengthen the pelvic floor.

Other types of urinary incontinence in women are usually secondary to a disease such as a stroke and have to be treated as part of the problem presented by that disease.

The first step in tackling incontinence is to try to find its cause and your doctor is in the best position to start the investigation. Old age by itself is not a cause of urinary incontinence and women should not be put off by the statement, 'What else can you expect at your age?' If a doctor proves unhelpful or has done all that he can do and the person is still left with the problem, then the district nurse is an invaluable source of advice.

VARICOSE VEINS

Varicose veins are swollen veins which can be easily seen under the skin and the surface of one or both legs. The basic cause is blockage of deep veins within the calf muscles with leakage of blood from the deep veins to the veins under the skin.

In women this blockage appears to occur most often at around the time of childbirth, although the varicose veins may not appear for many years afterwards. In men the causes are not clear, although there is an hereditary element which may affect either sex.

If you develop varicose veins, keep your weight down; and wear support stockings; ask your pharmacist or general practitioner for advice. Avoid standing, but take as much exercise as you can to improve circulation; when sitting try to keep your feet up so your legs are horizontal. Try to avoid getting knocks on the veins as ulcers might develop (see page 195).

The two main types of treatment for varicose veins are injection treatment or operation. In injection treatment, the doctor tries to identify the places where the blocked deep veins link up with the veins under the skin. If these connections are blocked then blood can sometimes flow again through the deep veins.

Sometimes an operation is needed to remove the varicose vein. This is a relatively minor operation which is usually successful provided that the person continues to take exercise after the operation to prevent a recurrence of varicose veins.

RESOURCES AND BACK-UP

The following sections give suggestions as to where you might go to get further information and advice about particular services and activities or with particular problems. All the information included is correct at the time of going to press. However, organizations very occasionally move office at short notice, and publications may go out of print. If you have any difficulty with any of the information here, your local Citizens Advice Bureau or Age Concern office will be able to help (see under 'General', below).

CONTENTS OF CATEGORIES

GENERAL

Citizens Advice Bureaux (CAB) are voluntary organizations which give confidential and impartial advice to people of all ages on a wide range of subjects. To find your nearest CAB, look in your telephone directory or contact the appropriate Association below.

The National Association of Citizens Advice Bureaux
Myddelton House,
115–123 Pentonville Road,
London, N1 9LZ
Telephone (01) 833 2181

The Scottish Association of Citizens Advice Bureaux
26 George Square,
Edinburgh, EH8 9LD
Telephone (031) 667 0156/8

The Northern Ireland Association of Citizens Advice Bureaux
New Forge Lane,
Belfast, BT9 5NW
Telephone (0232) 681117

The Federation of Independent Advice Centres
13 Stockwell Road,
London, SW19 9AU
Telephone (01) 274 1839/1878
Many advice centres which are not CABs belong to the Federation which can put you in contact with centres local to you.

The National Council for Voluntary Organisations
26 Bedford Square,
London, WC1B 3HU
Telephone (01) 636 4066
The Council publishes an annual guide to voluntary organizations, *The Voluntary Agencies Directory*. You may be able to consult this directory and the Family Welfare Association's directory *Charities Digest*, in a local reference library if you are wanting to track down an appropriate agency.

For older people
There are many agencies which work to help older people and a number of them are listed in the sections that follow. Age Concern, Help the Aged, and the Centre for Policy on Ageing are three major agencies which work together, contributing in different ways. They may be able to put you in touch with the appropriate agencies to assist you.

Age Concern England
60 Pitcairn Road,
Mitcham,
Surrey, CR4 3LL
Telephone (01) 640 5431

Age Concern Scotland
33 Castle Street,
Edinburgh, EH2 3DN
Telephone (031) 225 5000

Age Concern Wales
1 Park Grove,
Cardiff,
South Glamorgan, CF1 3BJ
Telephone (0222) 371821/371566

Age Concern Northern Ireland
6 Lower Crescent,
Belfast, BT7 1NR
Telephone (0232) 245729
Age Concern serves older people through independent local groups providing a range of community services such as lunch clubs, day centres, visiting schemes, transport schemes, family support and other schemes. The national centres campaign to develop and promote improved policies and sup-

port and advise the local groups. Look in your telephone directory to find your nearest group.

Help the Aged
16–18 St James' Walk,
London, EC1R 0BE
Telephone (01) 253 0253
A major fundraiser. Help the Aged assigns money to support activities both in Britain and overseas. In Britain, the emphasis is on day centres and day hospitals, minibuses, alarm systems, research and education. The information service produces a range of advice leaflets.

The Centre for Policy on Ageing
25–31 Ironmonger Row,
London, EC1V 3QP
Telephone (01) 253 1787
This is an independent unit which aims to promote better services and policies for older people, providing policy-makers and professionals with research studies, reports and information.

ADULT EDUCATION

The Local Education Authority (LEA) is responsible for education in your area, including adult education – look in the phone book under the name of your county or borough. Your local library should also be able to give you details of adult education.

The Forum on the Rights of Elderly People to Education (FREE)
(FREE), c/o 60 Pitcairn Road,
Mitcham,
Surrey, CR4 3LL
Telephone (01) 640 5431
FREE can provide information on all aspects of education for older people. It also campaigns for rights to educational opportunities.

The University of the Third Age (U3A),
c/o BASSAC, ·
13 Stockwell Road,
London, SW9 9AU
Telepone (01) 737 2541
This promotes self-help educational activities among retired people of all ages. A network of branches across the country choose their own courses according to the interests of their members. Send a large stamped, addressed envelope for further information.

The Workers' Educational Association (WEA),
Temple House,
9 Upper Berkeley Street,
London, W1H 8BY
Telephone (01) 402 5608/9

Through its network of branches, the Association provides a wide range of adult education courses independently in co-operation with universities, LEAs and voluntary organizations.

The National Extension College
18 Brooklands Avenue,
Cambridge, CB2 2HN
Telephone (0223) 316644
This offers a range of correspondence courses for retired people.

The National Institute of Adult Continuing Education
19B De Montfort Street,
Leicester, LE1 7GE
Telephone (0533) 551451

The Scottish Institute of Adult and Continuing Education
30 Rutland Square,
Edinburgh, EH1 2BW
Telephone (031) 229 0331
Both the above provide information on all aspects of adult education.

The Open University
Walton Hall,
Milton Keynes,
Buckinghamshire, MK7 6AG
Telephone (0908) 74066
This offers degree studies and a continuing education programme, including retirement planning.

AIDS AND ADAPTATIONS

The NHS and Social Services Different parts of local authorities and the NHS are responsible for providing different aids and equipment. These can be supplied free or on loan, but some Social Services Departments charge for certain services. Contact your doctor or local Social Services Department (SSD) for help in getting aids and equipment supplied. Aids for washing, dressing and feeding, for example, may be obtained from your SSD, while your health authority will have aids for medical and nursing care at home and provide wheelchairs and artificial limbs and appliances. You can make an application for a wheelchair through your doctor. Occupational therapists can supply aids such as bath and toilet aids, chairs and handrails, but you will need to be referred by a social worker, health visitor or district nurse.

The British Red Cross Society
4 Grosvenor Crescent,
London, SW1X 7EQ

Telephone (01) 235 5454
The Society has various aids for short term loan, such as wheelchairs and walking frames, and local Age Concern groups may be able to advise on local stockists – look in the telephone book for your nearest group. The British Red Cross Society also produces a leaflet about equipment – contact the Supplies Department at the above number.

The Disabled Living Foundation
380–384 Harrow Road,
London, W9 2HU
Telephone (01) 289 6111
As well as a comprehensive information service on aids and equipment for disabled and older people, the Foundation also has a permanent exhibition of aids on site which you can visit (by appointment) and receive help from trained advisers. The aids on display are not for sale, but the leaflets available include lists of suppliers.

Equipment for the Disabled
Mary Marlborough Lodge,
Nuffield Orthopaedic Centre,
Headington, Oxford, OX3 7LD
Telephone (0865) 750103
This organization publishes a series of priced illustrated booklets on various aids, including ones on home management, housing and furniture, gardening, and hoists and lifts.

British Telecom supplies devices to help people who may find using the telephone difficult. Ask at local BT offices for their booklet on equipment and services to disabled customers.

Your local social services department and/or the housing department or environmental health department of your local authority may be able to help with the financing and arranging of adaptations to your home if they are necessary.

The Centre on Environment for the Handicapped
(CEH),
35 Great Smith Street,
London, SW1P 3BJ
Telephone (01) 222 7980
Through its information service on technical and design matters and its architectural advisory service, the Centre can help you to find people in their area with experience in designing for disabled and older people. They also produce publications about access and fund the Access Committee for England which supports local access initiatives and local groups.

Useful publications
The Directory of Aids for Disabled and Elderly People is published by Woodhead-Faulkner for

RADAR (Royal Association for Disability and Rehabilitation). Ask at bookshops or contact the publishers direct at Fitzwilliam House, 32 Trumpington Street, Cambridge, CB2 1QY, Telephone (0223) 66733.

The free DSS leaflet HB2 is called *Equipment for the Disabled* – ask at your local DSS office or CAB or write to the address given in the section on 'Benefits' (below).

ALARMS

The Disabled Living Foundation
380–384 Harrow Road,
London, W9 2HU
Telephone (01) 289 6111
The Foundation can supply a list of firms operating and installing alarm systems.

Help the Aged
16-18 St James' Walk,
London, EC1R OBE
Telephone (01) 253 0253
The Community Alarms Department can provide information and advice on alarms.

Age Concern England
60 Pitcairn Road,
Mitcham,
Surrey, CR4 3LL

In conjunction with *Which?* magazine, Age Concern England has produced a buyer's guide, entitled *Calling for Help*, which reviews alarms that are available and discusses points to consider when buying one. Contact the Marketing Department for details. You should also contact your local authority housing department or social services department to see if they run a scheme of any kind to provide alarms. Other sources are commercial firms, housing associations and charities.

BENEFITS

To find out about your entitlement to pension and social security benefits, ask at an advice centre.

DSS leaflets
The DSS Leaflets Unit
PO Box 21,
Stanmore,
Middlesex, HA7 1AY.
The DSS produce free leaflets about all aspects of state pensions and benefits. These leaflets should be available from your local DSS office, or from large post offices, or you can write to the Unit above.

Leaflet FB2, *Which Benefit?*, lists all available benefits and details the leaflets that describe them. FB6, '*Retiring? Your Pension and Other Benefits*' covers those particularly relevant for older people. These include for example:

H11	*Fares to Hospital*
HB1	*Services and Benefits for Disabled People*
HB2	*Equipment for Disabled People*
HB4	*Help with Mobility: Getting Around*
NI51	*National Insurance for Widows*
NI205	*Attendance Allowance*
NI211	*Mobility Allowance*
NI212	*Invalid Care Allowance*
NI229	*Christmas Bonus*
NP32	*Your Retirement Pension*
NP32A	*Your Retirement Pension If You Are Widowed or Divorced*
NP32B	*Retirement Benefits for Married Women*
NP35	*Your Benefit as a Widow for the First 26 Weeks*
RR1	*Housing Benefit: Help with Rent and Rates*
SB1	*Income Support: Cash Help*
SB17A	*Extra Help with Heating Costs When It Is Very Cold*

The DSS also has a freephone information and advice line on 0800 666555. The service can only send you leaflets and forms.

Independent advice
Age Concern England (see the 'General' section) publishes *Your Rights*, an annual guide to money benefits for retired people. Age Concern England also has available free factsheets on housing benefit (no. 17), income support (no. 25) and how capital and income affects benefit (no. 16) – send an s.a.e. to the Information Department.

The Child Poverty Action Group
Citizens' Rights Office,
4th Floor,
1–5 Bath Street,
London, EC1V 9PY
Telephone (01) 253 3406
Local groups can sometimes help with welfare rights problems. Contact the Citizens' Rights Office.

BEREAVEMENT AND DEATH

Cruse
Cruse House,
126 Sheen Road,
Richmond,
Surrey, TW9 1UR
Telephone (01) 940 4818/9047
A nationwide organization, Cruse offers support in the form of counselling, practical help, and opportunities for social contact.

The National Association of Widows
54–57 Allison Street
Digbeth
Birmingham,
B5 5TH
Telephone (021) 643 8348
Like Cruse, this also has a network of local branches which provide support, advice and social opportunities. It was originally set up to campaign to improve the financial status of widows.

The Jewish Bereavement Counselling Service
Woburn House,
4 Upper Woburn Place,
London, WC1H 0EZ
Telephone (01) 349 0839 (24 hour answer phone) or (01) 387 4300 extension 227 (during office hours)
The Service has trained volunteer counsellors who can visit the bereaved. The service operates in Greater London, but can refer people to other projects across the country.

Help for the bereaved
Some local Age Concern groups run bereavement counselling schemes or your local CAB will know of other local agencies. Your CAB will also be able to advise about the financial help that is available for bereaved families on low incomes. The DSS leaflet D49, *What to do after a death*, available free from your local DSS office, is a guide to what you must do and the help you can get. Leaflet FB29 entitled, *Help when someone dies* covers the benefits which may be available.

The Consumers' Association
Publications Department,
Castlemead, Gascoyne Way,
Hertford, SG14 1LH
Telephone (0992) 589031
What to do when someone dies, a Consumers Association publication, can be ordered from bookshops or direct from the Association.

Help for the dying
The Hospice Information Centre
St Christopher's Hospice,
51 Lawrie Park Road,
Sydenham,
London, SE26 6DZ
Telephone (01) 778 9252
If you want to find details of your nearest hospice, contact the Information Officer at the above address.

The Voluntary Euthanasia Society
13 Prince of Wales Terrace,
London, W8 5PG
Telephone (01) 937 7770
The society has declaration forms by which members can indicate their wishes in respect of medical treatment when they are unable to speak for themselves.

The Human Rights Society
27 Walpole Street,
London, SW3 4QS
Telephone (0263) 740404 (Hon Secretary)
This society is opposed to the idea of voluntary euthanasia and aims to inform people of the alternatives and the help that is available.

The Christian Council on Ageing
The Old Court,
Greens Norton,
Nr Towcester,
Northamptonshire, NN12 8BS
The Council runs counselling sessions and establishes local groups as part of its aim to improve the pastoral care of older people and integrate them into the local churches and communities.

Useful publications
Help the Aged have a free leaflet available on receipt of an s.a.e. from the Information Desk, Bereavement Leaflet, Help the Aged, St James' Walk, London, EC1R 0BE.

MIND produce a priced leaflet, *Understanding Bereavement*, on how to find help, which is available from MIND Mail Order, 24–32 Stephenson Way, London, NW1 2HD, Telephone (01) 387 9126.

CARERS

The Carers National Association (CNA) was formed from a merger of the former National Council for Carers and their Elderly Dependents and the Association of Carers. The CNA offers advice, support and opportunities for self-help to carers of older and disabled people. Local support networks have been set up across the country. The CNA also campaigns for better provision for carers and makes their needs known to practitioners and policy-makers. They are at either 29 Chilworth Mews, London, W2 3RG, Telephone (01) 724 7776, or 21–23 New Road, Chatham, Kent, ME4 4JQ, Telephone (0634) 813981

The St John Ambulance Brigade,
1 Grosvenor Crescent,
London, SW1X 7EF

Telephone (01) 235 5231
The Brigade can give advice on caring and runs courses for carers locally – ask at your CAB for the address of your county headquarters.

Help from social services In some areas short-term relief care may be available from social services. Often this involves someone sitting in with the elderly person or the person being admitted to a hospital or local authority residential home for a short time – ask your doctor or your SSD.

The Holiday Care Service
2 Old Bank Chambers,
Station Road,
Horley,
Surrey, RH6 9HW
Telephone (0293) 774535
This can provide information on agencies which can arrange for care in the home (see also the section on 'Companions and help in the home').

The Association of Crossroads Care Attendant Schemes
10 Regent Place,
Rugby,
Warwickshire, CV21 2PN
Telephone (0788) 73653
There are schemes in various parts of the country – care attendants give relief care while the regular carer has a break. Demand for this free service is high – ask at your local SSD or CAB if there is a scheme near you.

Financial help
Carers may be eligible for financial help – ask at your CAB about invalid care allowance and dependent relatives allowance – see leaflets NI 212 and NI 205 from your DSS office. The DSS Invalid Care Allowance Unit is at Palatine House, Lancaster Road, Preston, Lancashire, PR1 1HB, Telephone (0772) 561202.

Useful publications
A useful priced handbook called *Caring at Home* has been produced by the Kings Fund and the Health Education Authority. It contains basic information and practical advice to help carers and is available from the National Extension College, 18 Brooklands Avenue, Cambridge, CB2 2HN, Telephone (0223) 316644

A useful guide on *Taking a Break* is produced by the Kings Fund's Informal Caring Unit. Carers can get a free copy by writing to Taking a Break, Newcastle-upon-Tyne X, NE85 2AQ. For details of the Unit's other publications for carers, contact the Kings Fund Centre, 126 Albert Street, London, NW1 7NF, Telephone (01) 267 6111.

COMPANIONS AND HELP IN THE HOME

Domiciliary care and home nursing care of all kinds can be brought in privately. It can be difficult to find permanent companions and you may have to consider advertising in a journal such as *The Lady*, *Choice* magazine or the *Daily Telegraph*, or in local newspapers and magazines. You may wish to seek legal advice on whether a contract is needed. Your local CAB or Age Concern group may be able to suggest local employment agencies. These, and local nursing agencies, will be listed in your 'Yellow Pages'. There are private domestic agencies specializing in help in the home. Most will place staff for short periods only – again, look in 'Yellow Pages'.

The British Nursing Association
North Place,
82 Great North Road,
Hatfield, Hertfordshire, AL9 5BL
Telephone (07072) 63544
This is a commercial organization which can provide nursing help. They can be contacted at the above address, and will let you know if they have a branch local to you.

Counsel and Care for the Elderly
Twyman House,
16 Bonny Street,
London, NW1 9LR
Telephone (01) 485 1566
This organisation maintains lists of local agencies and produces a factsheet, 'Information on grants for help at home from CCE'.

CONSUMER ADVICE

If you have a problem about goods or services, contact the trading standards (or consumer protection) department of your local council or CAB.

The Office of Fair Trading
Field House,
Breams Building,
London, EC4A 1PR
Telephone (01) 242 2858
The function of the Office is to examine services to consumers and publish a range of leaflets on consumers' rights. Many of these leaflets will be available at your CAB.

The National Consumer Council
20 Grosvenor Gardens,
London, SW1W 0DN
Telephone (01) 730 3469
Set up by the government, the Council's rôle is to identify the interests of consumers and to represent

these to major service providers in government departments and industry.

The National Federation of Consumer Groups
12 Mosley Street,
Newcastle-upon-Tyne, NE1 1DE
Telephone (091) 261 8259
The Federation can let you know about local groups.

The Consumers' Association
2 Marylebone Road,
London, NW1 4DX
Telephone (01) 486 5544
This independent consumers 'watchdog' tests goods and investigates services and campaigns for improvements as well as producing a number of publications.

The Post Office Users' National Council
Waterloo Bridge House,
Waterloo Road,
London, SE1 8UA
Telephone (01) 928 9458

If you need help with doing your shopping, contact your local volunteer bureau or Age Concern group to see if they have any volunteers available who could help you.

CRIME AND CRIME PREVENTION

The Crime Prevention Officer at your local police station should be able to advise you about home security and neighbourhood watch schemes. Some local Age Concern groups run schemes which help with the fitting of security locks to doors and windows.

The National Supervisory Council for Intruder Alarms
Queensgate House,
14 Cookham Road,
Maidenhead,
Berkshire, SL6 8AJ
Telephone (0628) 37512
The Council operates a code of practice and a complaints service and can give you a list of its approved contractors.

The British Safety Council
62 Chancellors Road,
London, W6 9RS
On receipt of a large s.a.e., the Council will send you one of the Cards it has produced, which you can show to callers before you open your door. The card is displayed at the window and asks for the caller to show an identity card with a telephone number.

The National Association of Victim Support Schemes
17A Electric Lane,
London, SW9 8LA
Telephone (01) 737 2010
Victim support schemes offer practical advice and emotional support to victims of crime. Contact the Association to find your local scheme.

The Criminal Injuries Compensation Board
Whittington House,
19 Alfred Place,
London, WC1E 7LG
Telephone (01) 636 9501
This was set up by the government to pay compensation to victims of violent crime. Contact them for an application form.

Crisis Counselling for Alleged Shoplifters
c/o National Consumer Protection Council,
London, NW4 4NY
Telephone (01) 202 5787 or (01) 958 8859 (after 7pm)
This nationwide organization which provides counselling and advice to alleged shoplifters.

DISABILITY

If you are disabled and would like to contact a support group, your local Citizens Advice Bureau should be able to put you in touch with a local disability organization or one of the following national organizations.

The Royal Association for Disability and Rehabilitation (RADAR)
25 Mortimer Street,
London, W1N 8AB
Telephone (01) 637 5400
As well as giving help and advice on welfare services, access, holidays and mobility, RADAR supports the National Key Scheme for Toilets for Disabled People and produces a monthly bulletin and other publications.

Disabled Living Foundation – see the section on 'Aids and Adaptations', p. 199.

DIAL UK (National Association of Disablement Information and Advice Lines)
DIAL House
117 High Street,
Clay Cross, Near Chesterfield,
Derbyshire, S45 9DZ
Telephone (0246) 250055
DIAL UK can provide information, and, in some cases, practical help on all aspects of disability. There are local branches across the UK.

The Disability Alliance
ERA, 25 Denmark Street,
London, WC2 8NJ
Telephone (01) 240 0806
This is an umbrella organization which campaigns on behalf of disabled people, and publishes *The Disability Rights Handbook*, an annual guide to rights, benefits and services for all disabled people and their families.

The Disablement Income Group
(DIG),
Millmead Business Centre,
Millmead Road,
London, N17 9QU
Telephone (01) 801 8013
The Group campaigns to ensure that disabled people do not suffer financial hardship, and provides personal advice and publications.

The Scottish Council on Disability
Princes House,
5 Shandwick Place,
Edinburgh, EH2 4RG
Telephone (031) 229 8632
The Council's Information Department offers a 24-hour service and produces a range of free literature.

Wales Council for the Disabled
Caerbragdy Industrial Estate,
Bedwas Road,
Caerphilly,
Mid Glamorgan, CF8 3SL
Telephone (0222) 887325

Northern Ireland Council on Disability
2 Annadale Avenue,
Belfast, BT7 3JR
Telephone (0232) 491911

ETHNIC MINORITIES

Most areas have a Community Relations Council (CRC) although they may be called something else. They aim to promote good race relations and may be able to help you get the services you need. You can also ask your local CAB and Age Concern group about what is available to help with your particular needs and whether there are any other support groups in the community.

The Standing Conference of Ethnic Minority Senior Citizens
(SCEMSC),
5 Westminster Bridge Road,
London, SE1 7XW
Telephone (01) 928 0095

This organization works to improve the quality of life for older people of ethnic origin and can arrange for interpreting services.

The British Refugee Council
Bondway House,
Bondway,
London, SW8 1SJ
Telephone (01) 582 6922
The Council works with refugees of all ages and can help with the welfare problems of older refugees, from Eastern Europe and Vietnam in particular.

The Commission for Racial Equality
Elliot House,
10–12 Allington Street,
London, SW1E 5EH
Telephone (01) 828 7022
The Commission's rôle, is to promote equality of opportunity.

EYESIGHT

If you are on a low income, you may not be charged for eye tests. Some opticians will make home visits but they may charge extra – ask your local Family Practitioner Committee or Community Health Council.

The DSS leaflet AB11 explains the low income voucher scheme for spectacles – ask at your local DSS or CAB or write to the DHSS Leaflets Unit (see section on 'Benefits' on p. 200).

The Royal National Institute for the Blind
(RNIB),
224 Great Portland Street,
London, W1N 6AA
Telephone (01) 388 1266
The RNIB has a welfare advisory service and sells aids for blind and partially sighted people. It also has Talking Book Service, based at Mount Pleasant, Wembley, Middlesex, HA0 IRR, Telephone (01) 903 6666. The annual subscription for this subsidized cassette service includes the loan of a playback machine.

The Partially Sighted Society
Queens Road,
Doncaster,
South Yorkshire, DN1 2NX
Telephone (0302) 68998
The Society advises and assists partially sighted people and produces large print publications and aids to vision. Contact and support is also provided through a network of local groups.

The International Glaucoma Association
Ophthalmology Department,
Kings College Hospital,
Denmark Hill,
London, SE5 9RS
Telephone (01) 274 6222 extension 2466/2453
The Association can provide information and leaflets for sufferers.

Macular Degeneration Support Group
c/o Gordon Thompson, The Secretary,
1 Herbert Road,
Hornchurch,
Essex, RM11 3LA
Telephone (04024) 40759

The Optical Information Council
Temple Chambers,
Temple Avenue,
London, EC4Y 0DT
Telephone (01) 353 3556
Contact the Council for free written information about eye care, spectacles and contact lenses, including *Eye Care and the Elderly* and *Eye Care after Cataract.*

The Eye Care Information Bureau
4 Ching Court,
Shelton Street,
London, WC2H 9DG
Telephone (01) 836 1765
This also provides information on all aspects of eye care and has free leaflets available.

BBC Radio 4
Broadcasting House,
London, W1A 1AA
Telephone (01) 927 5966
Radio 4's 'In Touch' programme publishes the *In Touch Handbook* for visually handicapped people, which includes, for example, details of organizations providing books and/or newspapers on tape.

FEET

Chiropody should be free of charge to people of pensionable age if they apply through their doctor. But in some areas the NHS services can be very over-subscribed. Ask your doctor, district nurse or health visitor or ring your District Health Authority and ask the district chiropody service for a list of state registered chiropodists. Chiropodists hold clinics in surgeries, health centres, hospitals and other venues (transport may be provided) and some may come to your home.

Private chiropodists will be listed in your 'Yellow Pages'. In some areas, if there is a shortage of NHS

chiropodists, the NHS will pay the fee for private treatment – ask your district health authority whether you are able to do this.

The Society of Chiropodists,
53 Welbeck Street,
London, W1M 7HE
Telephone (01) 486 3381
The Society produces information leaflets about general foot care and can also supply addresses of local NHS chiropodists.

FITNESS

The Central Council of Physical Recreation
Francis House,
Francis Street,
London, SW1P 1DE
Telephone (01) 828 3163/4
The Council can advise about all sports.

Extend
(Exercise Training for the
Elderly or Disabled),
3 The Boulevard,
Sheringham,
Norfolk, N26 8LJ
Telephone (0263) 822479
Through its groups across the country, this organization provides lessons in movement by trained teachers; it also publishes exercise booklets and music cassettes.

The International Margaret Morris Movement
39 Hope Street,
Glasgow, G2 6AG
The organization has developed a system for physical movement with graded levels of achievement.

The Keep Fit Association
16 Upper Woburn Place,
London, WC1H 0QG
Telephone (01) 387 4349
This can give you addresses for local teachers and classes for all ages and also publishes leaflets on home exercises.

Running Sixties
120 Norfolk Avenue,
Sanderstead,
Surrey, CR2 8BS
Telephone (01) 657 7660

Slimnastics
14 East Sheen Avenue,
London, SW14 8AS
Telephone (01) 876 1838

The Sports Council
16 Upper Woburn Place,
London WC1H 0QP
Telephone (01) 388 1277
Contact the Council for information about the sports centres in your area; it also runs a 50-plus sports campaign.

See also the section on 'Health' below.

FUNERALS

The DSS leaflet D49, 'What to Do After a Death', includes a section on arranging a funeral. You can get a copy from your local DSS office or advice centre or by writing to the address given in the section on 'Benefits' (p. 200).

The National Association of Funeral Directors
57 Doughty Street,
London, WC1N 2NE
Telephone (01) 242 9388
The Association has a code of practice which they encourage members to display. They also operate a complaints procedure and a pre-payment scheme.

The British Institute of Funeral Directors
11 Regent Street,
Kingswood,
Bristol, BS15 2JX
Telephone (0272) 673609
The Institute produces a leaflet called Taking Care of the Future.

The Cremation Society of Great Britain
Brecon House,
16/16A Albion Place,
Maidstone,
Kent, ME14 5DZ
Telephone (0622) 688292/3
The Society offers free advice and help on any aspect of cremation and has a booklet which explains cremation services.

Non-religious ceremonies
The British Humanist Association
13 Prince of Wales Terrace,
London, W8 5PG
Telephone (01) 937 2341

The National Secular Society
702 Holloway Road,
London, N19 3NL
Telephone (01) 272 1266
If you do not want a religious ceremony, either of the above organizations may be able to help you find someone to conduct a ceremony or send a form of words which can be used.

Pre-payment schemes
The Independent Order of Odd Fellows at Manchester Unity Friendly Society
Odd Fellows House,
40 Fountain Street,
Manchester, M2 2AB
Telephone (061) 832 9361
The Order has its own funeral pre-payment scheme. Age Concern England's factsheet no. 27, which is available free from the Information Department on receipt of an s.a.e., includes details of financial help from the Social Fund and of planning and paying for a funeral in advance, including the Chosen Heritage scheme., for details of their scheme.

GARDENING

If you are finding it difficult to manage your garden, contact your local volunteer bureau or Age Concern group to see if they have any volunteers available who can help.

Horticultural Therapy
Goulds Ground,
Vallis Way,
Frome,
Somerset, BA11 3DW
Telephone (0373) 64782
This is a charity which aims to encourage the use of horticulture, agriculture and gardening for older as well as disabled and disadvantaged people. They have local groups and can give advice and support to groups and individuals.

Gardens for the Disabled Trust and Garden Club
Peening Farmhouse,
Wittersham,
Tenterden,
Kent, TN30 7NP
Telephone (0797) 7202
If you are disabled and want to garden actively, this organization may be able to give you practical and financial help.

The National Society of Allotment and Leisure Gardeners Ltd
Hunters Road,
Corby,
Northamptonshire, NN17 1JE
Telephone (0536) 66576
The Society encourages local gardening associations and gives its members free help and advice.

British Association of Landscape Industries
9 Henry Street,
Keighley,
West Yorkshire, BD21 3DR
Telephone (0535) 606139

Help the Aged have an advice leaflet on gardening which is available free of charge from the Information Desk, Gardening Leaflet, Help the Aged, St James' Walk, London, EC1R 0BE on receipt of a 23 × 18 cm (9 × 7 in) s.a.e.

GRANDPARENTS

POPETS
(Parents of Parents Eternal Triangle),
15 Calder Close,
Higher Compton,
Plymouth, PL3 6NT
Telephone (0752) 777036
A support group which counsels grandparents seeking access to their grandchildren, POPETS also campaigns to get the law changed to give grandparents access as a legal right.

National Association of Grandparents
8 Kirklee Drive,
Ashington, NE63 9RD
Telephone (0670) 817036
This also aims to secure access for concerned grandparents and to give them a platform. Membership of the organization entitles you to newsletters, sample conciliation letters, legal guidelines and the opportunity to join a friendship club.

HEALTH

General health information
The College of Health
2 Marylebone Road,
London, NW1 4DX
Telephone (01) 935 3251
An independent body aiming to promote health, the College supports self-help groups and produces information leaflets on various aspects of the NHS and alternative medicine.

Healthline
PO Box 499,
London E2 9PU
Telephone (01) 980 4848 (to listen to tapes)
Healthline is a free telephone health information service run by the Health Information Trust. The confidential service gives information about health and medical issues, for example hip replacement operations or hypothermia, in the form of pre-recorded tape messages. Most tapes detail symptoms, methods of treatment as appropriate and agencies and self-help groups to contact for further advice. For a list of the tapes available, write to the address above. The telephone line is open 24 hours a day.

The Health Education Authority (HEA),
Hamilton House,
Mabledon Place,
London WC1H 9TX
Telephone (01) 631 0930

In conjunction with Age Concern, the Authority is running the 'Age Well Campaign', which is a national campaign aimed at promoting positive attitudes to health in later life. The HEA also runs 'Look After Yourself' classes across the country. You can contact your local health education unit through your health authority.

Alternative therapies
The Institute for Complementary Medicine
21 Portland Place,
London, W1N 3AF
Telephone (01) 636 9543

This is a charity which promotes natural therapies. Send an s.a.e. to the Information Centre for information about practitioners in your area.

General Council and Register of Osteopaths
1–21 Suffolk Street,
London, SW1Y 4HG
Telephone (01) 839 2060

British Homoeopathic Association
27A Devonshire Street,
London, W1N 1RJ
Telephone (01) 935 2163.

Food and health
The British Nutrition Foundation
15 Belgrave Square,
London, SW1X 8PS
Telephone (01) 235 4904

The Foundation publishes a free booklet called *Healthy Eating for the Elderly*.

The Vegetarian Society of the UK Ltd
Parkdale,
Dunham Road,
Altrincham,
Cheshire, WA14 4QG
Telephone (061) 928 0793

On receipt of an s.a.e., the Society will send a free pack of literature.

Specific health problems
There are many organizations and self-help groups in existence which can provide advice and support for particular health problems. Some of these national organizations (many of which have networks of local groups) are listed below, but ask at a CAB or your GP about any others.

The National Council for Voluntary Organisations
26 Bedford Square,
London, WC1B 3HU
Telephone (01) 636 4066

The Council publishes a directory called *Health Help*, which lists health and disability organisations.

Alcoholics Anonymous
PO Box 1,
Stonebow House,
Stonebow,
York, YO1 2NJ
Telephone (0904) 644026

Arthritis Care
(formerly the British Rheumatism and Arthritis Association),
6 Grosvenor Crescent,
London, SW1X 7ER
Telephone (01) 235 0902

Back Pain Association
Grundy House,
31–33 Park Road
Teddington,
Middlesex, TW11 0AB
Telephone (01) 977 5754

BACUP
(British Association of Cancer United Patients),
121–123 Charterhouse Street,
London, EC1M 6AA
Telephone (01) 608 1661

British Diabetic Association
10 Queen Anne Street,
London, W1M 0BD
Telephone (01) 323 1531

Brittle Bone Society
Unit 4,
Block 20,
Carlunie Road,
Dunsinane Estate,
Dundee, DD2 3QT
Telephone (0382) 670603/817771

Cancer Link
17 Britannia Street,
London, WC1X 9JN
Telephone (01) 833 2451

Chest, Heart and Stroke Association
Tavistock House North,
Tavistock Square,
London, WC1H 9JE
Telephone (01) 387 3012

Depressives Associated
PO Box 5,
Castletown,
Portland,
Dorset, DT5 1BQ.

International Stress and Tension Control Society
The Priory Hospital,
Priory Lane,
London, SW15 5JJ.

Multiple Sclerosis Society
25 Effie Road,
London, SW6 1EE
Telephone (01) 736 6267/8

The National Osteoporosis Society
PO Box 10,
Barton Meade House,
Radstock,
Bath, BA3 3YB

This produces a range of mostly free material about the problems associated with brittle bones.

Parkinsons Disease Society of the UK
36 Portland Place,
London, W1N 3DG
Telephone (01) 323 1174

Voluntary Stroke Scheme,
Manor Farm,
Appleton,
Abingdon,
Oxfordshire, OX13 5JR
Telephone (0865) 862954

See also the sections on 'Fitness' (p. 203), 'Eyesight' (p. 203), 'Feet' (p. 203) and 'Hearing' (p. 206), as well as 'Health Services' (p. 205).

HEALTH SERVICES

Health service provision varies from area to area. In most areas health services are managed by the District Health Authority. Doctors (general practitioners), dentists, opticians and chemists, however, are managed by Family Practitioner Committees. Doctors are usually your first point of contact with the NHS. As well as diagnosing and treating many illnesses, they can refer you to other parts of the health service to get the help you need. Most GPs will make home visits if necessary.

Family Practitioner Committees (FPCs) administer and oversee the GP, dental and optical services in each area. They keep a list of local GPs, dentists, and opticians and can help with questions and complaints about the GP service.

The Association of CHCs for England and Wales
30 Drayton Park,
London, N5 1PB
Telephone (01) 609 8405
Community Health Councils (CHCs) represent the patients' views of the NHS and can give you information about the health services in your area. They can also help you sort out complaints about doctors, hospital treatment and other health services. Look in the telephone book for your nearest one or contact the above address.

Going to hospital

The geriatric hospital service focuses mainly on the physical problems of older people. If you have to make regular trips to an out-patient clinic, you may be entitled to help with your fares. Ask at your DSS office or CAB for the DSS leaflet H11 *Fares to Hospital*. The British Red Cross Society are sometimes able to provide a car service for out-patient appointments or if you are visiting someone in hospital – look in the telephone book for the branch nearest to you. If you are in hospital for more than a few weeks, your pension is affected. DSS leaflet N19 explains what happens to your social security benefit or pension – ask for a copy at your DSS office or CAB. Medical social workers in hospital can help you with problems on leaving hospital – make an appointment before you are discharged.

The Patients Association
Room 33,
18 Charing Cross Road,
London, WC2H 0HR
Telephone (01) 240 0671
The Association gives help and advice to individuals on any question relating to patient care and publishes booklets on patients' rights.

Other health workers

Health visitors do not undertake practical nursing tasks but visit patients in their home to help and advise with problems. They can help you contact other services and obtain aids and adaptations. Health visitors can be contacted via your GP or at a local health centre or clinic.

The Health Visitors Association
50 Southwark Street,
London, SE1 1UN
Telephone (01) 378 7255

Speech therapists can help with speech or language disorders or swallowing difficulties. They are usually based at health centres and clinics but do sometimes make home visits. Ask your doctor or hospital specialist.

Voluntary Organizations Communication and Language (VOCAL)
336 Brixton Road,
London, SW9 7AA
Telephone (01) 274 4029

District nurses visit patients in their homes at the request of a doctor. They provide nursing care, including the co-ordination of other services.

Occupational therapists (OTs) can usually only be seen if you are referred by a social worker, health visitor or district nurse. OTs help patients and their carers to manage daily tasks that have become difficult. If you are leaving hospital, ask a nurse to contact the hospital's OT for you.

Physiotherapists can visit patients at home and help with pain relief and mobility and other physical problems, but referral must be through your doctor or hospital.

Community psychiatric nurses (CPNs) visit people with mental health problems at home and advise and help patient and carer. Some health authorities have very few CPNs – ask your doctor or contact the health authority.

How to complain

MIND Publications
4th Floor, 24–32 Stephenson Way,
London, NW1 2HD
Telephone (01) 387 9126
MIND produces *Proper Channels* which is a priced guide on how to complain about any aspect of the health service.

HEARING

The Royal National Institute for the Deaf
(RNID),
105 Gower Street,
London, WC1E 6AH
Telephone (01) 387 8033
The RNID can give advice on devices to aid the deaf and hard of hearing. It publishes information leaflets and can also supply lists of public places fitted with an induction loop. The charity campaigns in the interests of deaf people and can provide funds for special needs.

The British Association for the Hard of Hearing
(BAHOH),
7–11 Armstrong Road,
London, W3 7JL
Telephone (01) 743 1110
Contact the Association for advice on any problem related to impaired hearing, particularly the use of

hearing aids. BAHOH has clubs and classes across the country and runs a pen-pal scheme. They have free leaflets available, including one called *Thinking about a Hearing Aid?*

The British Tinnitus Association
105 Gower Street,
London WC1E 6AH
Telephone (01) 387 8033 extension 244
The Association offers support to sufferers and has a network of self-help groups.

A free booklet entitled *How to Use Your Hearing Aid* is available from the DSS Leaflets Unit (see p. 200).

HEATING

Your local CAB will be able to give advice on general heating problems and your local DSS office will also be able to tell you what State help is available.

If you are worried about paying your bills, contact your local gas region or electricity board to see if they operate any payment schemes. This may involve 'slot' meters, monthly budgeting, saving stamps or flexible payments.

If you are threatened with disconnection or have already been disconnected, the Fuel Industries Code of Practice offers protection to consumers in certain 'hardship' categories. Contact your CAB as soon as possible. Your local SSD may be able to lend you appliances if you are disconnected or arrange for you to stay elsewhere for a short time.

There is a Winter Warmthline freefone advice service run by Age Concern, Help the Aged and Neighbourhood Energy Action, which can be contacted on Freefone 0800 289404. Age Concern England's Information Department also produces a factsheet *Help with Heating* and Help the Aged have a booklet called *Keep Warm This Winter*. Both publications are available free on receipt of a 23×18 cm (9×7 in) s.a.e., from the addresses given in the 'General' section (p. 198).

Advice on heating
GAS AND ELECTRICITY
If you are over 60 and live alone, ask your local gas board to arrange a free safety check on your gas appliances. British Gas produces a leaflet describing the services they offer to older and disabled people. It is available from the address below. For advice on various aspects of heating, such as how best to use appliances and get the most from your heating system, contact your local gas region or electricity board. Home Service Advisers (for gas)

and Energy Marketing Teams (for electricity) may be able to call on you in your home. Some electricity boards do free visual wiring checks for older and disabled people.

BRITISH GAS
PO Box 16,
Blandford Forum,
Dorset DT11 7UZ

SOLID FUEL
To get advice on solid fuel heating dial freephone 100 and ask for 'Real fires'.

OIL-FIRED HEATING
The Heating and Ventilating Contactors' Association
ESCA House,
34 Palace Court,
London, W2 4HY
Telephone (01) 229 2488
The Association can advise on oil central heating. Their home heating line is on (01) 229 5543.

Complaints
The Gas Consumers Council
6th floor, Abford House,
15 Wilton Road,
London, SW1V 1LT
Telephone (01) 931 9151

The Electricity Consultative Council
Brook House,
2–16 Torrington Place,
London, WC1E 7LL
Telephone (01) 636 5703
If you have a complaint about your gas or electricity, contact the Council concerned (head office addresses above). The addresses of the local Councils are on the back of your fuel bills.

The Domestic Coal Consumers' Council
Dean Bradley House,
52 Horseferry Road,
London, SW1P 2AG
Telephone (01) 233 0583
The Council will try and help sort out disputes with coal merchants.

Useful publications
A priced booklet called *Keeping Warm on a Pension* is published by the London Energy and Employment Network, 99 Midland Road, London, NW1 2AH, Telephone (01) 387 4393.
An annual guide to fuel rights is published by SHAC, 189A Old Brompton Road, London, SW5 0AR, Telephone (01) 373 7276

HOLIDAYS
The Holiday Care Service
2 Old Bank Chambers,
Station Road,
Horley,
Surrey, RH6 9HW
Telephone (0293) 774535
This provides free specialist information on all types of holidays for disabled and older people, including finance. It also runs the Holiday Helpers scheme, which puts enquirers in touch with volunteers.

RADAR
(Royal Association for Disability and Rehabilitation),
25 Mortimer Street,
London, W1N 8AB
Telephone (01) 637 5400
RADAR publishes holiday factsheets and books, including the annual guides *Holidays for Disabled People* and *Holidays and Travel Abroad*.

Some Age Concern groups organize their own holidays or may know of other local groups which do. Your SSD may have information about special facilities too.

Special holidays for older people
A number of commercial organizations also offer special holidays for older people.

Cosmos
Cosmos House,
1 Bromley Common,
Bromley,
Kent, BR2 9LX
Telephone (01) 464 3400

Intasun Golden Days
Intasun House,
2 Cromwell Avenue,
Bromley,
Kent, BR2 9AQ
Telephone (01) 290 0511

Portland Travel Trust
218 Great Portland Street,
London, W1N 5HG
Telephone (01) 388 3299

SAGA
(Senior Citizens Holidays) Ltd,
The Saga Building
Middelburg Square
Folkestone
Kent CT20 1AZ
Telephone (0303) 40000

Thomson Young At Heart Holidays
Greater London House,
Hampstead Road,
London, NW1 7SD
Telephone (01) 387 8484.

General holiday information
The appropriate tourist boards can give general travel advice and will have books and leaflets available. National tourist centres for foreign countries are usually in London.

The English Tourist Board
Thames Tower,
Blacks Road,
London, W6 9EZ
Telephone (01) 846 9000

The Welsh Tourist Board
Brunel House,
2 Fitzalan Road,
Cardiff, CF2 1UY
Telephone (0222) 499909

The Scottish Tourist Board
23 Ravelston Terrace,
Edinburgh, EH4 3EU
Telephone (031) 332 2433

The Northern Ireland Tourist Board
River House,
48 High Street,
Belfast, BT1 2DS
Telephone (0232) 231221/7

The Field Studies Council
Information Office,
Preston Montford,
Montford Bridge,
Shrewsbury, SY4 1HW
Telephone (0743) 850674
This runs courses at its centres nationwide.

The Association of British Travel Agents
55–57 Newman Street,
London, W1P 4AH
Telephone (01) 637 2444
The Association has an agreed code of conduct and runs a scheme to deal with complaints.

Travel Companions
63 Mill Lane,
London, NW6 1NB
Telephone (01) 431 1984 or 202 8478
Aimed at people aged 30 to 75 this organisation provides a service for those who are looking for company to share a holiday.

Home exchange and caretaking
Home Exchange Holidays
377 Fishponds Road,
Fishponds,
Bristol, BS5 6RS
Telephone (0272) 654564
For an annual fee, this organisation provides members with international and local home exchange holiday services.

Homesitters
The Old Bakery,
Western Road,
Tring,
Hertfordshire, HP23 4BB
Telephone (0442) 891188

Universal Aunts
250 Kings Road,
London, SW3 5UE
Telephone (01) 351 5767
You can have a paid holiday by being a caretaker when a family is away on holiday. Both the above agencies provide and recruit for homesitting services.

Wartime reminiscence
The Pilgrimage Department
Royal British Legion,
Pall Mall,
London, SW1Y 5JY

The Commonwealth War Graves Commission
2 Marlow Road,
Maidenhead,
Berkshire, SL6 7DX
If you are a war widow and wish to visit your husband's grave, write to either of the above.

Battlefield Tours
Golden Key House,
15 Market Street,
Sandwich,
Kent, CT13 9DA
Telephone (0304) 612248
This organizes pilgrimages for the Royal British Legion.

HOUSING
The availability and quality of housing advice will vary greatly, depending on where you live, but your local authority housing department, local housing advice or housing aid centre, if there is one, and your local CAB will be able to provide information on the housing situation in your area.

Shelter
88 Old Street,
London, EC1V 9AX
Telephone (01) 253 0202
This is a national organization which gives advice to the homeless or anyone with a housing problem.

SHAC
(London Housing Aid Centre),
189A Old Brompton Road,
London, SW5 0AR
Telephone (01) 373 7276
SHAC provides Londoners with an independent telephone housing advice service and publishes a priced leaflet called *Moving Home in Retirement.*

Useful publications
Your Home in Retirement is a free booklet, produced by the Department of the Environment (DOE). It is available from CABs and housing advice centres or you can write to the Public Enquiry Unit, DOE, Room P1/003, 2 Marsham Street, London, SW1P 3EB.

Housing Options for Older People is a book published by Age Concern England. It also publishes a number of housing factsheets and booklets including one on *Sharing Your Home* which looks at the pros and cons of moving in with relatives.

The Housing Yearbook is published every year by Longmans. Ask if your local reference library has a copy, as it lists all the housing agencies.

Moving on
The British Association of Removers
277 Gray's Inn Road,
London, WC1X 8SY
Telephone (01) 837 3088
Contact the Association a free leaflet on moving house and a list of approved companies.

Moving abroad. If you are thinking of moving abroad, you may like to buy, or borrow from a library, *Retiring Abroad* by Harry Brown (published by Expatextra Ltd), or *Living and Retiring Abroad* by Michael Furnell (Kogan Page Ltd) – ask at bookshops for more details.

The Federation of Overseas Property Developers, Agents and Consultants
International House,
15–19 Kingsway,
London, WC2B 6UU
The Federation can tell you which builders are members and can put you in touch with solicitors specializing in overseas property sales.

Mobile homes. If you are considering a mobile (or 'park') home, a DOE booklet, *Mobile Homes – a Guide for Residents and Site Owners* (Housing booklet no. 16), is available free from your CAB or advice centre. Shelter publishes a free guide to buying mobile homes – send an s.a.e. to the Mobile Homes Unit at the address given on the left.

The Park Homes Residents' Guild
6 Morngate Park,
Bridport,
Dorchester, DT2 9JS
Telephone (0305) 88491

Rented accommodation
If you are interested in moving to rented housing in a different area, ask your council's housing department about the National Mobility Scheme or write direct to the Scheme, PO Box 170, London, SW1P 3PX. Only a few places are available under the Scheme. Council tenants can ask about the Tenants Exchange Scheme at their housing department or CAB or write to the same address. The Locatex Bureau, PO Box 1, March, Cambridgeshire, PE15 8HJ, Telephone (0354) 54050, is a private bureau which offers, for a fee, to help council and housing association tenants move to another area.

Lists of housing associations with special rented accommodation for older people are available from Age Concern England if you send an s.a.e. to the Information Department and indicate which counties or boroughs you are interested in. (See the section on 'General Information' at the beginning of this chapter for the address.) Or you can contact some of the larger national associations given below to see if accommodation is available in particular areas.

The Abbeyfield Society
186–192 Darkes Lane,
Potters Bar,
Hertfordshire, EN6 1AB
Telephone (0707) 44845
The Society provides extra care in small 'family' households.

Anchor Housing Association
Anchor House,
269A Banbury Road,
Oxford, OX2 7HU
Telephone (0865) 31151/311511

Hanover Housing Association
168D High Street,
Egham,
Surrey, TW20 9HX
Telephone (0784) 38361/5

Royal British Legion Housing Association
PO Box 32,
Unit 2, St John's Industrial Estate,
Penn,
High Wycombe,
Buckinghamshire,
HP10 9JF
Telephone (0494) 813771

Servite Houses Ltd
125 Brompton Road,
London, SW7 3RP
Telephone (01) 370 5466

The Housing Corporation
Maple House,
149 Tottenham Court Road,
London W1P 0BW
Telephone (01) 387 9466

The National Federation of Housing Associations
175 Grays Inn Road,
London, WC1X 8UP,
Telephone (01) 278 6571
Further information about housing association accommodation can be obtained from either of the above.

The National Association of Almshouses
Billingbear Lodge,
Wokingham,
Berkshire, RG11 5RU
Telephone (0344) 52922/3
The Association can provide information on local charities which administer almshouses.

Sheltered housing
The New Homes Marketing Board
82 New Cavendish Street,
London, W1M 8AD
Telephone (01) 580 5588
Sheltered housing to buy is available from many private companies. On receipt of a large s.a.e., the Board can send a list of those offering it.

The Housing Enquiry Service 'Hotline'
Telephone (01) 935 7464
Telephone the 'Hotline' for details of new homes being built in specific areas, including some sheltered developments.

Sheltered Housing Services Ltd
8–9 Abbey Parade,
London, W5 1EE
Telephone (01) 997 9313
This nationwide estate agency keeps details of sheltered housing in particular areas. A small fee is refunded after a purchase is made.

Park Housing Association
Brett House,
Park Road,
London, W10 4HT
Telephone (01) 961 2277
Contact the Association for details of their 'Sundowner' Scheme.

'Home for Life'
Concept House,
193 Bridges Road,
Crawley,
West Sussex, RH10 1LG
Telephone (0293) 552751
Contact the above address for details of this scheme.

Useful publications
Retirement Homes, a magazine available in large newsagents, lists all current developments across the country.

A Buyer's Guide to Sheltered Housing is published by Age Concern England and their factsheet no. 2 is about sheltered housing for sale. ACE's factsheet no. 24 outlines the options for those not able to buy outright. Both factsheets are available free on receipt of an s.a.e. from the Information Department. If you are interested in shared ownership, ask for the DOE's booklet on the subject from your CAB or advice centre.

Staying in your own home
Help the Aged
13 High Street,
Horley,
Surrey, RH6 7BH
Telephone (0293) 820282
Contact the housing department to find out about Help the Aged's 'gifted' scheme.

If you are thinking about taking in lodgers, ask at your CAB or advice centre for the free government leaflets *Letting Rooms in Your Home* and/or *Letting Your Home or Retirement Home*.

If you have been a council tenant for more than two years, you may want to find out about the *Right to Buy* scheme – ask for the free leaflet *Your Right to Buy Your Home*.

If you are considering a home income plan or a home reversion scheme, details of schemes known are included in Age Concern England's factsheet no. 12, *Raising an Income from Your Home*. A priced booklet called *Using Your Home as Capital* is also available.

See also the sections on 'Residential and nursing homes' (p. 216) and 'Repairs and Improvements' (p. 215).

INSULATION

Insulation and draught-proofing are the best ways to save money on heating bills. If you receive income support or housing benefit, contact your local council's grant section to see if you are eligible for a grant to pay for part of the cost of loft insulation. You can also get a copy of a free DOE booklet, *Save Money on Loft Insulation*, from your council's housing department.

Loft insulation is a simple do-it-yourself task, but if you are unable to carry out insulation yourself, ask your local Age Concern group if they can help you or if they know of anyone who can.

Neighbourhood Energy Action
2–4 Bigg Market,
Newcastle-upon-Tyne, NE1 1UW
Telephone (091) 261 5677
This organization will be able to tell you if there is a local energy project in your area. Many of these projects also give advice on how to use fuel efficiently.

The National Association of Loft Insulation Contractors

The Draught Proofing Advisory Association

The National Cavity Insulation Association
PO Box 12,
Haslemere,
Surrey, GU27 3AN
Telephone (0428) 54011
All the above organizations, at the same address, can give further information about insulation.

The Energy Efficiency Office
Room 1312, Thames House South,
London, SW1 4AJ
Telephone (01) 211 3850
This publishes free guides on insulating and heating your home (see also Heating, p. 206).

INSURANCE

The British Insurers' Association
BIBA House,
14 Bevis Marks,
London, EC3A 7NT
Telephone (01) 623 9043
The Association can help you find an insurance broker. The Association produces various free

leaflets and operates a conciliation service.

The Association of British Insurers
Aldermary House,
10–15 Queen Street,
London, EC4N 1TT
Telephone (01) 248 4477
This also produces leaflets about different types of insurance.

The Institute of Insurance Brokers
Barclays Bank,
Bank Chambers,
College Street,
Rushden,
Northamptonshire, NN10 0NW
Telephone (0933) 410003
This provides similar information to the above.

Discounts and special policies
Some insurance companies offer discounts or special policies for older people. These include:

Age Concern Insurance Services Ltd
Orbital House,
85–87 Croydon Road,
Caterham,
Surrey, CR3 6PD
Telephone (0883) 46964

Hill House Hammond Ltd
Retired Householders Insurance Department,
Freepost BS1162,
Lewins Mead,
Bristol, BS1 2BR
Telephone (0272) 292906

Legal and General
Temple Court,
11 Queen Victoria Street,
London, EC4N 4TP
Telephone (01) 248 9678

Norwich Union
Surrey Street,
Norwich, NR1 3NG
Telephone (0603) 62200

Royal Insurance plc
New Hall Place,
Liverpool, L69 3HS
Telephone (051) 227 4422

Scarborough Building Society
PO Box 6, 442 Scalby Road,
Scarborough,
N. Yorkshire, YO12 6EQ
Telephone (0723) 368155

Zurich Insurance Company
PO Box 20,
Zurich House,
Stanhope Road,
Portsmouth, PO1 1DU
Telephone (0705) 82200.

Health insurance
The Exeter Hospital Aid Society
5–7 Palace Gate,
Exeter, EX1 1UE
Telephone (0392) 75361

Kent Insurance and Securities Services (Overseas) Limited
PO Box 30,
27A Bank Street,
Ashford,
Kent, TN24 9YY
Telephone (0233) 38374
It can be very difficult for older people to obtain private health insurance – contact an independent insurance broker for advice. These two companies specialize in healthcare overseas and accept older age groups.

Complaints about insurance
If you have a complaint about a claim and you feel that the company is not being co-operative, you contact one of the organizations below.

The Insurance Ombudsman Bureau
31 Southampton Row,
London, WC1B 5HJ
Telephone (01) 242 8613

The Personal Insurance Arbitration Service
Chartered Institute of Arbitrators,
75 Cannon Street,
London, EC4N 5BH
Telephone (01) 236 8761

See also the section on 'Savings and investments' (see p. 217).

ISOLATION

Conversation by Correspondence
(Friends by Post),
6 Bollin Court,
Macclesfield Road,
Wilmslow,
Cheshire, SK9 2AP
Telephone (0625) 527044
This organization aims to fight loneliness by linking people of all ages with someone to write to once a

week or fortnight. If you want further information enclose an s.a.e.

Contact
15 Henrietta Street,
Covent Garden,
London, WC2E 8QH
Telephone (01) 240 0630
Contact aims to encourage older people living alone to establish contact with others. In a particular area, a small group of volunteers and housebound elderly people meet for tea once a month on a Sunday afternoon at the home of a volunteer.

Wider Horizons
'Westbrook',
Back Lane,
Malvern,
Worcester, WR14 2HJ
Telephone (06845) 64462
This promotes wider interests among housebound and lonely people by providing opportunities for new interests and friendships between members.

If you would like someone to visit you in your home on a regular basis, get in touch with your local Age Concern group or volunteer bureau (both addresses should be in the telephone book) to see if they have any volunteers available.

LEGAL HELP

Your local Citizens Advice Bureau will be able to supply lists of local solicitors and some Bureaux run free legal sessions.

If your income is below certain limits free legal advice may be available. Ask at your CAB for the free government leaflet 'Legal Aid Financial Limits' to see what the current limits are. Your CAB or the Law Society can tell you which solicitors in your area work under the legal aid scheme.

The Law Society
113 Chancery Lane,
London, WC2A 1PL
Telephone (01) 242 1222

The Law Society of Scotland
26 Drumsheugh Gardens,
Edinburgh, EH3 7YR
Telephone (031) 226 7411

The Law Society of Northern Ireland
Law Society House,
90–106 Victoria Street,
Belfast, BT1 3JZ
Telephone (0232) 231614

The Legal Aid Head Office
Newspaper House,
8–16 New Street,
London, EC4N 3BN
Telephone (01) 353 7411
Head Office can send free leaflets about the scheme. These leaflets are also available in some ethnic languages.

Law Centres Federation
Duchess House,
18–19 Warren Street,
London, W1P 5DB
Telephone (01) 387 8368
There may be a law centre giving free legal advice in your area – check in the telephone book, ask at a CAB, or contact the Federation.

The Solicitors Complaints Bureau
Portland House,
Stag Place,
London, SW1E 5Bl
Telephone (01) 834 2288
The Bureau has a leaflet called *Complaints About Solicitors' Charges*.

Lawline
Telephone (0898) 600600
This is a 24-hour telephone service which gives tape-recorded advice on over a hundred legal problems, including disputes with neighbours for example. At the time of writing, calls cost 22p per minute off-peak and 35p per minute at peak periods.

The Solicitors Family Law Association
24 Croydon Road,
Keston,
Kent, BR2 6EJ
Telephone (0689) 502271
The Association can put you in touch with specialist divorce solicitors in your area.

LEISURE

The leisure and recreation department of your local authority will be able to give you information about local facilities – look in the telephone book under the name of your county or borough.

Your local library, as well as being able to supply books, journals, cassettes and videos, will also be able to tell you about local and national activities.

There are many organizations that you can contact depending on your interests. Some of these are listed in the other sections such as 'Adult education' (p. 199), 'Fitness' (p. 203), 'Gardening' (p. 204),

'Holidays' (p. 207), 'Volunteering' (p. 220) and 'Work' (p. 221). Others include:

The Arts Council of Great Britain
105 Piccadilly,
London, W1V 0AU
Telephone (01) 629 9495

The Crafts Council
12 Waterloo Place,
London, SW1Y 4AE
Telephone (01) 930 4811

The National Trust
36 Queen Anne's Gate,
London, SW1H 9AS
Telephone (01) 222 9251

The National Trust for Scotland
5 Charlotte Square,
Edinburgh, EH2 4DU
Telephone (031) 226 5922

The Royal Society for Nature Conservation
The Green,
Nettleham,
Lincoln, LN2 2NR
Telephone (0522) 752326

The Royal Society for the Protection of Birds
(RSPB),
The Lodge,
Sandy,
Bedfordshire, SG19 2DL
Telephone (0767) 80551

Hobbies

ADULT EDUCATION
Adult Residential Colleges Association
19B De Montfort Street,
Leicester, LE1 7GE

Open University
Walton Hall,
Milton Keynes, MK7 6AA

University of The Third Age
(USA)
6 Parkside Gardens,
London, SW19 5EY

AMATEUR RADIO
Radio Society of Great Britain
LAMBDA House,
Cranbourne Road,
Potters Bar,
Hertfordshire, EN6 3JW

ANGLING
National Anglers Council
11 Cowgate,
Peterborough,
Cambridgeshire, PE1 1LZ

National Federation of Anglers
2 Wilson Street,
Derby, DE1 1PG

ANTIQUE COLLECTING
Antique Collectors Club
5 Church Street,
Woodbridge,
Suffolk, IP12 1DS

ARCHAEOLOGY
Council of British Archaeology
112 Kennington Road,
London, SE11 6RE

ASTRONOMY
British Astronomical Association
Burlington House,
Piccadilly,
London, W1V 0NL

BAND PLAYING
British Federation of Brass Bands
21 Woulds Court,
Moira,
Burton-on-Trent,
Staffordshire, DE12 6HB

BASKET MAKING
Basketmakers Association
Dean Way,
Chalfont St Giles,
Buckinghamshire, HP8 4JL

BEE KEEPING
International Bee Research Association
Hill House,
Chalfont St Peter,
Gerrards Cross,
Buckinghamshire, SL9 0NR

BIRD WATCHING
Royal Society for The Protection of Birds
The Lodge,
Sandy,
Bedfordshire, SG19 2DL

BOATING
Inland Waterways Association
114 Regent's Park Road,
London NW1 8UQ

Royal Yachting Association
Victoria Way,
Woking,
Surrey, GU21 1EQ

BRASS RUBBING
Monumental Brass Society
c/o Society of Antiquaries,
Burlington House,
Piccadilly,
London, W1V 0HS

BRIDGE
English Bridge Union
15B High Street,
Thame,
Oxfordshire, OX9 2BZ

CALLIGRAPHY
Society of Scribes and Illuminators
c/o BCC,
43 Earlham Street,
London, WC2H 9LD

CAMPING
Camping and Caravanning Club of Great Britain and Ireland Ltd
11 Lower Grosvenor Place,
London, SW1W 0EY

CHESS
British Chess Federation
9A Grand Parade,
St Leonards-on-Sea,
East Sussex, TN38 0DD

CINEMATOGRAPHY
Institute of Amateur Cinematographers
63 Woodfield Lane,
Ashtead,
Surrey, KT21 2BT

COIN COLLECTING
British Association of Numismatic Societies
Department of Coins and Metals,
Manchester Museum,
The University,
Oxford Road,
Manchester, M13 9PL

British Numismatic Society
Warburg Institute,
Woburn Square,
London, WC1H 0AB

CONJURING
Magic Circle
84 Chenies Mews,
London, WC1E 6AH

CROQUET
Croquet Association
Hurlingham Club,
London, SW6 3PR

DANCING
The Imperial Society of Teachers of Dancing
Euston Hall,
Birkenhead Street,
London, WC1H 8BE
The Society can supply addresses of teachers in your area.

DOG SHOWING
Kennel Club
1–5 Clarges Street,
Piccadilly,
London, W1Y 8AB

EMBROIDERY
Embroiderers' Guild
Apartment 41A,
Hampton Court Palace,
East Molesey,
Surrey, KT8 9AL

ENVIRONMENTAL CONSERVATION
Conservation Trust
c/o George Palmer School,
Northumberland Avenue,
Reading,
Berkshire

FLOWER ARRANGING
National Association of Flower Arrangement Societies of Great Britain
21 Denbigh Street,
London, SW1V 2HF

FOLK DANCING/FOLK SINGING
English Folk Dance and Song Society
2 Regent's Park Road,
London, NW1 7AY

GARDENING
National Society of Allotment and Leisure Gardeners Ltd
O'Dell House,
Hunters Road,
Corby,
Northamptonsire, NN17 1JE

The Royal Horticultural Society
Vincent Square,
London, SW1P 2PE
and RHS Garden,
Wisley, Surrey

GENEALOGY
Society of Genealogists
14 Charterhouse Buildings,
Goswell Road,
London, EC1M 7BA

GEOLOGY
The Geologists' Association
Burlington House,
Piccadilly,
London, W1V 0JU

HANDBELL RINGING
Handbell Ringers of Great Britain
36 Kensington Drive,
Bury,
Lancashire, BL8 2DE

HERALDRY
The Heraldry Society
44–45 Museum Street,
London, WC1A 1LY

HISTORY
The British Association for Local History
The Mill Manager's House,
Cromford, Matlock,
Derbyshire, DE4 3RQ

Historical Association
59A Kennington Park Road,
London, SE11 4JH

HOSPITAL BROADCASTING
National Association of Hospital Broadcasting Organizations
5 Portreath Drive,
Allestree,
Derby, DE3 2BJ

JIGSAW PUZZLES
British Jigsaw Puzzle Library
Old Homend,
Stretton Grandison,
Ledbury,
Hereford, HR8 2TW

MARQUETRY
Marquetry Society
2A The Ridgeway,
St Albans,
Herts, AL4 9RU

MATCHBOX COLLECTING
British Matchbox Label and Booklet Society
22 Githa Road,
Hastings,
East Sussex, TN35 5JU

MILITARY HISTORY
Military Historical Society
30 Edgeborough Way,
Bromley,
Kent, BR1 2UA

MODEL MAKING
Historical Model Railway Society
21 St James Road,
Harpenden,
Hertfordshire, AL5 4PB

Miniature Armoured Fighting Vehicle Association
15 Berwick Avenue,
Heaton Mersey,
Stockport,
Cheshire, SK4 3AA

Model Power Boat Association Ltd
36 Broadmeads,
Ware,
Herts

Model Railway Club
4 Calshot Street,
London, N1 9AT

Society of Model and Experimental Engineers
Marshall House,
28 Wanless Road,
London, SE24

Scottish Aeromodellers Association
6 Crookston Path,
Glasgow, G52 3LN

Society of Model Aeronautical Engineers Ltd
47 Vaughan Way,
Leicester, LE1 4SE

Society of Model Shipwrights
8 Alan Close,
Dartford,
Kent, DA1 5AX

MUSIC/DRAMA
National Operatic and Dramatic Association
1 Crestfield Street,
London, WC1H 8AU

ORGAN PLAYING
Incorporated Association of Organists
15th Floor,
Kennedy Tower,
St Chad's Queensway,
Birmingham, B4 6JG

Royal College of Organists
Kensington Gore,
London, SW7 2QS

PAINTING AND DRAWING
Federation of British Artists
17 Carlton House Terrace,
London, SW1Y 5AH

PHILATELY
National Philatelic Society
27 King Street,
London, WC2 8JD

Royal Philatelic Society Ltd
41 Devonshire Place,
London, W1N 1PE

PHOTOGRAPHY
Camera Club
8 Great Newport Street,
London, WC2H 7JA

Royal Photographic Society of Great Britain
The Octagon,
Milsom Street,
Bath,
Avon, BA1 1DN

POETRY WRITING
Poetry Society
21 Earls Court Square,
London, SW5 9DE

PUPPETRY
British Puppet and Model Theatre Guild
18 Maple Road,
Yeading,
Hayes,
Middlesex, UB4 9LP

RAILWAYS
Railway Club
202 High Holborn,
London, WC1V 6JS

Railway Correspondence and Travel Society
1 Elmore Close,
Coventry, CV3 2QS

Stephenson Locomotive Society
25 Regency Close,
Chigwell,
Essex, IG7 5NY

RECORDER PLAYING
Society for Recorder Players
469 Merton Road,
London, SW18 5LD

RIFLE SHOOTING
National Small Bore Rifle Association
Lord Roberts House,
Bisley Camp,
Brookwood,
Woking,
Surrey, GU24 0NP

SCRABBLE
Write to the Scrabble Club Coordinator
42 Elthiron Road,
London, SW6 4BW
The Co-ordinator will tell you whether there is a scrabble club near you.

SHELL COLLECTING
British Shell Collectors' Club
8 Ely Close,
New Malden,
Surrey, KT3 4LG

Conchological Society of Great Britain and Ireland
51 Wychwood Avenue,
Luton,
Bedfordshire, LU2 7HT

TAPE RECORDING
Federation of British Tape Recordists
20 Plantation Close,
Saffron Walden,
Essex, CB11 4DS

THEATRE/DRAMA
British Theatre Association
9 Fitzroy Square,
London, W1P 6AE

MANAGEMENT OF CONTINENCE

Some district health authorities have continence advisers who can assess and advise, and tell you about available aids. Ask your district nurse if you have one, or your doctor, or look up the number of your health authority in the telephone book and ring direct.

The Disabled Living Foundation
380–384 Harrow Road,
London, W9 2HU,
Telephone (01) 289 6111
The Foundation has an Incontinence Advisory Service, which is open Monday–Thursday – ask for the Incontinence Adviser.

In some areas, the district health authority or social services department run laundry services. Ask your doctor or social worker if there is one in your area.

Several companies which manufacture or retail incontinence products are now providing Freefone helplines (individuals still need to be assessed by a doctor or nurse):

Bard Helpline
(0800) 591 783 or write to
Bard Limited,
Freepost,
Sunderland, SR1 0BR

Coloplast Service
dial 100 and ask for Freefone Coloplast Services, or write to Nurse Advisor,
Incontinence,
The Coloplast Service,
Peterborough,
Cambridgeshire, PE2 0FX

In Care Helpline
dial 100 and ask for Freefone In Care Helpline or write to Incare Medical Products,
43 Castle Street,
Reading,
Berkshire, RG1 7SN

MENTAL ILLNESS

Services available to people with mental confusion or dementia and their carers vary greatly from area to area. Your Local Social Services Department, Age Concern or carers' group should be able to tell you about local provision. Older people who become confused may be referred by their doctor to the psychiatric service, which assesses whether the person can manage at home with help, if they need to go to a day hospital for part of the week or if they should go on the waiting list for a long-term hospital bed.

The Alzheimer's Disease Society
158–160 Balham High Road,
London, SW12 9BN
Telephone (01) 675 6557
The Society gives counselling, information and support to the families of people suffering from dementia or the sufferers themselves. The Society forms local support groups for relatives, can tell you about the illness and the help that is available and has produced a guide to caring for someone with dementia.

MIND
22 Harley Street,
London, W1N 2ED
Telephone (01) 637 0741
MIND can give advice on all aspects of mental illness, particularly legal and welfare rights. They

also produce a range of publications – write for a list to MIND Mail Order, 24–32 Stephenson Way, London, NW1 2HD, Telephone (01) 387 9126

The Scottish Association for Mental Health
Atlantic House,
38 Gardner's Crescent,
Edinburgh, EH3 8DQ
Telephone (031) 229 9687

The Northern Ireland Association for Mental Health
84 University Street,
Belfast, BT7 1HE
Telephone (0232) 328474

MENCAP
(Royal Society for People with Mental Handicaps),
12A Maddox Street,
London, W1R 9PL
Telephone (01) 491 0727
MENCAP has an information service that carers can contact.

Booklets and other information

Caring for Someone with Dementia is a Channel 4 booklet available free on receipt of an A5 envelope, from PO Box 4000, London W3 6XJ.

To collect and spend pension or benefits for someone else, you have to apply to become an 'appointee' (as opposed to an 'agent' who merely collects the money) – ask at your local DHSS office.

For information leaflets about Enduring Powers of Attorney and the Court of Protection, send an s.a.e. to the Public Trustee Office, 24 Kingsway, London, WC2B 6JX, Telephone (01) 269 7000.
MIND have produced a book about the Court of Protection – contact MIND Publications at the address left.

PENSIONS

Ask at your local DSS office or CAB for material about state pensions. The free DSS leaflet FB6 is called *Retiring? Your Pension and Other Benefits* and is a good introduction – leaflet NP32, *Your Retirement Pension* gives more details. Or you can ring the social security Freefone on 0800 666555.

Age Concern England have three factsheets which may be useful – numbers 20–22 cover National Insurance contributions and retirement pensions up to 1948, from 1948 to 1975, and 1975 onwards respectively. The priced annual guide, *Your Rights*, also includes a digest of the state pension.

The Occupational Pensions Advisory Service
(OPAS),
8A Bloomsbury Square,
London, WC1A 2VA
Telephone (01) 831 5511
This is a charity with a network of unpaid advisers who can be contacted through CABs.

The Society of Pension Consultants
Ludgate House,
Ludgate Circus,
London, EC4A 2AB
Telephone (01) 353 1688
The Society can tell you about consultants operating in your area – it may be worth going to a consultant if a lot of money is involved.

The Company Pensions Information Centre
7 Old Park Lane,
London, W1Y 3LJ
Telephone (01) 493 4757
The Centre does not deal with individual cases, but publishes booklets on pension schemes.

If you are thinking of going abroad ask for leaflet NI 38 *Social Security Abroad* or write to the DSS Overseas Office, Longbenton, Newcastle-upon-Tyne, NE98 1YX.

PENSIONER ORGANIZATIONS

The National Federation of Retirement Pensions Associations (Pensioners Voice)
14 St Peter Street,
Blackburn,
Lancashire, BB2 2HD
Telephone (0254) 52606
This is a pressure group with branches across the UK, which campaign for an improvement in older people's quality of life.

The British Pensioners and Trade Unions Action Association
Norman Dodd's House,
315 Bexley Road,
Erith, Kent, DA8 3EZ
Telephone (0322) 335464
The Association is open to all pensioners. Members are grouped into Pensioner Action Groups which campaign at local level for older people.

The National Pensioners Convention
c/o The Secretary,
Congress House,
Great Russell Street,
London, WC1B 3LS
Telephone (01) 636 4030
This operates under the aegis of the TUC and

organizes local and national rallies.

Pensioners for Peace International
c/o The Secretary,
43 Dickerage Road,
Kingston-upon-Thames,
Surrey, KT1 3SR
Telephone (01) 942 0204
This organization mobilizes older people who want to become active in the cause of peace and disarmament.

The Campaign for Equal State Pension Ages
c/o the Secretary,
'Constables',
Windsor Road,
Ascot, Berkshire, SL5 7LF
Telephone (0990) 21167
The Campaign works on behalf of older men who face discrimination in pension age benefits and concessions.

Pensioners Link (formerly Task Force)
17 Balfe Street,
London, N1 9EB
Telephone (01) 278 5501/4
This is a pressure group which sets up pensioner groups and projects across London.

The London Joint Council for Senior Citizens
c/o The General Secretary,
Transport House,
Smith Square,
London, SW1P 3JD
Telephone (01) 929 3866
The Council acts as an umbrella organization.

Occupational groups
Many pensioner organizations have developed from employers' or trade unions' concern about the welfare of their retired employees – contact your former employer or union to see if there is an appropriate group. Five larger ones are:

Civil Service Pensioners Alliance
c/o Hon. General Secretary,
9 Woodend Drive,
South Ascot,
Berkshire, SL5 9BD
Telephone (0990) 23886

National Federation of Post Office and British Telecom Pensioners
Carlton Court,
64 Alma Street,
Luton,
Bedfordshire, LU1 2PR
Telephone (0582) 459105

National Health Retirement Fellowship
St Mary Abbot's Hospital,
Marloes Road,
London, W8 5LQ
Telephone (01) 937 4931

National and Local Government Officers Association (NALGO),
Retired Members Assistant,
1 Mabledon Place,
London, WC1H 9AJ
Telephone (01) 388 2366

Transport and General Workers Union Retired Members Association
c/o The President, TGWU,
Transport House,
Smith Square,
London, SW1P 3JB
Telephone (01) 828 3806

RELATIONSHIPS

The British Association for Counselling
37A Sheep Street,
Rugby,
Warwickshire, CV21 3BX
Telephone (0788) 78328/9
If you want to find out what counselling services are available in your area, contact the Association, which publishes directories of organizations providing individual counsellors.

Relate (formerly the National Marriage Guidance Council)
Herbert Grey College,
Little Church Street,
Rugby, CV21 3AP
Telephone (0788) 73241

The Scottish Marriage Guidance Council
26 Frederick Street,
Edinburgh, EH2 2JR
Telephone (031) 225 5006

The Divorce Conciliation Advisory Service
38 Ebury Street,
London, SW1W 0LU
Telephone (01) 730 2422
The Service will give you the addresses of local services which offer conciliation and counselling.

The Catholic Marriage Advisory Council
Clitheroe House
1 Blythe Mews
London W14 0NW
Telephone (01) 371 1341

The Jewish Marriage Council
23 Ravenshurst Avenue,
London, NW4 4EL
Telephone (01) 203 6311

The Association to Aid the Sexual and Personal Relationships of People with Disabilities
(SPOD) 286 Camden Road,
London, N7 0BJ
Telephone (01) 607 8851
SPOD can put you in contact with appropriate counsellors as well as providing information.

London Lesbian and Gay Switchboard
BM Switchboard,
London, WC1N 3XX
Telephone (01) 837 7324
This is a 24-hour information and help service for lesbians and gay men and can refer you to Evergreens, a social/support group for older gay men, or the Older Lesbian Network.

The Family Planning Association
27–35 Mortimer Street,
London, W1N 7RJ
Telephone (01) 636 7866
Your local family planning association will be able to give advice about sexual therapy – look in the phone book or contact their headquarters at the above address.

REPAIRS AND IMPROVEMENTS

If you are a tenant and you are having problems getting repairs done, contact your tenants association if you have one or your CAB or advice centre. Council tenants and most housing association tenants, now have the 'right to repair', i.e. to carry out certain minor repairs themselves and claim payment back. Ask your CAB about the scheme and for a copy of the free government leaflet *Right to Repair* (Housing Booklet no. 2)

SHAC
189A Old Brompton Road,
London, SW5 0AR
Telephone (01) 373 7276
SHAC publishes priced guides on rights to repair for private, housing association and council tenants.

Extensive repairs
For larger repair work, homeowners can ask for the free government leaflet *Paying for Repairs and Improvement to Your Home* at your CAB or advice centre. Disabled people are given priority for council grants. 'Maturity' (interest-only) loans from building societies are also difficult to obtain and you will have to ask around local societies. To pay for

smaller repair work you may have to investigate unsecured loans from societies or bank loans. If you receive income support you may be able to get a loan from the social fund – ask for details at your CAB and see DSS leaflet SB16, *A Guide to the Social Fund.*

Help for older home-owners

In some areas there are special 'Staying Put' or 'Care and Repair' agency advice schemes which help older home-owners arrange repairs and improvements. Your local CAB or your council's housing department should be able to tell you if there is one in your area.

Age Concern England's factsheet no. 13 is about sources of financial help for older home-owners. (See the 'General' section on p. 196 for the address.) A priced booklet, *Are You Living Comfortably?*, is also available.

The National Home Improvement Council

26 Store Street,
London, WC1E 7BT
Telephone (01) 636 2562
The Council can supply lists of contractors.

The Federation of Master Builders

Gordon Fisher House,
33 John Street,
London, WC1N 2BB
Telephone (01) 242 7583

The Building Employers Confederation

82 New Cavendish Street,
London, W1M 8AD
Telephone (01) 580 5588

The National House Building Council

58 Portland Place,
London, W1N 4BU
Telephone (01) 637 1248/9
All of the above three organizations run guarantee schemes.

The Royal Institute of Chartered Surveyors

12 Great George Street,
Parliament Square,
London, SW1P 3AD
Telephone (01) 222 7000
The Institute can tell you about surveyors in your area and send, on receipt of an s.a.e., a leaflet called *What Will It Cost?*.

The Chartered Surveyors Voluntary Service helps people who are not sure how to obtain professional advice. Ask at your CAB or local advice centre for details of the service.

RESIDENTIAL AND NURSING HOMES

Residential care. If you need, or your relative needs, a high degree of personal care, you may consider residential care. If you hope to find a place in a council residential home you should apply to your social services department, not to an individual home. Contact your social worker if you have one or write to the 'Residential Care Services Section' at the main office of the SSD.

If you want to move to another area, or if you cannot or do not want to obtain a place in a local authority home, you will have to consider a private or voluntary home. Contact the Registration Officer for Residential Care Homes at your SSD for a list of such homes in the area. You usually have to apply to the individual home which will detail the charges and conditions for you.

Nursing homes provide a greater amount of nursing care. Almost all are privately run but your District Health Authority will have a list of homes in your area – look in the telephone book or ask your doctor for the address. The Yellow Pages of the telephone directory will have the addresses of a number of homes, and local agencies, such as your community health council, may be able to help.

Counsel and Care for the Elderly

Twyman House,
16 Bonny Street,
London, NW1 9LR
Telephone (01) 485 1566
This is a charity which acts as a general advice agency for older people and provides information on homes. Telephone lines are open 10.30am–4.00pm, Monday to Friday.

The Elderly Accommodation Counsel Ltd

1 Durward House,
31 Kensington Court,
London, W8 5BH
Telephone (01) 995 8320
This charity can provide computer print-outs for a small fee on all types of accommodation for older people in the area and price range they want.

Grace Link

Upper Chambers,
7 Derby Street,
Leek,
Staffordshire, ST13 6HN
Telephone (0345) 023300
A fee-based advisory service, Grace Link is intended for people wanting private, residential or nursing homes. They have a database of homes, which they visit and assess annually, which they will match against your needs.

The Association of Charity Officers

2nd Floor, Tavistock House North,
Tavistock Square,
London, WC1H 9RJ
Telephone (01) 387 0578
This has member funds, some of which run homes for particular professional, commercial and occupational groups.

The National Care Association

8 Southampton Place,
London, WC1A 2EF
Telephone (01) 405 2277
Among its members are local associations of proprietors of private homes. The Association can advise, through its local associations, on any aspect of private residential care.

The Registered Nursing Home Association

Calthorpe House,
Hagley Road,
Edgbaston,
Birmingham, B16 8QY
Telephone (021) 454 2511
This provides information on those homes which they have visited.

Useful publications

Age Concern England has a factsheet (no. 29) on finding residential care which lists some other private agencies, and two factsheets (nos. 10 and 11) on the charging system for residential and nursing care. Counsel and Care for the Elderly have a leaflet called *Claiming Income Support Towards the Fees of a Registered Private or Voluntary Home* – send an s.a.e. to the address above.

RETIREMENT PREPARATION

Your employer may arrange a pre-retirement course for you. If not, some adult education centres run courses – look in the telephone book under the name of your council for the address of your nearest centre. Many financial institutions and firms offer courses as they are good marketing opportunities for the companies. SAGA (see 'Holidays' section, p. 205) have retirement planning holidays.

The Pre-Retirement Association of Great Britain and Northern Ireland

19 Undine Street,
London, SW17 8PP
Telephone (01) 767 3225/6
The Association can provide guidance on what is available and supply a list of its affiliated organizations.

The Retirement Education Centre
6 Rothsay Gardens,
Bedford, MK40 3QB
Telephone (0234) 60304
This offers courses at different levels.

The Mid-Life Centre
318 Summer Lane,
Birmingham, B19 3RL
Telephone (021) 359 3563
The Centre studies mid-life (35–55 years) and can offer personal advice on pre-retirement and changing lifestyles.

SAFETY

The Royal Society for Prevention of Accidents
(RoSPA),
Cannon House,
The Priory,
Queensway,
Birmingham, B4 6BS
Telephone (021) 200 2461
The Society produces a range of useful material including a priced leaflet called *Safety in Retirement*.

National Association for Safety in the Home
Surrey Fire Brigade Headquarters,
St David's,
70 Wray Park Road,
Reigate, Surrey, RH2 0EJ
Telephone (0737) 242444
The Association's aim is to promote all aspects of home safety.

Accident prevention

Local branches of the Red Cross give training to the public on accident prevention.

Information on accident prevention and safety in the home is also available from the fuel industries. Your local gas and electricity showrooms may have leaflets or you could contact the organizations mentioned in the section on 'Heating' (p. 206). *Help Yourself to Gas Safety* is a leaflet available from gas companies.

Help the Aged have a free leaflet about fire hazards called *Fire – Let's Talk About It*. Send a 23 × 18cm (9 × 7in) s.a.e. to the Information Desk, Fire Leaflet, Help the Aged, St James' Walk, London, EC1R 0BE.

See also the sections on 'Crime and crime prevention' (p. 202), 'Heating' (p. 206), 'Insurance' (p. 209), and 'Repairs and improvements' (p. 215).

SAVINGS AND INVESTMENTS

If you are thinking of opening a savings account, compare the details of different accounts by looking at the leaflets that banks and building societies have available.

Banking Information Service
10 Lombard Street,
London, EC3V 9AP
Telephone (01) 626 8486

The Building Society Shop
City House,
Maid Marion Way,
Nottingham, NG1 6BH
Telephone (0602) 472595
This can recommend the best buys in each type of saving.

The Building Societies Association
3 Savile Row,
London, W1X 1AF
Telephone (01) 437 0655
The Association has free leaflets available about society accounts.

Building Society Choice is a monthly magazine available from larger newsagents.

The Banking Ombudsman
Citadel House,
5–11 Fetter Lane,
London, EC4A 1BR
Telephone (01) 583 1395

The Building Society Ombudsman
35–37 Grosvenor Gardens,
London, SW1X 7AW
Telephone (01) 931 0044
If you have a complaint about a bank or building society, contact the appropriate Ombudsman above, to arbitrate your grievance.

National Savings
Durham, DH99 1NS
Write to the above for information about certificates, yearly plans and SAYE.

National Savings
Glasgow, G58 1SB
Write to the above for information about ordinary and investment accounts and deposit bonds.

For further information about all National Savings products, ring (01) 605 9461; (0253) 723714; or (041) 632 2766.

The Bonds and Stock Office
Blackpool,
Lancashire, FY3 9YP
Telephone (0253) 697333
Contact the above for information about government stocks and income bonds.

Cipfa-Sterling
65 London Wall,
London, EC2M 5TU
Telephone (01) 638 6361
These are money brokers who publish a weekly list of town hall bonds.

The Unit Trust Association
65 Kingsway,
London, WC2B 6TD
Telephone (01) 831 0898
The Association publishes a booklet, *Everything You Need to Know About Unit Trusts*, which is available free on receipt of an s.a.e. sent to the above address.

The Association of Investment Trust Companies
6th floor, Park House,
16 Finsbury Circus,
London, EC2M 7JU
Telephone (01) 588 5347/8
The Association can send you information about investment trusts and a list of brokers dealing in this kind of investment.

Investing in shares
The Stock Exchange
Throgmorton Street,
London, EC2N 1HP
Telephone (01) 588 2355
Write to the Stock Exchange for their free booklet, *An Introduction to Buying and Selling Shares*, and a list of brokers who deal for small investors. Or you can ask your bank to order shares for you through one of their specialists.

Useful publications

If you are interested in buying a PEP, you can buy the Stock Exchange's *PEP Investor* from newsagents. Or you can buy *The Good PEP Guide* from Money Guides, Riverside House, Rattlesden, Bury St Edmunds, Suffolk, IP30 0SF.

Age Concern England publish an annual guide to taxes and savings in retirement.

A free booklet called *Self Defence for Investors* is published by the Securities and Investment Board, 3 Royal Exchange Buildings, London, EC3V 3NL, Telephone (01) 283 2474.

Independent financial advice

If you are looking for an independent financial adviser, you can dial (01) 200 3000 and the Campaign for Independent Financial Advice (CAMIFA) will send a list of their ten nearest advisers and a free copy of *Your Guide to Independent Financial Advice*.

SOCIAL SERVICES

You can find the telephone number of your local Social Services Department (SSD) – they are called Social Work Departments in Scotland – by looking in the telephone book under the name of your local authority (county or London borough). Your SSD should have leaflets available about the services it provides. Social workers deal with all kinds of social and personal problems. They can also arrange for home helps, meals-on-wheels, holiday beds and residential care, for example. If you want to complain about your Social Services Department, write to the Director of Social Service or contact your local Councillor.

The Home Help Service gives practical help with tasks such as housework, shopping and meals. The service is free in some areas and means-tested in others. Contact the Home Help Organizer at your local SSD or you may need to be referred by a health visitor or your doctor.

Meals-on-wheels services are available to older people in their homes, provided partly through voluntary groups and partly by the SSD who organize them. Special diets can usually be catered for. Ask your district nurse, health visitor or social worker or contact the meals area organizer at your SSD.

'Good Neighbour' schemes. Some local authorities run these, which can help you with a variety of schemes – ask at your SSD or CAB.

Lunch clubs offer the chance to get out of the house, meet people and have a lunch at a low cost. Day centres can be particularly valuable to the housebound and isolated. Most are run by the SSD or voluntary organizations. Transport may be provided to and from the centre.

The Central Council for Jewish Social Services
221 Golders Green Road,
London, NW11 9DW
Telephone (01) 458 3282
The Council provides various social services for the Jewish community, primarily in London and the South East, but can put enquirers in touch with facilities throughout the UK.

TAXATION

If you have questions about income tax, ask at your nearest tax office, and remember to have all the necessary documentation. Look under Inland Revenue in the telephone book to find the address. Your CAB will also often be able to help with tax problems.

Free leaflets. Your tax office will have a range of free leaflets available, including:

IR4   *Income Tax and Pensioners*
IR4A   *Income Tax – Age Allowance*
IR22   *Personal Allowances*
IR23   *Income Tax and Widows*
IR30   *Income Tax: Separation and Divorce*
IR31   *Income Tax and Married Couples*
IR45   *What Happens When Someone Dies*
IR55   *Bank Interest – Paying Tax*
CGT6   *Retirement: Disposal of a Business*
CGT8   *Capital Gains Tax*

The Tax Payers Society
Room 22,
1st Floor,
4 Carmelite Street,
London, EC4Y 0BN
Telephone (01) 583 6020
The Society gives advice on tax problems for an annual subscription.

The Institute of Chartered Accountants in England and Wales
PO Box 433,
Chartered Accountants' Hall,
Moorgate Place,
London, EC2P 2BJ
Telephone (01) 628 7060

The Institute of Chartered Accountants in Scotland
27 Queen Street,
Edinburgh, EH2 1LA
Telephone (031) 225 5673

The Institute of Chartered Accountants in Ireland
87/89 Pembroke Road,
Dublin 4,
Eire.
If you want to find an accountant to help with your tax affairs, contact the relevant body above.

Useful publications

Look in your local library or bookshop for the many publications, up-dated annually, that are available to help with taxation.

Age Concern England publish *Your Taxes and*

Savings in Retirement each year, available from the Marketing Department. Factsheet no. 14 explains the way in which building society and bank deposit account interest is taxed for individuals, and no. 15 explains the earnings rule and how state pensions are taxed – both factsheets are available from the Information Department on receipt of an s.a.e.

For a copy of a free detailed booklet about Inheritance Tax (IHT1), write to the Capital Taxes Office, Minford House, Rockley Road, London, W14 0DF.

TEETH

If you are having problems finding a dentist, you can ask at your local Family Practitioner Committee (FPC) or at main post offices or libraries to see the FPC's lists of general dental practitioners. Your local Community Health Council (CHC) or CAB may be able to recommend a suitable dentist. Or you can contact the District Dental Officer of the local Community Dental Service. The addresses of these agencies will be in the telephone book, but if you cannot find them ask at your CAB. Some dentists do home visits; ask about availability at the Community Dental Service or at your local Family Practitioner Committee or CHC.

You have to pay about 75% of the cost of NHS dental treatment, unless you are on a low income. Ask for leaflets D11 and AB11 at your local DSS office, post office or advice centre for details of eligibility for free NHS treatment or help with costs.

If you have a complaint about your NHS dental treatment, contact the FPC as soon as possible.

Age Concern England have available a free factsheet (no. 5) which looks at some of the dental problems which older people face and gives information on improving dental fitness – send an s.a.e. to the Information Department.

The British Dental Health Foundation
88 Gurnards Avenue,
Fishermead,
Milton Keynes, MK6 2BL
Telephone (0908) 667063
The Foundation promotes dental health and has a range of free literature available.

TELEPHONES

There is no national scheme providing financial help with telephones for older people. Age Concern England's factsheet no. 28 *Telephone Costs – Sources of Financial Help* describes what help is available to older people for the cost of installing and using a telephone. The factsheet is available free if you send an s.a.e. to the Information Department.

If you are having problems using your phone, ask at your local British Telecom office for their free leaflet *Guide to Equipment and Services for Disabled Customers* or ask the operator for the Freefone number.

DIEL
Office of Telecommunications,
Atlantic House,
Holborn Viaduct,
London, EC1N 2HQ
Telephone (01) 822 1690
This can also give advice about special equipment, and help to deal with complaints.

TELEVISION LICENCES

The National Television Licence Records Office
Barton House,
Bond Street,
Bristol, BS98 1TL
Telephone (0883) 46964

Television licence concessions are available from the above office to retired people of pensionable age who live in certain specific types of accommodation. This is called a 'special' accommodation for residential care licence. Further information is available from the TV Licence Records Office.
Age Concern England's factsheet no. 3, *Television Licence Concessions*, explains the details of the scheme and is available free on receipt of an s.a.e. from the Information Department.

Registered blind people can get a small reduction off the cost of a full fee licence by showing their registration card at the post office when renewing their licence.

Some local authorities operate schemes for full or part payment of licences for older people. Contact your local social services department to see if there is a scheme in your area.

If you are housebound and in need, a social worker may be able to put you in touch with organizations which provide television and radio facilities.

From 1989 a pay-as-you-go scheme is to be introduced whereby everyone will be able to pay for a licence by instalment.

TRANSPORT AND MOBILITY

Contact your local Council for Voluntary Service – look in the phone book – to see if there are any community transport schemes in your area, or ask at your CAB.

If you need an escort taxi or ambulance, help may be available from the British Red Cross, St John Ambulance or the WRVS – look up the addresses of your nearest branches in the telephone book or ask at your CAB. Your local volunteer bureau or Age Concern group can help with occasional trips.

The British Nursing Association
North Place,
82 Great North Road,
Hatfield,
Hertfordshire, AL9 5BL
Telephone (07072) 63544
The Association has branches across the country which can sometimes provide escorts. You will have to negotiate fees with the branch.

The Federation of London Dial-a-Ride
St Margaret's,
25 Leighton Road,
London, NW5 2QD
Telephone (01) 482 2325
Dial-a-ride is a transport service available predominantly in London for disabled people who cannot use public transport. It uses adapted minibuses which can carry wheelchairs and has paid drivers. To get in touch with your local service in London, contact the Federation.

The Mobility Advice and Vehicle Information Service
Transport and Road Research Laboratory,
Crowthorne,
Berkshire, RG11 6AU
Telephone (0344) 770456
This offers government service advice and assessment to the disabled driver and has a number of other centres around the country.

Useful publications
Door to Door, a guide to transport for disabled people, is available free from your local DSS office or social services department or by post from the Department of Transport, Building No. 3, Door to Door Guide, Freepost, Victoria Road, South Ruislip, Middlesex, HA4 0BR.

A priced annual guide called *Traveller's Guide for the Disabled* is published by the Automobile Association (AA), Fanum House, Basingstoke, Hampshire, RG21 2EA, Telephone (0256) 21023

British Rail and Disabled Travellers is a free leaflet available from mainline stations or by post from the Public Affairs Department, British Railways Board, Euston House, 24 Eversholt Street, London, NW1 1DZ.

Care in the Air, is a free leaflet for disabled airline passengers available by post from the Air Transport Users Committee, 129 Kingsway, London, WC2B 6NN, Telephone (01) 242 3882.

Help for disabled drivers
Disabled drivers' groups
The Disabled Drivers' Association,
Ashwellthorpe Hall,
Norwich,
Norfolk, NR16 1EX
Telephone (050841) 449

The Disabled Drivers' Motor Club
1A Dudley Gardens,
London, W13 9LU
Telephone (01) 840 1515
Both of the above organizations can answer queries about car conversions and special allowances. An annual membership fee entitles you to various discounts and to join the local groups.

The Orange Badge Scheme gives parking concessions to severely disabled or blind people and their drivers. Ask your SSD how to apply.

Mobility Allowance is a weekly cash benefit paid to anyone under a certain age who is unable or virtually unable to walk. For more details, get a copy of DSS leaflet NI 211 from your local DSS office or CAB.

Motability
2nd Floor, Gate House,
West Gate,
The High,
Harlow,
Essex, CM20 1HR
Telephone (0279) 635666
Motability operates leasing and hire purchase schemes to enable disabled people to use their mobility allowance to the best advantage.

RADAR
25 Mortimer Street,
London, W1N 8AB
Telephone (01) 637 5400
RADAR have a range of material available relating to travel and mobility for disabled people.

TRAVEL CONCESSIONS

Many local authorities offer concessionary travel to retired people at off-peak times, although conditions and availability vary. Some local authorities only give concessions to older people who are retired from work or on low incomes.

Bus and coach concessions. Contact your local council for details about bus concessions or ask at your local bus garage or post office. Ask your local travel agent about concessions on coach services or get in touch with the operator.

National Express Limited
Ensign Court,
4 Vicarage Road,
Edgbaston,
Birmingham, B15 3ES
Telephone (021) 456 1122
Contact this company for imformation about their services.

British Rail
Euston House,
24 Eversholt Street,
London, NW1 1DZ
Telephone (01) 928 5151 extension 41020
British Rail have a 'Senior Citizen's Railcard' which anyone aged 60 or over can buy and which offers reductions on certain journeys. A leaflet about the railcard is available from rail stations and includes an application form. Or you can write to the Railcard Manager at the address above. A Disabled Persons Railcard is also available – ask for a leaflet at your local station.

Air travel. If you are interested in air travel concessions, contact your travel agent or the relevant airline in plenty of time before you travel.

VOLUNTEERING

The National Association of Volunteer Bureaux
St Peter's College,
College Road,
Saltley,
Birmingham, B8 3TE
Telephone (021) 327 0265
Your local volunteer bureau (or Council of Voluntary Service or Rural Community Council in rural areas) will be able to tell you about local services provided by volunteers – look in the telephone book, ask at your CAB, or contact the Association above.

The Volunteer Centre UK
29 Lower King's Road,
Berkhamstead,
Hertfordshire, HP4 2AB
Telephone (0442) 873311
This is the national resource and advisory agency for volunteers and voluntary work.

Community Service Volunteers
(CSV),
237 Pentonville Road,
London, N1 9NJ
Telephone (01) 278 6601
CSV runs a scheme called the Retired and Senior Volunteer Programme (RSVP) for volunteers over 50 who want to do community work.

The Retired Executives Action Clearing House
(REACH),
89 Southwark Street,
London, SE1 0HD
Telephone (01) 928 0452
This recruits retired executives and professional people for voluntary work with charitable or community groups who need help. No fees are charged to the applicant or the organization and payment is usually expenses only.

Pro-Dog
Rocky Bank,
4 New Road,
Ditton, Maidstone,
Kent, ME20 6AD
Telephone (0732) 848499
This organization runs 'pat dog schemes' across the country, where volunteers take their pets into residential homes and hospitals on a regular basis.

Volunteers abroad
The following organizations all place volunteers overseas.

Voluntary Service Overseas
317 Putney Bridge Road,
London, SW15 2PN
Telephone (01) 780 2266

International Voluntary Service
Ceresole House,
53 Regent Road,
Leicester, LE1 6YL
Telephone (0533) 541862
You have to be under 65 to work for the service.

The Catholic Institute for International Relations
22 Coleman Fields,
London, N1 7AF
Telephone (01) 354 0883

The United Nations Association International Service
3 Whitehall Court,
London, SW1A 2EL
Telephone (01) 930 0679

British Executive Service Overseas
10 Belgrave Square,
London, SW1X 8PH
Telephone (01) 235 0991
The Service sends people out for shorter periods of time to help businesses in the third world.

WRVS – see the section on 'Women' (opposite).

WILLS

Even with a simple will it is advisable to go to a solicitor – see the section on 'Legal Help' (p. 210).

Wills and Probate is published by the Consumers' Association. You can borrow it from a library or order from bookshops or obtain direct from the Association's Publications Department, Castlemead, Gascoyne Way, Hertford, SG14 1LH, Telephone (0992) 589031.

The Law Society (see 'Legal Help' section) has a free booklet available – *Making a Will Won't Kill You*. Age Concern England's factsheet no. 7, *Making Your Will*, is available free from the Information Department on receipt of an s.a.e. Age Concern also publishes a leaflet, *Instructions for My Next of Kin and Executors Upon My Death*, which can be left to tell your family where all your important documents are, including your will.

Form PR48, *How to Obtain Probate*, is available free from CABs.

WOMEN

The Equal Opportunities Commission
Overseas House,
Quay Street,
Manchester, M3 3HN
Telephone (061) 833 9244
The Commission can advise about equal opportunity issues.

Your local CAB or Community Health Council should know if there is a women's group or centre in your area. Or you may be interested in contacting any of the following organizations which will be able to tell you if they have branches in your area.

National Association of Widows – see 'Bereavement' section, p. 200.

The National Association of Women's Clubs
5 Vernon Rise,
King's Cross Road,
London, WC1X 9EP
Telephone (01) 837 1434
This has a network of clubs which are open to women of all ages and interests.

The National Federation of Women's Institutes
39 Eccleston Street,
London, SW1W 9NT
Telephone (01) 730 7212
The Federation organizes activities for women of all ages mainly in rural areas.

The National Women's Register
245 Warwick Road,
Solihull,
West Midlands,
B92 7AH
Telephone (021) 706 1101
The Register offers women of all ages the opportunity to meet in discussion groups in each other's homes.

The Townswomen's Guild (Headquarters)
at 75 Harborne Road,
Birmingham, B15 3DA
Telephone (021) 456 3435

The Women's International League for Peace and Freedom
29 Great James Street,
London, WC1N 3ES
Telephone (01) 242 1521
The League campaigns for disarmament and human rights and the status of women.

The Women's Royal Voluntary Service
(WRVS),
234–244 Stockwell Road,
London, SW9 9SP
Telephone (01) 733 3388
This has a network of groups across the country which carry out independent community work and help other bodies with welfare and emergency work. Work for older people includes meals-on-wheels, books-on-wheels, and a driver service.

WORK

Ask at your local DSS office or CAB for copies of the free DSS leaflets NI92 about earning extra pension by postponing your retirement and NI196 about the earnings rule. You can ask at your local job centre about employment legislation and any material which the Department of Employment has available.

A few Age Concern groups run employment bureaux. Information about the financial aspects of carrying on working after pension age is given in Age Concern England's factsheets nos. 18 and 19 – send an s.a.e. to the Information Department.

The Pre-Retirement Association
19 Undine Street,
London, SW17, 8PP
Telephone (01) 767 3225/6
The Association has a free leaflet about work in retirement listing relevant organizations – send a large s.a.e.

Success after Sixty
40–41 Bond Street,
London, W1X 3AF
Telephone (01) 629 0672

Also at:
33 George Street,
Croydon,
Surrey, CR0 1LB
Telephone (01) 680 0858
This is a commercial employment agency for people aged 50 and over in the Greater London area.

Professional and Executive Recruitment. Professionals may want to find out about this service, about which your local job centre will be able to give you details.

Age Endeavour
Willowthorpe,
High Street,
Stansted Abbotts,
Ware,
Herts SG-12 8AS
Telephone (0920) 870158
Age Endeavour is a charity originally set up to help older people continue in part-time employment. Their emphasis has shifted slightly since the late 1970s' rise in unemployment.

The Association of British Chambers of Commerce
212A Shaftesbury Avenue,
London, WC2H 8EW
Telephone (01) 240 5831/6
Look in the telephone book for your local Chamber of Commerce or contact the Association.

The Small Firms and Tourism Division
Department of Employment,
Steel House,
Tothill Street,
London, SW1H 9NF
Telephone (01) 213 3000
Contact the above to find out where your nearest small firms centre is.

Council for Small Industries in Rural Areas
(COSIRA), (formerly the Rural Development commission)
141 Castle Street,
Salisbury,
Wiltshire, SP1 3TP
Telephone (0722) 336255

British Franchise Association
75A Bell Street,
Henley-on-Thames,
Oxfordshire, RG9 2BD
Telephone (0491) 578049/578050

Hotel and Catering Training Board
International House,
High Street,
Ealing,
London, W5 5DB
Telephone (01) 579 2400

INDEX

Numbers in **Bold** indicate pictures